Revision Notes and Model Answers for A-level Pure Mathematics

Revision Notes and Model Answers for A-level Pure Mathematics

D J Heath MSc PhD

Lecturer in Mathematics
Carshalton College of Further Education

Stanley Thornes (Publishers) Ltd

First published in 1985 by

Stanley Thornes (Publishers) Ltd
Old Station Drive
Leckhampton
CHELTENHAM GL53 0DN

British Library Cataloguing in Publication Data

Heath, D J
Revision notes and model answers for A-level pure mathematics.
1. Mathematics – 1961–
I. Title
510 QA39.2

ISBN 0-85950-153-1

Typeset in 9/10pt Press Roman by Tech-Set, Gateshead.
Printed and bound in Great Britain at The Pitman Press, Bath.

CONTENTS

PREFACE

This book is a revision course for A-level mathematics students. It is assumed that the student has already completed an initial reading of the A-level syllabus and requires a systematic revision course with examples and worked solutions to examination questions. There are a number of textbooks available providing introductions to the subject. Some of these also include selections of A-level questions without, however, providing worked solutions. It is the aim of this book to bridge the gap between an introductory textbook and a revision course by providing both short notes and comprehensive model answers to examination questions.

The main principles of each topic have been summarised and illustrated by worked examples, selected, where possible, from past examination papers. Concluding each section there is a collection of examination questions taken from different examining boards. The students may attempt these questions for revision purposes and, if necessary, refer to their worked solutions after the exercise.

The contents of this book cover the common core of the Pure Mathematics syllabuses of the different examining boards.

I gratefully acknowledge the use of examination questions from the following boards:

University of London (LU)
Northern Ireland Board (NI)
Oxford Delegacy of Local Examinations (O)
Southern Universities Joint Board (SUJB)
The Associated Examining Board (AEB)
Welsh Joint Education Committee (WJEC)

The worked solutions to these examination questions are the sole responsibility of the author and have not been provided by or approved of by the examining boards. The University of London University Entrance and School Examination Council accepts no responsibility whatsoever for the accuracy or method of working in the answers given. Part examination questions have been indicated by printing 'part' at the end of the question.

I am extremely grateful to my wife and daughter for providing me with the time that has been absorbed in the production of this book.

D J HEATH

1 ALGEBRAIC SERIES

SEQUENCES

A sequence is a set of numbers or algebraic quantities. Each element of the sequence is referred to as a term. Some of the most interesting and useful sequences are those in which each successive term, apart from the first, is derived from its predecessor by a definite rule.

Sequences can be either finite or infinite. In the case of an infinite sequence the relationship between successive terms must be established since it is impossible to list each element.

Example 1 $1, 2, 3, 4, 5$

This is a finite sequence of five terms in which each term is formed by adding 1 to its predecessor. If we denote the nth term by u_n, its successor in the sequence is u_{n+1} and is given by

$$u_{n+1} = u_n + 1 \quad \text{for} \quad n = 1, 2, 3, 4$$

where $u_1 = 1$. Since this defines a connection between the nth and $(n+1)$th terms, it is sometimes called a recurrence relationship.

Example 2 $a, ar, ar^2, ar^3, \ldots$

The dots indicate that this is an infinite sequence. Each term is obtained from its predecessor after multiplication by r. The recurrence relationship here is

$$u_{n+1} = ru_n$$

SERIES

In mathematics, a series is a sequence of terms that are combined by either addition or subtraction. For example, the terms of an arithmetic or geometric progression form a sequence. However, these terms can be united by either addition or subtraction to form a series. Because of their importance in the study of series, we now consider arithmetic and geometric progressions.

ARITHMETIC PROGRESSIONS

An arithmetic progression (AP) is a sequence in which successive terms have a constant difference. The terms in Example 1 form an AP.

The first term of an AP is usually denoted by the letter a, and the common difference between successive terms is d. The nth term of the AP is then written as

$$\boxed{n\text{th term} = a + (n-1)d} \tag{1.1}$$

We let S_n denote the sum of the first n terms of the AP. To obtain S_n, we write

$$S_n = a + (a+d) + (a+2d) + \ldots + [a+(n-2)d] + [a+(n-1)d] \tag{1.2}$$

This series can also be rewritten in reverse order as

$$S_n = [a+(n-1)d] + [a+(n-2)d] + \ldots + (a+2d) + (a+d) + a \tag{1.3}$$

Addition of each term in (1.2) to its corresponding term in (1.3) gives

$$2S_n = [2a+(n-1)d]+[2a+(n-1)d]+\ldots+[2a+(n-1)d] \qquad (1.4)$$

Since there are n terms on the RHS of (1.2) and (1.3), there will also be n terms on the RHS of (1.4). Consequently, we have

$$2S_n = n[2a+(n-1)d]$$

$$\therefore \quad \boxed{S_n = \frac{n}{2}[2a+(n-1)d]} \qquad (1.5)$$

An alternative formula for S_n is obtained if we let l represent the nth term given by (1.1). We then have

$$a+l = 2a+(n-1)d$$

which is the expression enclosed by the square bracket in (1.5). Substituting gives

$$\boxed{S_n = \frac{n}{2}(a+l)} \qquad (1.6)$$

In principle all A-level questions concerned with APs involve manipulation of the key results and definitions (1.1), (1.5) and (1.6) for their solution. Some illustrations of their use in practice are given in the following worked examples.

Worked Example

In an arithmetic progression the third term is four times the first term and the fifth term is 14. Find the tenth term. (LU 1981)

Solution

Let u_n denote the nth term of the AP, where

$$u_n = a+(n-1)d \qquad (1)$$

Putting $n=1$ in (1) $\quad u_1 = a$

Putting $n=3$ in (1) $\quad u_3 = a+2d$

Putting $n=5$ in (1) $\quad u_5 = a+4d$

If $u_3 = 4u_1$ (given) $\quad a+2d = 4a$

$$3a-2d = 0 \qquad (2)$$

If $u_5 = 14$ $\quad a+4d = 14 \qquad (3)$

We now solve (2) and (3) simultaneously.

(2) × 2 $\quad 6a-4d = 0 \qquad (4)$

(3) + (4) $\quad 7a = 14$

$$\therefore \quad a = 2$$

Substituting for a in (2)

$$6-2d = 0$$

$$\therefore \quad d = 3$$

Putting $n=10$ in (1) gives $u_{10} = a+9d$

Substituting the values of a and d, gives

$$u_{10} = 29$$

Worked Example

The first term of an arithmetic series is $(3p+5)$ where p is a positive integer. The last term is $(17p+17)$ and the common difference is 2.

Find, in terms of p (i) the number of terms,
(ii) the sum of the series

Show that the sum of the series is divisible by 14, only when p is odd.
(AEB 1980)

Solution

(i) Let the number of terms be n. We start by summarising the information given

$$a = 3p+5 \quad (1)$$
$$d = 2 \quad (2)$$

and the nth term
$$l = 17p+17 \quad (3)$$

Using the standard expression (1.1) for the nth term, we have
$$17p+17 = 3p+5+2(n-1)$$

Removing the bracket on the RHS this simplifies to
$$17p+17 = 3p+3+2n$$

Rearranging this so that $2n$ appears by itself on the LHS gives
$$2n = 14p+14$$
$$n = 7p+7 = 7(p+1) \quad (4)$$

(ii) To find the sum of the series we substitute (4) into (1.6) with a and l given by (1) and (3) respectively. Consequently, we have
$$S_n = \frac{7(p+1)}{2}(3p+5+17p+17)$$

or, simplifying
$$S_n = \frac{7(p+1)}{2}(20p+22) \quad (5)$$

which can be written as
$$S_n = 7(p+1)(10p+11)$$

This is a multiple of 14 when $p+1$ is even, i.e. p is odd or when $10p+11$ is even. This is impossible since $10p$ will always be even and hence $10p+11$ always odd.

GEOMETRIC PROGRESSIONS

A geometric progression (GP) is a sequence in which the ratio of each term to its predecessor is constant. Example 2 (p. 1) shows the terms of an infinite geometric progression. The recurrence relationship in this example shows the connection between the $(n+1)$th term and the nth term.

Following the same convention adopted for the arithmetic progression, the first term of the sequence will be denoted by a. The letter r is used for the ratio of one term in the sequence to its predecessor. By inspection of the terms in Example 2, we deduce that the expression for the nth term of a geometric progression is

$$\boxed{n\text{th term} = ar^{n-1}} \quad (1.7)$$

To find S_n, the sum of the first n terms of the GP, we write
$$S_n = a+ar+ar^2+\ldots+ar^{n-2}+ar^{n-1} \quad (1.8)$$

Multiplying (1.8) by r gives
$$rS_n = ar+ar^2+ar^3+\ldots+ar^{n-1}+ar^n \quad (1.9)$$

Subtracting (1.8) from (1.9) gives

$$rS_n - S_n = ar^n - a$$

which factorises to

$$S_n(r-1) = a(r^n - 1)$$

$$\therefore \quad \boxed{S_n = \frac{a(r^n-1)}{r-1} \quad \text{for} \quad r > 1} \qquad (1.10)$$

Although the result (1.10) is valid for all values of r it is usually used in this form when $r > 1$ since, in this case, both the numerator and the denominator are positive. If $r < 1$, (1.10) can be rewritten as

$$\boxed{S_n = \frac{a(1-r^n)}{1-r} \quad \text{for} \quad r < 1} \qquad (1.11)$$

INFINITE GPs

If $|r| < 1$, $|r^n| \to 0$ as $n \to \infty$. However, if $|r| > 1$, then as $n \to \infty$ $|r^n| \to \infty$. It is only in the former case that the sum to infinity, S_∞, of a geometric progression will exist and from (1.11) it will be given by

$$\boxed{S_\infty = \frac{a}{1-r} \quad \text{provided} \quad |r| < 1} \qquad (1.12)$$

The key results (1.7), (1.10), (1.11) and (1.12) are crucial for the solution of A-level problems on GPs.

Worked Example

The second and fifth terms of a geometric progression of real terms are $\sqrt{2}$ and $8\sqrt{2}$ respectively. Find the sum of the first nine terms of the progression. (LU 1981)

Solution

Generally $u_n = ar^{n-1}$

Putting $n = 2$ $\quad ar = \sqrt{2}$ $\quad$ (1) (Second term of the GP)

Putting $n = 5$ $\quad ar^4 = 8\sqrt{2}$ $\quad$ (2) (Fifth term of the GP)

Dividing (1) into (2) gives

$$r^3 = 8$$

$$\therefore \quad r = 2$$

Substituting for r in (1) gives

$$2a = \sqrt{2}$$

$$\therefore \quad a = \frac{\sqrt{2}}{2}$$

Using the formula (1.10) for S_n and replacing a and r by their numerical values, we have

$$S_9 = \frac{1}{\sqrt{2}} \frac{(2^9-1)}{1}$$

$$\therefore \quad S_9 = \frac{511}{\sqrt{2}} = \frac{511\sqrt{2}}{2}$$

ARITHMETIC AND GEOMETRIC MEANS

The arithmetic mean, $\bar{x}$, of a number of quantities $x_1, x_2, x_3, x_4, \ldots, x_n$ is given by

$$\bar{x} = \frac{1}{n}(x_1 + x_2 + x_3 + x_4 + \ldots + x_n)$$

The geometric mean, GM, of the same quantities is

$$\text{GM} = \sqrt[n]{x_1 x_2 x_3 \ldots x_n}$$

EXERCISE

1. Show that the arithmetic mean of two positive real numbers is greater than or equal to their geometric mean. Hence show that, when a, b, c, d are real

$$a^4 + b^4 + c^4 + d^4 \geqslant 4abcd$$ (LU 1981, part)

2. The first, second and third terms of an arithmetic series are a, b and c, respectively. Prove that the sum of the first ten terms can be expressed as

$$\tfrac{5}{2}(9c - 5a)$$

These numbers a, b and c are also the first, third and fourth terms, respectively, of a geometric series. Prove that $(2b - c)c^2 = b^3$. (AEB 1981)

3. An arithmetic series has first term 6, common difference 8 and the sum of the first n terms is S_n. Express S_n in terms of n and show that it is the product of two consecutive integers. Deduce that S_n is not an integral power of 2.

The sum of the first n terms of a geometric series is $\frac{4}{3}(4^n - 1)$ and the nth term is u_n. Express u_n in terms of n and show that u_n is an integral power of 2. (AEB 1983)

4. If $|r| \neq 1$, find the sum S_n of the series

$$r + r^3 + r^5 + \ldots + r^{2n-1}$$

Given that $r = \frac{1}{2}$ show that $S_n \to \frac{2}{3}$ as $n \to \infty$. (LU 1973, part)

5. (i) Given that the sum of the first and second terms of an arithmetic progression is x and that the sum of the $(n-1)$th and nth terms is y, prove that the sum of the first n terms is

$$\frac{n}{4}(x + y)$$

(ii) The sum of the first four terms of a geometric series of positive terms is 15 and the sum to infinity of the series is 16. Show that the sum of the first eight terms of the series differs from the sum to infinity by $\frac{1}{16}$. (LU 1977)

Worked Solutions

1. For any real quantities x_1 and x_2 we have

$$(x_1 - x_2)^2 \geqslant 0$$

$$x_1^2 - 2x_1x_2 + x_2^2 \geqslant 0$$

Rearranging

$$x_1^2 + x_2^2 \geqslant 2x_1x_2 \quad (1)$$

Adding $2x_1x_2$ to each side in order to make the LHS a perfect square

$$x_1^2 + 2x_1x_2 + x_2^2 \geqslant 4x_1x_2 \quad (2)$$

$$(x_1 + x_2)^2 \geqslant 4x_1x_2 \quad (3)$$

$$\tfrac{1}{4}(x_1 + x_2)^2 \geqslant x_1x_2$$

Taking the square root gives

$$\tfrac{1}{2}(x_1+x_2) \geqslant (x_1x_2)^{1/2} \quad (4)$$

The square root on the RHS will be real since both x_1 and x_2 are positive.

(4) $\Rightarrow$ arithmetic mean $\geqslant$ geometric mean as required.

We now let $x_1=ab$ and $x_2=cd$. Substituting in (3) gives

$$(ab+cd)^2 \geqslant 4abcd$$

$$\therefore \quad a^2b^2+c^2d^2 \geqslant 2abcd \quad (5)$$

Now $(a-b)^2 \geqslant 0$

$$\therefore \quad a^2+b^2 \geqslant 2ab$$

Squaring each side

$$(a^2+b^2)^2 \geqslant 4a^2b^2$$

$$a^4+2a^2b^2+b^4 \geqslant 4a^2b^2$$

$$\therefore \quad a^4+b^4 \geqslant 2a^2b^2 \quad (6)$$

Similarly it follows that

$$c^4+d^4 \geqslant 2c^2d^2 \quad (7)$$

(6) + (7) gives

$$a^4+b^4+c^4+d^4 \geqslant 2(a^2b^2+c^2d^2)$$

Using the inequality (5) on the RHS gives the result

$$a^4+b^4+c^4+d^4 \geqslant 4abcd$$

2.

$$\text{First term of AP} = a \quad (1)$$

$$\text{Second term of AP is } a+d = b \quad (2)$$

$$\text{Third term of AP is } a+2d = c \quad (3)$$

From (2) $\quad d = b-a \quad (4)$

Substituting (4) in (3)

$$a+2(b-a) = c$$

$$2b-a = c$$

$$\therefore \quad b = \tfrac{1}{2}(a+c) \quad (5)$$

Using the formula (1.5) for S_n and putting $n=10$ gives

$$S_{10} = 5[2a+9(b-a)]$$

$$S_{10} = 5(9b-7a) \quad (6)$$

We need to eliminate b from (6). Substituting (5) into (6) gives

$$S_{10} = 5[\tfrac{9}{2}(a+c)-7a]$$

$$= \tfrac{5}{2}[9(a+c)-14a]$$

$$\therefore \quad S_{10} = \tfrac{5}{2}(9c-5a)$$

which is the required answer.

$$\text{First term of GP} = a \quad (7)$$

$$\text{Third term of GP is } ar^2 = b \quad (8)$$

$$\text{Fourth term of GP is } ar^3 = c \quad (9)$$

From (8) $\quad r^2 = \dfrac{b}{a} \quad (10)$

Dividing (9) by (8) gives

$$r = \frac{c}{b} \quad (11)$$

EXERCISE

Squaring each side of (11)

$$r^2 = \frac{c^2}{b^2} \qquad (12)$$

Comparing the RHS of (10) and (12) gives

$$\frac{c^2}{b^2} = \frac{b}{a}$$

$$a = \frac{b^3}{c^2} \qquad (13)$$

Rearranging (5) gives

$$a = 2b - c \qquad (14)$$

Equating the RHS of (13) and (14) gives

$$2b - c = \frac{b^3}{c^2}$$

$$\therefore \quad (2b-c)c^2 = b^3 \text{ as required}$$

3. Using the normal notation for an AP

$$a = 6 \text{ (given)}$$

$$d = 8 \text{ (given)}$$

The formula for S_n is

$$S_n = \frac{n}{2}[2a + (n-1)d]$$

Substituting for a and d gives

$$S_n = \frac{n}{2}[12 + 8(n-1)]$$

giving

$$S_n = \frac{n}{2}(8n+4)$$

$$= n(4n+2)$$

$$= 2n(2n+1)$$

$\therefore$ S_n is a product of two consecutive integers

Since the factor $(2n+1)$ is always odd, it can never be an integral power of 2, from which it follows that S_n itself is not an integral power of 2.

Comparing the standard formula for the sum of n terms of a GP with the given expression we have

$$S_n = \frac{a(r^n - 1)}{r-1} = \tfrac{4}{3}(4^n - 1)$$

$\therefore$ $r = 4$ and $a = 4$ by inspection

nth term of GP $u_n = ar^{n-1}$

Substituting for a and r

$$u_n = 4 \times 4^{n-1}$$

$$= 4^n$$

$$\therefore \quad u_n = 2^{2n}$$

which shows u_n is an integral power of 2 as required.

EXERCISE

4. The ratio of successive terms is given by

$$\frac{r^3}{r} = r^2 \quad (1)$$

and

$$\frac{r^5}{r^3} = r^2 \quad (2)$$

Since the ratios (1) and (2) are identical it follows that this must be a geometric series. The condition $|r| \neq 1$ ensures that the magnitude of each term in the series is unique. The common ratio, R, of the series is

$$R = r^2 \quad (3)$$

The number of terms in the series is found by adding 1 to the power of the last term and then dividing by 2. For example, r^5 is the third term. The power of the last term is $(2n-1)$, from which we deduce that the series has n terms.

The sum of the first n terms of the series is

$$S_n = \frac{a(1-R^n)}{1-R} \quad (4)$$

The first term of this geometric series is r. Putting $a = r$ and substituting (3) into (4) gives

$$S_n = \frac{r(1-r^{2n})}{1-r^2} \quad (5)$$

as the required expression for the sum of the first n terms. If $r = \frac{1}{2}$, $r^n \to 0$ as $n \to \infty$. The sum to infinity is given by

$$S_\infty = \frac{\frac{1}{2}}{1-(\frac{1}{2})^2}$$

$$S_\infty = \frac{2}{3} \quad \text{as required}$$

5. (i) Using the normal notation for an AP

$$\text{first term} + \text{second term} = a + (a+d) = 2a + d$$

but

$$\text{first term} + \text{second term} = x \quad \text{(given)}$$

$$\therefore \quad x = 2a + d \quad (1)$$

$$(n-1)\text{th term} + n\text{th term} = a + (n-2)d + a + (n-1)d = 2a + (2n-3)d$$

but

$$(n-1)\text{th term} + n\text{th term} = y$$

$$\therefore \quad y = 2a + (2n-3)d \quad (2)$$

Adding (1) and (2) gives

$$x + y = 4a + (2n-2)d$$

which factorises to

$$x + y = 4a + 2(n-1)d$$

giving

$$\frac{x+y}{2} = 2a + (n-1)d \quad (3)$$

EXERCISE

The formula for S_n is

$$S_n = \frac{n}{2}[2a+(n-1)d]$$

Replacing the square bracket by the LHS of (3) gives

$$S_n = \frac{n}{2}\frac{(x+y)}{2}$$

$$\text{or} \quad S_n = \frac{n}{4}(x+y) \quad \text{as required}$$

(ii) Using the normal notation for a GP

$$S_4 = 15 \quad \therefore \quad \frac{a(1-r^4)}{1-r} = 15 \qquad (4)$$

$$S_\infty = 16 \quad \therefore \quad \frac{a}{1-r} = 16$$

hence

$$a = 16(1-r) \qquad (5)$$

Substituting (5) in (4) gives

$$16(1-r^4) = 15$$

$$r^4 = \tfrac{1}{16}$$

$$\therefore \quad r = \tfrac{1}{2}$$

Now

$$S_8 = \frac{a(1-r^8)}{1-r} = S_\infty(1-r^8)$$

Removing the brackets

$$S_8 = S_\infty - S_\infty r^8$$

$$S_\infty - S_8 = S_\infty r^8$$

$$S_\infty - S_8 = 16r^8 \qquad (\text{since } S_\infty = 16)$$

hence

$$S_\infty - S_8 = 16 \times (\tfrac{1}{16})^2$$

giving

$$S_\infty - S_8 = \tfrac{1}{16} \quad \text{as required}$$

EXERCISE

2 QUADRATIC FUNCTIONS, INEQUALITIES AND EQUATIONS

THE QUADRATIC FUNCTION

The general form of the quadratic function is

$$y = ax^2 + bx + c \tag{2.1}$$

where in this text we take a, b and c to be constant real numbers and x a variable in the range $-\infty < x < \infty$.

We can obtain information about the general behaviour of the quadratic function by noting that for large values of x the quadratic term contributes most to the value of y. As an approximation, we can take $y = ax^2$ for large values of x. However, since x^2 is always positive, we conclude that if $a > 0$, $y \to \infty$ if $x \to \pm\infty$ as in Figs. 2.1, 2.2 and 2.3. Conversely, if $a < 0$, $y \to -\infty$ if $x \to \pm\infty$ and this possibility is shown in Figs. 2.4, 2.5 and 2.6. In the former case, when $a > 0$, y will have a minimum value, y_{min}, and in the latter case, when $a < 0$, y will have a maximum value y_{max}.

We now investigate the quadratic function in more detail. The RHS of (2.1) can be rearranged as

$$y = a\left(x^2 + \frac{bx}{a} + \frac{c}{a}\right)$$

$$\frac{y}{a} = x^2 + \frac{bx}{a} + \frac{c}{a}$$

$$\frac{y}{a} - \frac{c}{a} = x^2 + \frac{bx}{a}$$

Completing the square on the RHS gives

$$\frac{y}{a} - \frac{c}{a} = \left(x + \frac{b}{2a}\right)^2 - \frac{b^2}{4a^2}$$

$$\frac{y}{a} - \frac{c}{a} + \frac{b^2}{4a^2} = \left(x + \frac{b}{2a}\right)^2 \tag{2.2}$$

However, the RHS is always positive, which implies that

$$\frac{y}{a} - \frac{c}{a} + \frac{b^2}{4a^2} \geqslant 0$$

If we put $x = -\dfrac{b}{2a}$ on the RHS of (2.2), we have

$$\frac{y}{a} - \frac{c}{a} + \frac{b^2}{4a^2} = 0$$

$$y = \frac{4ac - b^2}{4a} \tag{2.3}$$

Depending on the sign of a this is either the maximum or the minimum value of y.

If $a > 0$, we have $y_{\text{min}} = \dfrac{4ac - b^2}{4a}$ when $x = \dfrac{-b}{2a}$ and, if $a < 0$, we have $y_{\text{max}} = \dfrac{4ac - b^2}{4a}$ when $x = \dfrac{-b}{2a}$.

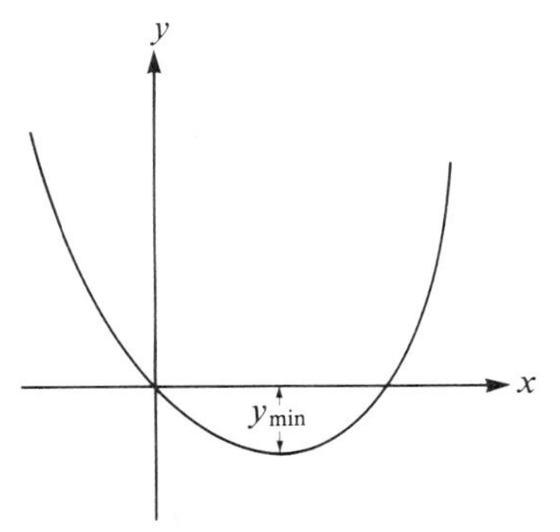

Fig. 2.1 $a > 0$. Real, distinct roots. Curve concave upwards

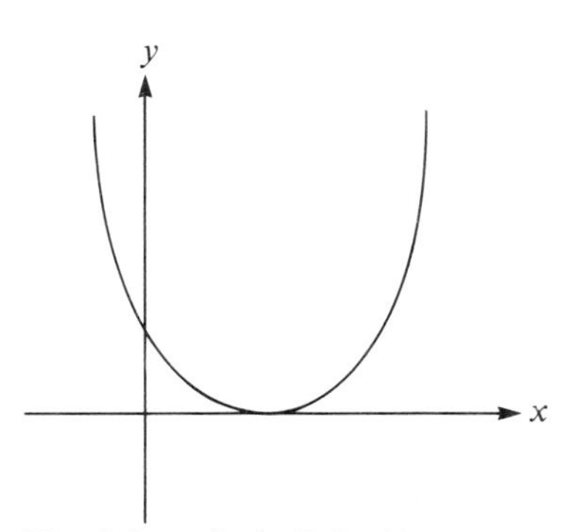

Fig. 2.2 $a > 0$. Coincident roots, $y_{\text{min}} = 0$. Curve concave upwards.

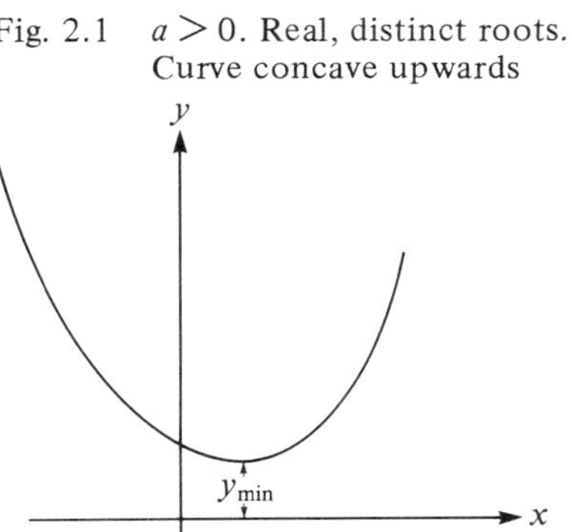

Fig. 2.3 $a > 0$. No real roots. Curve concave upwards.

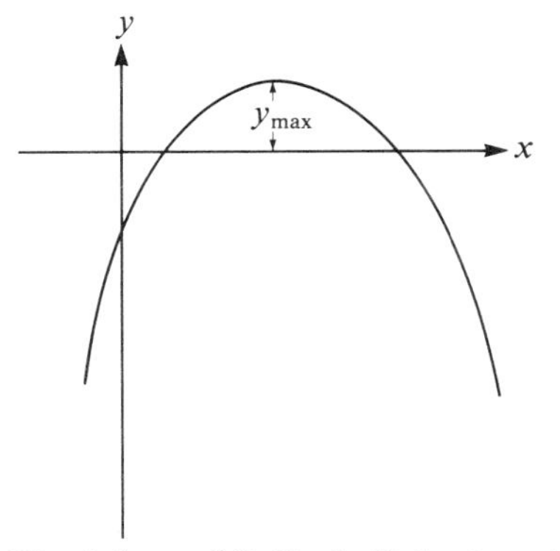

Fig. 2.4 $a < 0$. Real, distinct roots. Curve concave downwards.

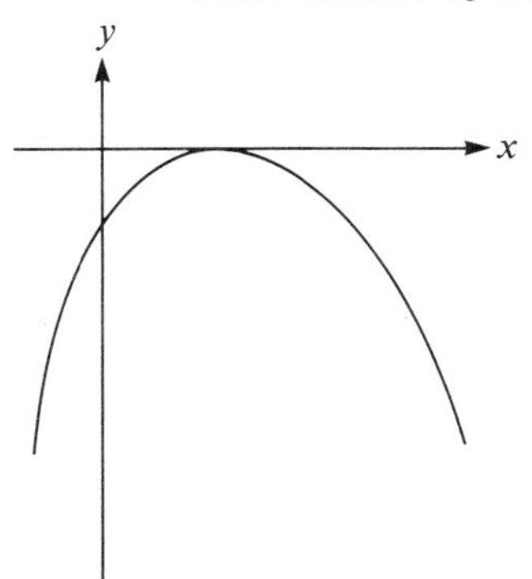

Fig. 2.5 $a < 0$. Coincident roots, $y_{\text{max}} = 0$. Curve concave downwards.

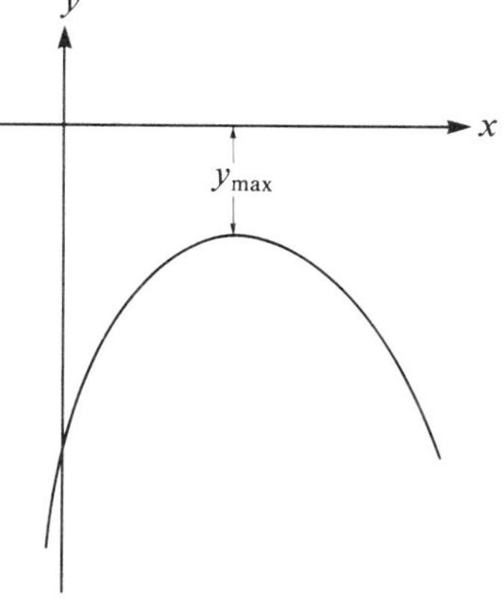

Fig. 2.6 $a < 0$. No real roots. Curve concave downwards.

THE QUADRATIC EQUATION

The general form of a quadratic equation is

$$ax^2+bx+c = 0 \tag{2.4}$$

which occurs when $y = 0$ in (2.1). We can determine the values of x that satisfy (2.4) by putting $y = 0$ in (2.2). This gives

$$\left(x+\frac{b}{2a}\right)^2 = \frac{b^2}{4a^2}-\frac{c}{a}$$

Taking the square root

$$x+\frac{b}{2a} = \pm\sqrt{\frac{b^2}{4a^2}-\frac{c}{a}}$$

$$\therefore \quad x = \frac{-b\pm\sqrt{b^2-4ac}}{2a}$$

The quantity (b^2-4ac) appearing under the root sign is referred to as the discriminant of the quadratic equation because it distinguishes between the three different types of solution.

Case 1	$b^2 > 4ac$	Real, distinct roots (see Figs. 2.1 and 2.4)
Case 2	$b^2 = 4ac$	Coincident roots (see Figs. 2.2 and 2.5)
Case 3	$b^2 < 4ac$	Imaginary roots (see Figs. 2.3 and 2.6)

The use of these different conditions is shown in the following example.

Worked Example

Given that the equation

$$x^2+2(m+1)x+4 = 0$$

has equal roots, find the possible values of the constant m. (LU 1981)

Solution

For equal roots we require $b^2 = 4ac$ (Case 2 above). In this equation we have $a = 1$, $b = 2(m+1)$ and $c = 4$. For $b^2 = 4ac$

$$4(m+1)^2 = 4\times 4$$

$$(m+1)^2 = 4$$

$$\therefore \quad m+1 = \pm 2$$

$$\therefore \quad m = -3 \quad \text{or} \quad m = 1$$

QUADRATIC INEQUALITIES

The topic of quadratic inequalities is closely related to the theory of the quadratic function. In order to solve a quadratic inequality we require the range of x for which y, defined as in (2.1), is such that either $y > 0$ or $y < 0$. Before examining this problem in more detail, we state without proof the rules for dealing with inequalities.

(1) Each side of an inequality may be increased or decreased by the same amount without changing the inequality.

(2) Each side of an inequality may be multiplied or divided by a positive number without changing the inequality.

(3) If each side of an inequality is multiplied or divided by a negative number the inequality sign is reversed.

Example $10-2x < 6$

Multiplying each side by -1 gives

$$2x-10 > -6 \quad \text{(Note the inequality sign is reversed)}$$
$$2x > 10-6$$
$$\therefore \quad 2x > 4$$
$$\text{i.e.} \quad x > 2$$

The solution to a quadratic inequality is determined by finding the roots (if any) of the equation $y = 0$. If there are no roots or the roots are coincident, either $y \geqslant 0$ or $y \leqslant 0$ for all values of x, depending on whether $a > 0$ or $a < 0$. In the case of real, distinct roots (Figs. 2.1 and 2.4), we note that if $a > 0$, $y < 0$ for $\alpha < x < \beta$ and if $a < 0$, $y > 0$ for $\alpha < x < \beta$, where α and β are the roots of the quadratic equation $y = 0$.

Worked Example

Find the set of values of x for which

$$x^2+x-3 > 3x \qquad \text{(LU 1981)}$$

Solution

$$x^2+x-3 > 3x$$
$$x^2-2x-3 > 0$$

Factorising to

$$(x-3)(x+1) > 0$$

The quadratic equation $(x-3)(x+1) = 0$ gives either $x = 3$ or $x = -1$. Since the coefficient of x^2 is 1 and is positive we know that the curve is concave upwards and will cut the x-axis at $x = 3$ and $x = -1$, descending to a minimum value below the x-axis. Consequently, the inequality will be satisfied for all values of x outside the range $-1 < x < 3$. The solution is, therefore

$$x > 3 \quad \text{or} \quad x < -1$$

THE GRAPHS OF $y = f(x)$ and $y = 1/f(x)$

The technique of curve sketching exhibits the main features of the graph without producing an accurate plot of the function. In the case of a quadratic function the most important points are those where the function intersects the x- and y-axes and has either a maximum or a minimum value. To find where it cuts the y-axis we put $x = 0$, and for the points of intersection on the x-axis we solve the quadratic equation.

If $f(x) = ax^2+bx+c$ the curve will be concave upwards for $a > 0$ and has a minimum point at $x = -b/2a$. Conversely, if $a < 0$ the curve will be concave downwards and will have a maximum value at $x = -b/2a$. These general considerations are sufficient to sketch the curve of $y = f(x)$.

The graph of the reciprocal function, $y = 1/f(x)$, is more complicated and the roots of the equation $f(x) = 0$ are particularly important in determining the main features of the graph. We denote these roots by $x = \alpha$ and $x = \beta$. The function $f(x)$ can then be expressed as

$$f(x) = a(x-\alpha)(x-\beta)$$

with the result that

$$y = \frac{1}{a(x-\alpha)(x-\beta)}$$

We will assume without loss of generality in the following discussion that $a > 0$. Since α and β are distinct numbers, we will take $\alpha < \beta$. If $x < \alpha$ and

$x \to \alpha$ both factors in the denominator will have negative values and their product will be positive. However, the factor $(x-\alpha)$ can be made as small as we wish with the result that $y \to +\infty$ as $x \to \alpha$. If $x > \alpha$ and $x \to \alpha$ the opposite occurs, $y \to -\infty$. The straight line $x = \alpha$ is called an asymptote and it touches the curve at infinity. The point $x = \alpha$ produces a break or discontinuity in the curve.

Similar considerations apply to $x = \beta$. However, in this case, if $x < \beta$ and $x \to \beta$ only the factor $(x-\beta)$ in the denominator will be negative with the result that $y \to -\infty$. If $x > \beta$ and $x \to \beta$, $y \to +\infty$. Again, the straight line $x = \beta$ is an asymptote to the curve and the curve is discontinuous at $x = \beta$.

We also need to investigate the behaviour of the curve for very large values of x. The quadratic factor in the denominator can be approximated by taking $f(x) = ax^2$ for very large values of x which shows that as $x \to \pm\infty$, $y \to 0$. Consequently, the x-axis is an asymptote to the curve in both directions. Moreover, we note that a minimum value of $f(x)$ will produce a maximum value for $y = 1/f(x)$ and, conversely, the maximum value of $f(x)$ will give a minimum value for $y = 1/f(x)$.

Worked Example

(i) By completing the square, or otherwise, find the least possible value of $2x^2-8x+9$ for real values of x and *sketch* the graph of $y = 2x^2-8x+9$.

(ii) Find the range of possible values of c such that $2x^2-8x+c > 0$ for all real values of x.

(iii) Find the value of k if $2x^2-8x+k \geqslant -2$ for all real x and, with this value of k, *sketch* the graphs of $y = 2x^2-8x+k$ and $y = 1/(2x^2-8x+k)$. (SUJB 1978)

Solution

(i) Let $y = 2x^2-8x+9$

Taking out 2 as a factor, we have

$$y = 2(x^2-4x+\tfrac{9}{2})$$
$$y = 2(x^2-4x+4+\tfrac{1}{2})$$

The expression x^2-4x+4 forms a perfect square, $(x-2)^2$. Consequently

$$y = 2[(x-2)^2+\tfrac{1}{2}]$$
$$\therefore \quad y = 2(x-2)^2+1$$

In this form it is seen that the minimum value of y occurs when $x = 2$ and is $y = 1$. Since $y = 1$ is a minimum value the curve will not intersect the x-axis. Furthermore, we note that $x = 0$ gives $y = 9$ as the point of intersection on the y-axis. This information is sufficient to sketch the graph of the function (Fig. 2.7).

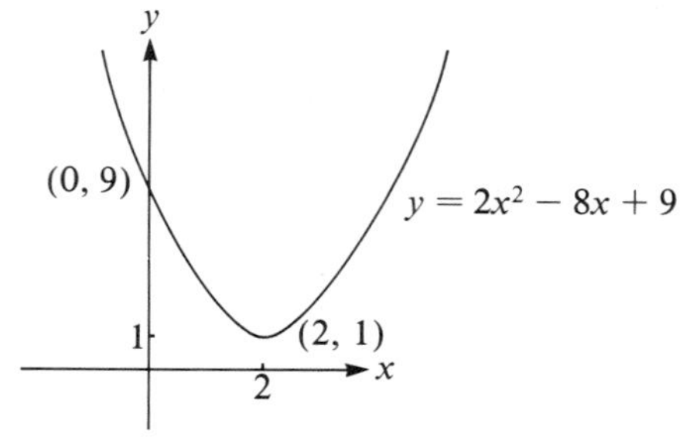

Fig. 2.7

THE GRAPHS OF $y = f(x)$ and $y = 1/f(x)$

(ii) $$2x^2 - 8x + c > 0 \quad \forall x$$

$\therefore$ y has no real roots

The condition for this is $b^2 < 4ac$

$$64 < 8c \quad \therefore \quad c > 8$$

(iii) $$2x^2 - 8x + k \geqslant -2$$

$$2x^2 - 8x + (k+2) \geqslant 0$$

Hence the curve just touches the x-axis as in Fig. 2.2 and has coincident roots.

For coincident roots we require $b^2 = 4ac$

$$64 = 8(k+2)$$

$$k = 6$$

hence $$y = 2x^2 - 8x + 6$$

$$= 2(x^2 - 4x + 3)$$

Factorising $$y = 2(x-3)(x-1)$$

Since the coefficient of $x^2 > 0$, the curve is concave upwards and cuts the x-axis at $x = 3$ and $x = 1$. For $1 < x < 3$ the graph goes beneath the x-axis. When $x = 0$ we have $y = 6$, giving the point of intersection on the y-axis. The minimum value of y occurs when $x = -b/2a = 2$, which gives $y = -2$. With this information we can now sketch the graph of y (Fig. 2.8).

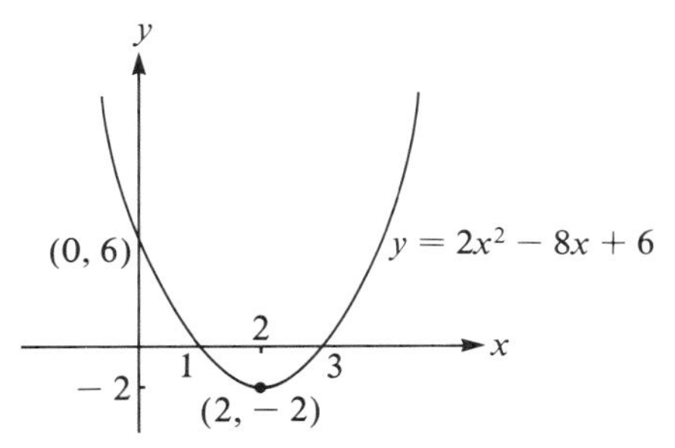

Fig. 2.8

In order to sketch $y = 1/(2x^2 - 8x + 6)$, we start by drawing the asymptotes $x = 3$ and $x = 1$. When $x < 1$ and $x \to 1$, $y \to +\infty$ and when $x > 1$ and $x \to 1$, $y \to -\infty$. Also, when $x < 3$ and $x \to 3$, $y \to -\infty$ and when $x > 3$ and $x \to 3$, $y \to +\infty$. The maximum value of y occurs when $x = 2$ and is $y = -\frac{1}{2}$. The x-axis is a horizontal asymptote to the curve, since as $x \to \pm\infty$, $y \to 0$. The y-axis intersection is found by putting $x = 0$, giving $y = \frac{1}{6}$ (Fig. 2.9).

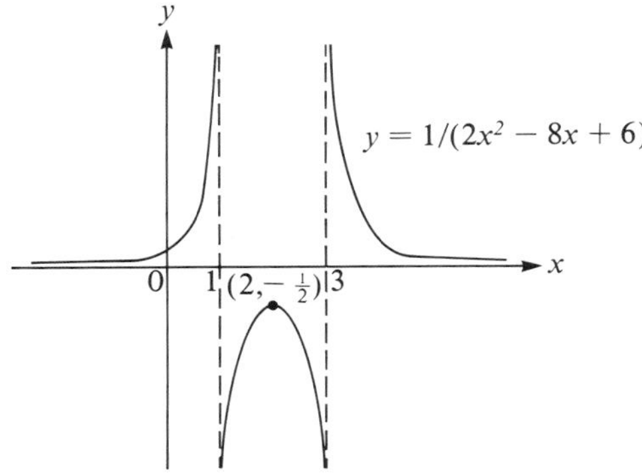

Fig. 2.9

<u>THE GRAPHS OF $y = f(x)$ and $y = 1/f(x)$</u>

EXERCISE

1. Find the set of values of x for which $2x^2+3x+2<4$. (LU 1980)

2. Find the set of real values of x for which $\dfrac{x(x-5)}{(x-3)}>6$. (LU 1981)

3. (i) Solve the inequality $\dfrac{3}{3x-2}>\dfrac{4}{4x-3}$.

   (ii) If $y=\dfrac{1}{(x-1)(x-2)}$ and x is real, show that y cannot lie between 0 and -4.

   Sketch the graph of $y=\dfrac{1}{(x-1)(x-2)}$ showing the main features clearly. (SUJB 1978)

4. Given that $f(x)\equiv 6x^2+x-12$, find the minimum value of $f(x)$ and the values of x for which $f(x)=0$.

   Using the same axes, sketch the curves $y=f(x)$ and $y=\dfrac{1}{f(x)}$ labelling each clearly.

   Deduce that there are four values of x for which $[f(x)]^2=1$. Find these values, each to two decimal places. (LU 1980)

Worked Solutions

1.
$$2x^2+3x+2 < 4$$
$$2x^2+3x-2 < 0$$
$$\therefore\quad (2x-1)(x+2) < 0$$

The roots of the quadratic $(2x-1)(x+2)=0$ are $x=\frac{1}{2}$ and $x=-2$. Since the coefficient of $x^2>0$, in the quadratic equation, the curve will be concave upwards and will go below the x-axis between $x=\frac{1}{2}$ and $x=-2$. Hence, the required range is

$$\tfrac{1}{2} < x < -2$$

2. If $\dfrac{x(x-5)}{(x-3)}>6$

$$x(x-5) > 6(x-3) \quad \text{provided} \quad (x-3) > 0$$
$$x^2-5x > 6x-18$$
$$x^2-11x+18 > 0 \qquad (1)$$
$$(x-9)(x-2) > 0$$

hence $x<2$ or $x>9$

However, if $(x-3)>0$, $x>3$. Hence, the only possible solution is $x>9$.

We now investigate the possibility $(x-3)<0$. Since multiplying throughout by a negative quantity reverses the sign of an inequality, (1) now becomes

EXERCISE

$$x^2 - 11x + 18 < 0$$
$$(x-9)(x-2) < 0$$

hence $$2 < x < 9 \quad (2)$$

But $$(x-3) < 0$$
$$\therefore \quad x < 3 \quad (3)$$

The values of x satisfying both ranges (2) and (3) is
$$2 < x < 3 \quad (4)$$

The solution to the inequality is $x > 9$ or $2 < x < 3$.

3. (i) $$\frac{3}{3x-2} > \frac{4}{4x-3}$$

We multiply throughout by $(3x-2)^2(4x-3)^2$, which is a positive quantity, so that the inequality sign remains unchanged. This gives, after cancelling common factors,

$$3(4x-3)^2(3x-2) > 4(4x-3)(3x-2)^2$$
$$3(4x-3)^2(3x-2) - 4(4x-3)(3x-2)^2 > 0$$
$$(4x-3)(3x-2)[3(4x-3) - 4(3x-2)] > 0$$
$$(4x-3)(3x-2)(12x - 9 - 12x + 8) > 0$$
$$(4x-3)(3x-2)(-1) > 0$$
$$(4x-3)(3x-2) < 0$$

If $(4x-3)(3x-2) = 0$
$$x = \tfrac{3}{4} \quad \text{or} \quad x = \tfrac{2}{3}$$

The curve $y = (4x-3)(3x-2)$ is concave upwards and goes underneath the x-axis for $\frac{2}{3} < x < \frac{3}{4}$. Hence, the required solution is $\frac{2}{3} < x < \frac{3}{4}$.

(ii) $$y = \frac{1}{(x-1)(x-2)}$$

$$y(x-1)(x-2) = 1$$
$$y(x^2 - 3x + 2) = 1$$
$$x^2y - 3xy + (2y-1) = 0$$

We require real values of x, and the condition for this is $b^2 \geqslant 4ac$.

$$9y^2 > 4y(2y-1)$$
$$9y^2 > 8y^2 - 4y$$
$$y^2 + 4y > 0$$
$$y(y+4) > 0$$
$$\therefore \quad y > 0, \; y < -4$$

In order to sketch the graph we start with the asymptotes $x = 1$ and $x = 2$. When $x < 1$ and $x \to 1$, $y \to +\infty$ and returns from $-\infty$ on the other side of $x = 1$. The curve has a maximum at $x = \frac{3}{2}$ (using $x = -b/2a$), which gives $y = -4$. When $x < 2$ and $x \to 2$, $y \to -\infty$ and returns from $+\infty$ on the other side of $x = 2$. The point of intersection on the y-axis is $(0, \frac{1}{2})$ (Fig. 2.10).

EXERCISE

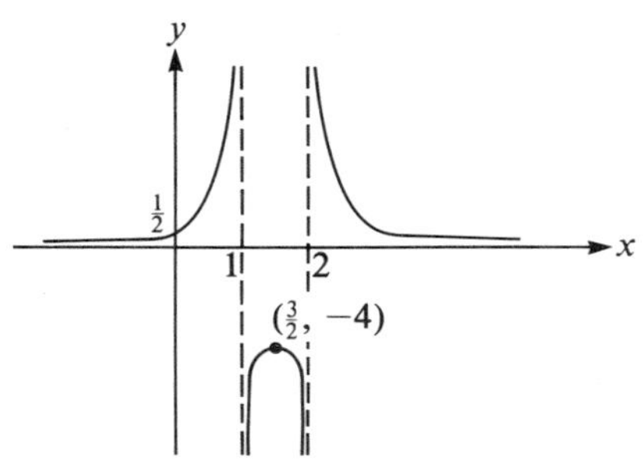

Fig. 2.10

4.

$$f(x) = 6x^2+x-12$$
$$= 6\left(x^2+\frac{x}{6}-2\right)$$

A standard technique for finding maximum or minimum values of a quadratic expression is to complete the square. This gives

$$f(x) = 6\left[\left(x+\frac{1}{12}\right)^2-\frac{289}{144}\right]$$

Since the squared term in the square bracket is always positive, the minimum value of $f(x)$ will occur when this term is zero, i.e. when $x=-\frac{1}{12}$.

$$f\left(\frac{-1}{12}\right) = 6\left(\frac{-289}{144}\right) = \frac{-289}{24}$$

If $f(x)=0$

$$6x^2+x-12 = 0$$
$$(3x-4)(2x+3) = 0$$
$$\therefore \quad 3x-4 = 0 \qquad \therefore \quad x = \frac{4}{3}$$
$$\text{or} \quad 2x+3 = 0 \qquad \therefore \quad x = \frac{-3}{2}$$

To sketch $y=f(x)$ we note that $f(\frac{4}{3})=0$ and $f(-\frac{3}{2})=0$, giving the points of intersection on the x-axis. Since the coefficient of x^2 is positive the curve is concave upwards, dropping below the x-axis in the range $-\frac{3}{2}<x<\frac{4}{3}$ to its minimum value when $x=-\frac{1}{12}$ (Fig. 2.11). The point of intersection on the y-axis is given by $f(0)=-12$.

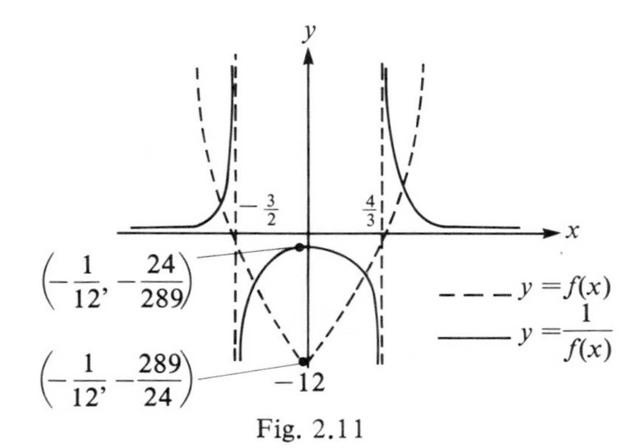

Fig. 2.11

EXERCISE

In order to sketch $y = 1/f(x)$ we note that the curve has vertical asymptotes at $x = \frac{4}{3}$ and $x = -\frac{3}{2}$, and the x-axis is a horizontal asymptote (Fig. 2.11). The minimum value of $f(x)$ at $x = -\frac{1}{12}$ will correspond to a maximum value of $y = 1/f(x)$.

If $[f(x)]^2 = 1$

$$(6x^2+x-12)^2 = 1$$

$$6x^2+x-12 = 1 \qquad (1)$$

$$\text{or} \quad 6x^2+x-12 = -1 \qquad (2)$$

Rearranging (1) we have

$$6x^2+x-13 = 0$$

$$x = \frac{-1 \pm \sqrt{1-4(6)(-13)}}{12}$$

giving

$$x = \frac{-1 \pm \sqrt{313}}{12}$$

$$x = 1.39 \quad \text{or} \quad x = -1.56$$

Rearranging (2) we have

$$6x^2+x-11 = 0$$

$$x = \frac{-1 \pm \sqrt{1-4(6)(-11)}}{12}$$

giving

$$x = -1.44 \quad \text{or} \quad x = 1.27$$

RELATIONSHIPS BETWEEN ROOTS AND COEFFICIENTS OF QUADRATIC EQUATIONS

If $a \neq 0$ the general form of a quadratic equation may be written as

$$x^2+\frac{bx}{a}+\frac{c}{a} = 0 \qquad (2.5)$$

Denoting the roots of this equation by α and β we have

$$(x-\alpha)(x-\beta) = 0$$

Multiplying out the brackets and collecting like terms gives

$$x^2-(\alpha+\beta)x+\alpha\beta = 0 \qquad (2.6)$$

Comparing (2.5) and (2.6) we find

$$\alpha+\beta = -\frac{b}{a} \qquad (2.7)$$

$$\alpha\beta = \frac{c}{a} \qquad (2.8)$$

These results are essential to the solution of many A-level questions.

Worked Example

If α, β are the roots of the quadratic equation

$$3x^2+4x+7 = 0$$

(i) evaluate $\alpha+\beta$, $\alpha\beta$ and $\alpha^2+\beta^2$;

(ii) form the quadratic equation whose roots are

$$\frac{\alpha-1}{\beta} \quad \text{and} \quad \frac{\beta-1}{\alpha}$$

(NI 1982)

EXERCISE/RELATIONSHIPS BETWEEN ROOTS AND COEFFICIENTS

Solution

(i)

$$\text{Sum of roots} = \frac{-b}{a}$$

$$\Rightarrow \quad \alpha+\beta = \frac{-4}{3}$$

$$\text{Product of roots} = \frac{c}{a}$$

$$\Rightarrow \quad \alpha\beta = \frac{7}{3}$$

Also

$$\alpha^2+\beta^2 = (\alpha+\beta)^2-2\alpha\beta = \left(\frac{-4}{3}\right)^2-2\left(\frac{7}{3}\right)$$

giving

$$\alpha^2+\beta^2 = \frac{-26}{9}$$

(ii)

$$\text{Sum of roots} = \frac{\alpha-1}{\beta}+\frac{\beta-1}{\alpha} = \frac{\alpha^2+\beta^2-(\alpha+\beta)}{\alpha\beta} = \frac{-2}{3}$$

$$\text{Product of roots} = \left(\frac{\alpha-1}{\beta}\right)\left(\frac{\beta-1}{\alpha}\right) = \frac{\alpha\beta-(\alpha+\beta)+1}{\alpha\beta} = 2$$

The required quadratic is given by

$$x^2-(\text{sum of roots})x+\text{product of roots} = 0$$

$$\therefore \quad x^2+\frac{2x}{3}+2 = 0$$

EXERCISE

1. Form the quadratic equation whose roots are α^2, β^2 given that α, β are the roots of $x^2-6x+2=0$. (NI 1980, part)

2. If the roots of the quadratic equation $x^2-3px+p^2=0$ are α and β where $\alpha>\beta$, find the values of $\alpha^2+\beta^2$ and $\alpha-\beta$ when p is positive. Find, in terms of p, a quadratic equation whose roots are α^3/β and $-\beta^3/\alpha$. (AEB 1980)

3. Find the set of values of k for which the equation

$$(2k-1)x^2+(2k+1)x+(k+1) = 0$$

has real roots.

Given that the sum of the roots of the equation

$$(2k-1)x^2+(2k+1)x+(k+1) = 0$$

is 7, find k and hence, or otherwise, find the numerical value of the product of these roots.

4. Given that α and β are the roots of the equation $x^2-bx+c=0$,

(i) show that $(\alpha^2+1)(\beta^2+1)=(c-1)^2+b^2$

(ii) find, in terms of b and c, a quadratic equation whose roots are $\dfrac{\alpha}{\alpha^2+1}$ and $\dfrac{\beta}{\beta^2+1}$ (AEB 1983)

Worked Solutions

1.
$$\text{Sum of roots} = -b/a$$
$$\therefore \quad \alpha+\beta = 6$$
$$\text{Product of roots} = c/a$$
$$\alpha\beta = 2$$
$$\therefore \quad \alpha^2\beta^2 = 4$$

and
$$\alpha^2+\beta^2 = (\alpha+\beta)^2-2\alpha\beta$$
$$= 36-4$$
$$= 32$$

Hence the required equation is $x^2-32x+4=0$.

2.
$$\alpha+\beta = 3p \quad \text{(sum of roots)}$$
$$\alpha\beta = p^2 \quad \text{(product of roots)}$$
$$(\alpha+\beta)^2 = \alpha^2+2\alpha\beta+\beta^2$$
$$\alpha^2+\beta^2 = 9p^2-2p^2$$
$$= 7p^2$$

Also
$$(\alpha-\beta)^2 = \alpha^2-2\alpha\beta+\beta^2$$
$$= (\alpha^2+\beta^2)-2\alpha\beta$$
$$= 7p^2-2p^2$$
$$\therefore \quad (\alpha-\beta)^2 = 5p^2$$
$$(\alpha-\beta) = \pm p\sqrt{5}$$

Since $\alpha > \beta$, we take
$$\alpha-\beta = p\sqrt{5}$$

The required quadratic must have
$$\text{Sum of roots} = \frac{\alpha^3}{\beta}-\frac{\beta^3}{\alpha}$$
$$= \frac{\alpha^4-\beta^4}{\alpha\beta}$$
$$= \frac{(\alpha^2+\beta^2)(\alpha-\beta)(\alpha+\beta)}{\alpha\beta}$$
$$\therefore \quad \text{Sum of roots} = \frac{7p^2\times p\sqrt{5}\times 3p}{p^2}$$

Cancelling gives
$$\text{Sum of roots} = 21\sqrt{5}\,p^2$$
$$\text{Product of roots} = \frac{\alpha^3}{\beta}\times\frac{-\beta^3}{\alpha}$$
$$= -\alpha^2\beta^2$$
$$= -p^4$$

Hence the required quadratic equation is
$$x^2-21\sqrt{5}\,p^2x-p^4 = 0$$

3. For real roots $b^2 \geqslant 4ac$
$$\therefore \quad (2k+1)^2 \geqslant 4(2k-1)(k+1)$$
$$4k^2+4k+1 \geqslant 8k^2+4k-4$$

reducing to $$4k^2 \leqslant 5$$

$$\therefore \quad k \leqslant \tfrac{1}{2}\sqrt{5} \quad \text{or} \quad k \geqslant -\tfrac{1}{2}\sqrt{5}$$

$\therefore$ The range of values is

$$\frac{-\sqrt{5}}{2} \leqslant k \leqslant \frac{\sqrt{5}}{2}$$

$$\text{Sum of roots} = -b/a$$

$$\therefore \quad \frac{-(2k+1)}{(2k-1)} = 7$$

$$-2k-1 = 14k-7$$

$$\therefore \quad k = \tfrac{3}{8}$$

$$\text{Product of roots} = \frac{k+1}{2k-1}$$

Substituting for k gives

$$\text{the product of roots} = -\tfrac{11}{2}$$

4. (i)

$$\alpha+\beta = b \qquad \text{(sum of roots)}$$

$$\alpha\beta = c \qquad \text{(product of roots)}$$

$$\begin{aligned}(\alpha^2+1)(\beta^2+1) &= \alpha^2\beta^2+\alpha^2+\beta^2+1 \\ &= (\alpha\beta)^2+(\alpha+\beta)^2-2\alpha\beta+1 \\ &= c^2+b^2-2c+1 \\ &= (c^2-2c+1)+b^2 \\ &= (c-1)^2+b^2\end{aligned}$$

(ii) Sum of roots

$$\begin{aligned}\frac{\alpha}{\alpha^2+1}+\frac{\beta}{\beta^2+1} &= \frac{\alpha(\beta^2+1)+\beta(\alpha^2+1)}{(\alpha^2+1)(\beta^2+1)} \\ &= \frac{\alpha\beta^2+\alpha+\alpha^2\beta+\beta}{(\alpha^2+1)(\beta^2+1)} \\ &= \frac{\alpha\beta(\alpha+\beta)+(\alpha+\beta)}{(\alpha^2+1)(\beta^2+1)} \\ &= \frac{bc+b}{(c-1)^2+b^2} \\ &= \frac{b(c+1)}{(c-1)^2+b^2}\end{aligned}$$

$$\begin{aligned}\text{Product of roots} = \left(\frac{\alpha}{\alpha^2+1}\right)\left(\frac{\beta}{\beta^2+1}\right) &= \frac{\alpha\beta}{(\alpha^2+1)(\beta^2+1)} \\ &= \frac{c}{(c-1)^2+b^2}\end{aligned}$$

The required quadratic equation is given by

$$x^2-(\text{sum of roots})x+(\text{product of roots}) = 0$$

$$\therefore \quad x^2-\frac{b(c+1)x}{(c-1)^2+b^2}+\frac{c}{(c-1)^2+b^2} = 0$$

giving $$[(c-1)^2+b^2]x^2-b(c+1)x+c = 0$$

EXERCISE

3 INDICES AND LOGARITHMS

INDICES

There are four basic rules in connection with indices and these are summarised below.

Multiplication $$a^m \times a^n = a^{m+n} \tag{3.1}$$

Division $$\frac{a^m}{a^n} = a^{m-n} \tag{3.2}$$

Powers $$(a^m)^n = a^{mn} \tag{3.3}$$

Roots $$(a^m)^{1/n} = a^{m/n} \tag{3.4}$$

THE ZERO INDEX

Putting $n = m$ in (3.2) gives

$$\frac{a^m}{a^m} = a^{m-m} = a^0 \tag{3.5}$$

but

$$\frac{a^m}{a^m} = 1 \tag{3.6}$$

The result (3.6) follows since division of the numerator by itself must give unity. Comparing the RHS of (3.5) and (3.6) gives

$$a^0 = 1 \tag{3.7}$$

This is a very important and useful result.

NEGATIVE INDICES

If we put $m = 0$ in (3.2) we have

$$\frac{a^0}{a^n} = a^{0-n}$$

Since $a^0 = 1$ this can be rewritten as

$$\frac{1}{a^n} = a^{-n}$$

This shows that a negative index is equivalent to the reciprocal of the corresponding positive index.

DEFINITION OF A LOGARITHM

The logarithm of a number is the power to which the base has to be raised to give that number.

Example 1

Since $10^2 = 100$

we write $\log_{10}100 = 2$

Notice that the base used for calculating the logarithm is inserted as a subscript.

Example 2

$$8^3 = 512$$
$$\log_8 512 = 3$$

RULES FOR LOGARITHMS

Let $x = a^m$ and $y = a^n$ then $\log_a x = m$ and $\log_a y = n$.

MULTIPLICATION

$$\begin{aligned}\log_a xy &= \log_a(a^m \times a^n)\\ &= \log_a a^{m+n}\\ &= m+n\end{aligned}$$

$$\therefore \quad \boxed{\log_a xy = \log_a x + \log_a y} \qquad (3.8)$$

DIVISION

$$\begin{aligned}\log_a \frac{x}{y} &= \log_a \frac{a^m}{a^n}\\ &= \log_a a^{m-n}\end{aligned}$$

$$\therefore \quad \boxed{\log_a \frac{x}{y} = \log_a x - \log_a y} \qquad (3.9)$$

POWERS OR ROOTS

$$\begin{aligned}x^p &= (a^m)^p\\ &= a^{mp}\\ \log_a x^p &= \log_a a^{mp}\\ &= mp\end{aligned}$$

$$\therefore \quad \boxed{\log_a x^p = p\log_a x} \quad (\text{since } m = \log_a x) \qquad (3.10)$$

If we let $p = 1/q$ we obtain the result

$$\boxed{\log_a x^{1/q} = \frac{1}{q}\log_a x} \qquad (3.11)$$

Worked Example

Given that $\log_2(x-5y+4)=0$ and $\log_2(x+1)-1=2\log_2 y$ find the values of x and y. (AEB 1980)

Solution

$$\log_2(x-5y+4)=0 \quad\Rightarrow\quad x-5y+4 = 2^0$$
$$\therefore\quad x-5y+4 = 1$$
$$\therefore\quad x-5y = -3 \qquad (1)$$

and

$$\log_2(x+1)-1 = 2\log_2 y$$
$$\log_2(x+1)-2\log_2 y = 1$$
$$\log_2(x+1)-\log_2 y^2 = 1$$
$$\log_2\left(\frac{x+1}{y^2}\right) = 1$$
$$\frac{x+1}{y^2} = 2^1$$
$$\therefore\quad x+1 = 2y^2 \qquad (\text{since } 2^1=2)$$

hence

$$x = 2y^2-1 \qquad (2)$$

Substituting from (2) into (1) gives

$$2y^2-1-5y = -3$$

Rearranging $\quad 2y^2-5y+2 = 0$

Factorising $\quad (2y-1)(y-2) = 0$

$$y = \tfrac{1}{2}, \quad y = 2$$

Substituting in (2)

When $y=\frac{1}{2}$ $\quad x = 2(\frac{1}{4})-1 = -\frac{1}{2}$

When $y=2$ $\quad x = 2(2)^2-1 = 7$

The solutions are $x=-\frac{1}{2}$, $y=\frac{1}{2}$ and $x=7$, $y=2$.

CHANGE OF BASE FORMULA FOR LOGARITHMS

Let

$$N = b^x \qquad (3.12)$$
$$\therefore\quad \log_b N = x \qquad (3.13)$$

also, let

$$N = a^y \qquad (3.14)$$
$$\therefore\quad \log_a N = y \qquad (3.15)$$

Comparing the RHS of (3.12) and (3.14) gives

$$b^x = a^y$$
$$b = a^{y/x}$$

Taking logarithms $\quad \log_a b = \dfrac{y}{x}$

Substituting (3.13) and (3.15) gives

$$\log_a b = \frac{\log_a N}{\log_b N}$$

$$\boxed{\log_a N = \log_a b \times \log_b N} \qquad (3.16)$$

Worked Example

Given that $\log_2 x + 2\log_4 y = 4$, show that $xy = 16$. Hence solve for x and y the simultaneous equations

$$\log_{10}(x+y) = 1$$
$$\log_2 x + 2\log_4 y = 4 \qquad \text{(AEB 1981)}$$

Solution $\log_2 x = \log_2 4 \times \log_4 x$ (change of base formula)

$$= \log_2 2^2 \times \log_4 x$$
$$\therefore \quad \log_2 x = 2\log_4 x$$

Substituting in the given expression gives

$$2\log_4 x + 2\log_4 y = 4$$
$$\log_4 x + \log_4 y = 2$$
$$\log_4 xy = 2$$
$$xy = 4^2$$
$$\therefore \quad xy = 16$$

Since $\log_{10}(x+y) = 1$ $\quad x+y = 10 \quad (1)$

Since $\log_2 x + 2\log_4 y = 4$ $\quad xy = 16 \quad (2)$

From (1) $\quad x = 10-y \quad (3)$

Substituting (3) in (2) $\quad y(10-y) = 16$

Rearranging $\quad y^2 - 10y + 16 = 0$

$$(y-2)(y-8) = 0$$
$$\therefore \quad y = 2 \quad \text{or} \quad y = 8$$

When $y = 2$ in (2) $\quad 2x = 16$

$$\therefore \quad x = 8$$

When $y = 8$ in (2) $\quad 8x = 16$

$$\therefore \quad x = 2$$

The solutions are $x = 2, \; y = 8$ and $x = 8, \; y = 2$

SPECIAL CASE

The change of base formula (3.16) can be used to obtain a special result by putting $N = a$. This gives

$$\log_a a = \log_a b \times \log_b a$$

but

$$\log_a a = 1$$
$$\therefore \quad \log_a b \times \log_b a = 1$$
$$\log_a b = \frac{1}{\log_b a}$$

EXERCISE

1. Given that $\lg y = 3 - \frac{3}{4}\lg x$, express y in terms of x in a form not involving logarithms. ($\lg = \log_{10}$.) (LU 1980)

2. Solve, for real x, the equation
$$\log_2(x+4) = 2 - \log_2 x \qquad \text{(LU 1980)}$$

3. Define the logarithm of a number b to the given base a. Use this definition to show that $\log_2 32 = 5$. Obtain the logarithm of 0.04 to the base 5. (NI 1980)

4. (i) Find the values of x which satisfy the equation

$$4\log_3 x = 9\log_x 3$$

(ii) By taking $\log_{10}5 \approx 0.7$, obtain an estimate of the root of the equation

$$10^{y-5} = 5^{y+2}$$

giving your answer to the nearest integer. (AEB 1983)

Worked Solutions

1.

$$\begin{aligned} \lg y &= 3 - \tfrac{3}{4}\lg x \\ \lg y + \tfrac{3}{4}\lg x &= 3 \\ \lg y + \lg x^{3/4} &= 3 \quad \text{(power rule for logarithms)} \\ \text{giving} \quad \lg yx^{3/4} &= 3 \\ \therefore \quad yx^{3/4} &= 10^3 \\ \therefore \quad y &= 1000x^{-3/4} \end{aligned}$$

2.

$$\begin{aligned} \log_2(x+4) &= 2 - \log_2 x \\ \log_2(x+4) + \log_2 x &= 2 \\ \log_2 x(x+4) &= 2 \\ x(x+4) &= 2^2 \\ &= 4 \\ \therefore \quad x^2 + 4x - 4 &= 0 \end{aligned}$$

Using the standard formula for solving a quadratic equation we have

$$\begin{aligned} x &= \frac{-4 \pm \sqrt{32}}{2} \\ &= -2 \pm \sqrt{8} \end{aligned}$$

Since the expression $\log_2 x$ appears in the question, we require $x > 0$, so we take the positive root only

$$\begin{aligned} x &= -2 + \sqrt{8} \\ &= -2 + 2\sqrt{2} \end{aligned}$$

3. The logarithm of b to the base a is the power to which a has to be raised to equal b. If $b = a^x$, x is the logarithm of b to the base a and we write $\log_a b = x$.

Since $\quad 32 = 2^5$

$$\log_2 32 = 5$$

Now $\quad 0.04 = \frac{1}{25}$

Introducing powers of 5, we have $\quad 0.04 = \dfrac{1}{5^2}$

Using negative indices we have

$$= 5^{-2}$$

$$\therefore \quad \log_5 0.04 = -2$$

EXERCISE

4. (i) If $4\log_3 x = 9\log_x 3$

$$4\log_3 x = \frac{9}{\log_3 x} \quad \left(\text{using } \log_x 3 = \frac{1}{\log_3 x}\right)$$

$$4(\log_3 x)^2 = 9$$

$$(\log_3 x)^2 = \frac{9}{4}$$

$$\therefore \quad \log_3 x = \frac{3}{2} \quad \text{or} \quad \log_3 x = -\frac{3}{2}$$

$$x = 3^{3/2} \quad \text{or} \quad x = 3^{-3/2}$$

$$\therefore \quad x = 3\sqrt{3} \quad \text{or} \quad x = \frac{1}{3\sqrt{3}} = \frac{\sqrt{3}}{9}$$

(ii)

$$10^{y-5} = 5^{y+2}$$

Taking logarithms to base 10 throughout gives

$$(y-5)\log_{10}10 = (y+2)\log_{10}5$$

$$(y-5) \approx (y+2)\frac{7}{10} \quad \text{(using the approximation given)}$$

$$10y - 50 \approx 7y + 14$$

$$3y \approx 64$$

$$\therefore \quad y = 21 \quad \text{(nearest integer solution)}$$

EXERCISE

4 PARTIAL FRACTIONS AND THE BINOMIAL THEOREM

PARTIAL FRACTIONS

Partial fractions have several applications and some of these occur in later chapters in this book. In this chapter we look at the application of partial fractions in problems involving the binomial theorem and, with this aim in mind, we initially outline the basic rules for partial fractions.

The decomposition of an algebraic fraction into partial fractions is the reverse process to the addition or subtraction of simple algebraic fractions. We will initially demonstrate the method when the denominator can be factorised into linear factors.

LINEAR FACTORS

In this case each linear factor occurs as the denominator of a partial fraction whose numerator is a constant which has to be determined. The method of determining the constant is illustrated in the example below.

Example

Express in partial fractions

$$\frac{1}{x(x+1)(x+2)}$$

Corresponding to each linear factor in the denominator there is a partial fraction. We assume that

$$\frac{1}{x(x+1)(x+2)} = \frac{A}{x}+\frac{B}{x+1}+\frac{C}{x+2} \qquad (1)$$

To determine the values of A, B and C we multiply throughout by $x(x+1)(x+2)$. This gives

$$1 = A(x+1)(x+2)+Bx(x+2)+Cx(x+1) \qquad (2)$$

We now put $x = 0$ so that the 2nd and 3rd terms on the RHS of (2) vanish. Consequently

$$1 = 2A \qquad \therefore \quad A = \tfrac{1}{2}$$

We can now put $x = -2$ giving

$$1 = 2C \qquad \therefore \quad C = \tfrac{1}{2}$$

This determines the values of the constants A and C. We can now put $x = -1$ which removes the first and the third terms from the RHS of (2). This gives

$$B = -1$$

The complete breakdown into partial fractions is

$$\frac{1}{x(x+1)(x+2)} = \frac{1}{2x}-\frac{1}{x+1}+\frac{1}{2(x+2)}$$

REPEATED LINEAR FACTORS

Corresponding to each repeated factor in the denominator there will be at least one partial fraction. The number of partial fractions depends on the power of the repeated linear factor. If the repeated linear factor is $(x+1)^2$ there will be two partial fractions, one with a denominator of $(x+1)$ and the second with a denominator of $(x+1)^2$.

Example

Express in partial fractions

$$\frac{3x}{(x+2)(x-2)^2}$$

Let
$$\frac{3x}{(x+2)(x-2)^2} = \frac{A}{x+2} + \frac{B}{x-2} + \frac{C}{(x-2)^2}$$

Multiplying throughout by the denominator $(x+2)(x-2)^2$, gives

$$3x = A(x-2)^2 + B(x+2)(x-2) + C(x+2)$$

Putting $x = 2$

$$6 = 4C \qquad \therefore \; C = \frac{3}{2}$$

Putting $x = -2$

$$-6 = 16A \qquad \therefore \; A = \frac{-3}{8}$$

Putting $x = 0$

$$0 = 4A - 4B + 2C$$

Substituting the values of A and C, we have

$$0 = \frac{-3}{2} - 4B + 3$$

$$4B = \frac{3}{2}$$

$$\therefore \; B = \frac{3}{8}$$

The complete breakdown into partial fractions is

$$\frac{3x}{(x+2)(x-2)^2} = \frac{-3}{8(x+2)} + \frac{3}{8(x-2)} + \frac{3}{2(x-2)^2}$$

QUADRATIC FACTORS

If there is a quadratic factor in the denominator the corresponding partial fraction will have a numerator which is a linear polynomial of the form $Bx+C$ and a denominator equal to the quadratic factor. The unknown constants are determined in an analogous manner to the cases already given.

Example

Express in partial fractions

$$\frac{2x+6}{(2x+1)(5x^2+2x+1)}$$

Let
$$\frac{2x+6}{(2x+1)(5x^2+2x+1)} = \frac{A}{(2x+1)} + \frac{Bx+C}{(5x^2+2x+1)}$$

Multiplying throughout by $(2x+1)(5x^2+2x+1)$ gives

$$2x+6 = A(5x^2+2x+1)+(Bx+C)(2x+1) \tag{1}$$

Putting $x=-\frac{1}{2}$ gives

$$5 = A\left(\frac{5}{4}-1+1\right) \quad \therefore \quad A = 4 \tag{2}$$

Multiplying out the brackets on the RHS of (1), collecting like terms together and factorising, we have

$$2x+6 = (5A+2B)x^2+(B+2C+2A)x+(A+C) \tag{3}$$

This is an identity which is valid for all values of x. Equating coefficients of like powers of x, we have for x^2

$$0 = 5A+2B$$

since the LHS has no term involving x^2. Substituting the value of A given by (2) we have

$$0 = 20+2B$$

$$\therefore \quad B = -10 \tag{4}$$

Equating coefficients of x

$$2 = B+2C+2A$$

Substituting the values of A and B given by (2) and (4) we have

$$2 = -10+2C+8$$

$$\therefore \quad 4 = 2C \quad \text{i.e.} \quad C = 2$$

The complete decomposition into partial fractions is

$$\frac{2x+6}{(2x+1)(5x^2+2x+1)} = \frac{4}{(2x+1)}+\frac{2-10x}{(5x^2+2x+1)}$$

THE BINOMIAL THEOREM

The binomial theorem is

$$(1+x)^n = 1+\binom{n}{1}x+\binom{n}{2}x^2+\binom{n}{3}x^3+\ldots+\binom{n}{n}x^n \tag{4.1}$$

where $\binom{n}{r}$ represents the number of combinations of r objects from n items and is given by

$$\binom{n}{r} = \frac{n!}{r!(n-r)!} \quad \text{and may be written as } {}^nC_r \tag{4.2}$$

where $n! = n(n-1)(n-2)(n-3)\ldots(3)(2)(1)$. The quantities represented by $\binom{n}{r}$ are referred to as binomial coefficients. Using the definition of $r!$ and $(n-r)!$, the rth binomial coefficient is given by

$$\binom{n}{r} = \frac{n(n-1)(n-2)(n-3)\ldots(n-r+1)}{r!} \tag{4.3}$$

In the case where n is a positive integer the series terminates after $(n+1)$ terms, while if n is a negative integer or a rational number the resulting binomial expansion is infinite. The sum of the terms of a finite series resulting from a binomial expansion will always exist for finite values of x, while if the series is infinite its sum will only converge for $|x|<1$ and outside this range the expansion is invalid.

The series (4.1) can be adapted to obtain any binomial expansion. This is shown in the examples which follow.

Example

Find the terms in the expansion of $(x+y)^4$.

$$
\begin{aligned}
(x+y)^4 &= \left[x\left(1+\frac{y}{x}\right)\right]^4 \\
&= x^4\left(1+\frac{y}{x}\right)^4 \\
&= x^4\left[1+\frac{4y}{x}+\frac{4\times 3}{2\times 1}\left(\frac{y}{x}\right)^2+\frac{4\times 3\times 2}{3\times 2\times 1}\left(\frac{y}{x}\right)^3+\frac{4\times 3\times 2\times 1}{4\times 3\times 2\times 1}\left(\frac{y}{x}\right)^4\right] \\
&= x^4\left(1+\frac{4y}{x}+\frac{6y^2}{x^2}+\frac{4y^3}{x^3}+\frac{y^4}{x^4}\right)
\end{aligned}
$$

$$\therefore \quad (x+y)^4 = x^4+4x^3y+6x^2y^2+4xy^3+y^4$$

Note: $n = 4$ generates 5 terms in the resulting binomial expansion.

Worked Example

Find the numerical value of the term independent of x in the expansion of

$$\left(2x+\frac{1}{x^2}\right)^6 \qquad \text{(LU 1980)}$$

Solution

$$
\begin{aligned}
\left(2x+\frac{1}{x^2}\right)^6 &= \left[2x\left(1+\frac{1}{2x^3}\right)\right]^6 \\
&= (2x)^6\left(1+\frac{1}{2x^3}\right)^6 \\
&= 64x^6\left(1+\frac{1}{2x^3}\right)^6
\end{aligned}
$$

The term independent of x is obtained when x^6 is multiplied by x^{-6} (since $x^6 \times x^{-6} = x^0$). The third term in the expansion of $(1 + 1(2x)^3)^6$ will involve x^{-6} and is, consequently, the only term of interest in this problem. The required term is

$$
\begin{aligned}
& 64x^6 \times \frac{6\times 5}{2!}\left(\frac{1}{2x^3}\right)^2 \\
&= 64\times 15\times \tfrac{1}{4} \\
&= 240
\end{aligned}
$$

Example

Find the first four terms in the expansion of $(1+2x)^{-1}$ and state the range of values of x for which it is valid.

Putting $n = -1$ and replacing x by $2x$ in (4.1) gives

$$(1+2x)^{-1} = 1+(-1)2x+\frac{(-1)(-2)}{2\times 1}(2x)^2+\frac{(-1)(-2)(-3)}{3\times 2\times 1}(2x)^3+\ldots$$

Simplifying

$$(1+2x)^{-1} = 1-2x+4x^2-8x^3+\ldots$$

This series is valid for $|2x|<1$ or, equivalently, for the range $-1<2x<1$

$$-\tfrac{1}{2} < x < \tfrac{1}{2}$$

EXERCISE

1. Obtain partial fractions for the expression

$$\frac{(x+1)(4x-1)}{(2-x)(x^2+3)}$$ (NI 1981)

2. Given that $g(x) = \dfrac{5-x}{(1+x^2)(1-x)}$, express $g(x)$ in partial fractions.

Hence, or otherwise, show that the expansion of $g(x)$ as a series of ascending powers of x up to and including the term in x^4 is $5+4x-x^2+5x^4$.

(LU 1980)

3. Given that $f(x) = \dfrac{1+2x}{(1+x)(1-2x^2)}$, express $f(x)$ in partial fractions and find the first six terms in the expansion of $f(x)$ in ascending powers of x, when $|x|<1/\sqrt{2}$. (LU 1981)

4. When terms in x^n, $n \geqslant 4$, are omitted

$$\frac{3ax}{4}+\sqrt{4+ax}-\frac{2}{\sqrt{1-ax}} = -x^2+bx^3$$

Find the values of a and b. (AEB 1980)

5. Expand $(9+y)^{1/2}$ in ascending powers of y up to and including the term in y^2. Hence show that $(9-2\alpha+\alpha^2)^{1/2} = 3-\dfrac{\alpha}{3}+\dfrac{4\alpha^2}{27}$ if α is so small that terms in α^n, $n \geqslant 3$, may be neglected. Solve the quadratic equation $(x+1)(x-2)+\alpha x = 0$ by using the formula. Hence show that the positive root of this equation is approximately

$$2-\frac{2\alpha}{3}+\frac{2\alpha^2}{27}$$ (AEB 1981)

6. Given that $x>2$, use the binomial expansion to express $\left(\dfrac{x+2}{x}\right)^{-1/2}$ in the form

$$a+\frac{b}{x}+\frac{c}{x^2}+\frac{d}{x^3}+\ldots$$

evaluating the constants a, b, c and d. Taking $x = 100$, use your series to find an approximation for $\left(\dfrac{450}{51}\right)^{1/2}$ giving your answers to 4 decimal places. (AEB 1983)

Worked Solutions

1. Let $$\frac{(x+1)(4x-1)}{(2-x)(x^2+3)} = \frac{A}{2-x}+\frac{Bx+C}{x^2+3}$$

$$\therefore \quad (x+1)(4x-1) = A(x^2+3)+(Bx+C)(2-x) \qquad (1)$$

putting $x = 2$ $\quad 21 = 7A \quad$ giving $\quad A = 3$

Multiplying out the brackets on the LHS and RHS of (1) and collecting together like terms

$$4x^2+3x-1 = (A-B)x^2+(2B-C)x+(3A+2C)$$

Equating coefficients of like terms gives

for x^2 $\quad A-B = 4 \qquad (2)$

for x $\quad 2B-C = 3 \qquad (3)$

Substituting the value of A in (2) gives

$$3-B = 4 \quad \therefore \quad B = -1$$

Substituting the value of B in (3)

$$-2-C = 3 \quad \therefore \quad C = -5$$

$$\therefore \quad \frac{(x+1)(4x-1)}{(2-x)(x^2+3)} = \frac{3}{2-x}-\frac{(x+5)}{x^2+3}$$

2. Let $\quad g(x) = \dfrac{A}{1-x}+\dfrac{Bx+C}{(1+x^2)}$

Multiplying throughout by $(1-x)(1+x^2)$ gives

$$5-x = A(1+x^2)+(Bx+C)(1-x) \qquad (1)$$

$$5-x = (A-B)x^2+(B-C)x+(A+C) \qquad (2)$$

putting $x = 1$ in (1)

$$4 = 2A \quad \therefore \quad A = 2$$

Equating coefficients of x^2 on the LHS and RHS of (2)

$$0 = A-B \quad \therefore \quad B = 2$$

Equating coefficients of x on LHS and RHS of (2)

$$-1 = B-C$$

Substituting the value of B gives

$$-1 = 2-C \quad \therefore \quad C = 3$$

hence $\quad g(x) = 2(1-x)^{-1}+(2x+3)(1+x^2)^{-1} \qquad (3)$

Expanding by the binomial theorem

$$(1-x)^{-1} = 1+(-1)(-x)+\frac{(-1)(-2)}{2\times 1}(-x)^2+\frac{(-1)(-2)(-3)}{3\times 2\times 1}(-x)^3 + \frac{(-1)(-2)(-3)(-4)}{4\times 3\times 2\times 1}(-x)^4+\ldots$$

Simplifying to

$$(1-x)^{-1} = 1+x+x^2+x^3+x^4+\ldots \qquad (2)$$

$$(1+x^2)^{-1} = 1+(-1)(x^2)+\frac{(-1)(-2)}{2\times 1}(x^2)^2+\frac{(-1)(-2)(-3)}{3\times 2\times 1}(x^2)^3 + \frac{(-1)(-2)(-3)(-4)}{4\times 3\times 2\times 1}(x^2)^4+\ldots$$

$$= 1-x^2+x^4-x^6+x^8-\ldots \qquad (3)$$

EXERCISE

Substituting the expansions (2) and (3) in (1) gives

$$g(x) = 2(1+x+x^2+x^3+x^4+\dots)+(2x+3)(1-x^2+x^4-x^6+\dots)$$
$$= 2+2x+2x^2+2x^3+2x^4+3-3x^2+3x^4+2x-2x^3$$

Giving

$$g(x) = 5+4x-x^2+5x^4-\dots$$

3. Let

$$\frac{1+2x}{(1+x)(1-2x^2)} = \frac{A}{1+x}+\frac{Bx+C}{1-2x^2}$$
$$1+2x = A(1-2x^2)+(Bx+C)(1+x)$$

putting $x=-1 \Rightarrow \quad -1 = -A \quad \therefore \quad A = 1$

Multiplying out the brackets on the RHS and collecting like terms

$$1+2x = (B-2A)x^2+(B+C)x+(A+C)$$

Equating coefficients of x^2

$$0 = B-2A \qquad \therefore \quad B = 2$$

Equating coefficients of x

$$2 = B+C \qquad \therefore \quad C = 0$$

hence

$$f(x) = \frac{1}{1+x}+\frac{2x}{1-2x^2}$$

or

$$f(x) = (1+x)^{-1}+2x(1-2x^2)^{-1} \tag{1}$$

Expanding by the binomial theorem

$$(1+x)^{-1} = 1-x+x^2-x^3+x^4-x^5+\dots \tag{2}$$

$$(1-2x^2)^{-1} = 1+2x^2+\frac{(-1)(-2)}{2\times 1}(-2x^2)^2+\frac{(-1)(-2)(-3)}{3\times 2\times 1}(-2x^2)^3$$
$$+\frac{(-1)(-2)(-3)(-4)}{4\times 3\times 2\times 1}(-2x^2)^4$$
$$+\frac{(-1)(-2)(-3)(-4)(-5)}{5\times 4\times 3\times 2\times 1}(-2x^2)^5+\dots$$
$$= 1+2x^2+4x^4+8x^6+16x^8+32x^{10}+\dots \tag{3}$$

Substituting the expansions (2) and (3) in (1) gives

$$f(x) = (1-x+x^2-x^3+x^4-x^5)+2x(1+2x^2+4x^4+8x^6+16x^8+32x^{10})$$

Giving

$$f(x) = 1+x+x^2+3x^3+x^4+7x^5$$

4. Expanding by the binomial theorem

$$(1-ax)^{-1/2} = 1+(-\tfrac{1}{2})(-ax)+\frac{(-\frac{1}{2})(-\frac{3}{2})}{2!}(-ax)^2$$
$$+\frac{(-\frac{1}{2})(-\frac{3}{2})(-\frac{5}{2})}{3!}(-ax)^3$$

$$\therefore \quad (1-ax)^{-1/2} = 1+\frac{ax}{2}+\frac{3a^2x^2}{8}+\frac{5a^3x^3}{16} \tag{1}$$

$$(4+ax)^{1/2} = \left[4\left(1+\frac{ax}{4}\right)\right]^{1/2}$$
$$= 2\left(1+\frac{ax}{4}\right)^{1/2}$$

Expanding by the binomial theorem

$$\left(1+\frac{ax}{4}\right)^{1/2} = 1+\tfrac{1}{2}\left(\frac{ax}{4}\right)+\frac{\tfrac{1}{2}(-\tfrac{1}{2})}{2}\left(\frac{ax}{4}\right)^2+\frac{\tfrac{1}{2}(-\tfrac{1}{2})(-\tfrac{3}{2})}{3\times 2\times 1}\left(\frac{ax}{4}\right)^3+\ldots$$

$$= 1+\frac{ax}{8}-\frac{1}{128}a^2x^2+\frac{a^3x^3}{1024} \qquad (2)$$

$$\therefore \quad \frac{3ax}{4}+\sqrt{4+ax}-\frac{2}{\sqrt{1-ax}} = \frac{3ax}{4}+2\left(1+\frac{ax}{8}-\frac{a^2x^2}{128}+\frac{a^3x^3}{1024}\right)$$

$$-2\left(1+\frac{ax}{2}+\frac{3a^2x^2}{8}+\frac{5a^3x^3}{16}\right)$$

Multiplying out the brackets and collecting like terms together

$$\frac{3ax}{4}+\sqrt{4+ax}-\frac{2}{\sqrt{1-ax}} = \left(\frac{3a}{4}+\frac{a}{4}-a\right)x-\left(\frac{a^2}{64}+\frac{3a^2}{4}\right)x^2$$

$$+\left(\frac{a^3}{512}-\frac{5a^3}{8}\right)x^3$$

$$= \frac{-49}{64}a^2x^2-\frac{319}{512}a^3x^3$$

$$\equiv -x^2+bx^3 \qquad \text{(the given expression)}$$

Equating coefficients

$$\frac{49}{64}a^2 = 1 \qquad \therefore \quad a = \pm\frac{8}{7}$$

$$b = \frac{-319}{512}a^3$$

$$= \frac{-319}{512}\times\frac{512}{343}$$

$$= \pm\frac{319}{343}$$

5. Expanding by the binomial theorem

$$(9+y)^{1/2} = \left[9\left(1+\frac{y}{9}\right)\right]^{1/2}$$

$$= 3\left(1+\frac{y}{9}\right)^{1/2}$$

$$= 3\left[1+\tfrac{1}{2}\left(\frac{y}{9}\right)+\frac{\tfrac{1}{2}(-\tfrac{1}{2})}{2}\left(\frac{y}{9}\right)^2+\ldots\right]$$

$$= 3\left(1+\frac{y}{18}-\frac{1}{648}y^2\right)$$

$$= 3+\frac{y}{6}-\frac{y^2}{216}$$

<u>EXERCISE</u>

We now put $\quad y = \alpha^2 - 2\alpha$

$$(9-2\alpha+\alpha^2)^{1/2} = 3+\frac{1}{6}(\alpha^2-2\alpha)-\frac{1}{216}(\alpha^2-2\alpha)^2$$

$$= 3+\frac{\alpha^2}{6}-\frac{\alpha}{3}-\frac{1}{216}(\alpha^4-4\alpha^3+4\alpha^2)$$

$$= 3-\frac{\alpha}{3}+\alpha^2\left(\frac{1}{6}-\frac{1}{54}\right) \qquad \text{(neglecting terms} \geqslant \alpha^3\text{)}$$

$$= 3-\frac{\alpha}{3}+\frac{4\alpha^2}{27} \qquad \text{the required result} \qquad (1)$$

$$(x+1)(x-2)+\alpha x = 0$$

$$x^2+(\alpha-1)x-2 = 0$$

The solution to this quadratic is

$$x = \frac{(1-\alpha)\pm\sqrt{\alpha^2-2\alpha+9}}{2} \qquad (2)$$

Using the approximation (1) in (2) and taking the positive root

$$x = \frac{(1-\alpha)+(3-\alpha/3+4/27\alpha^2)}{2}$$

$$\therefore \quad x = 2-\frac{2}{3}\alpha+\frac{2}{27}\alpha^2$$

The answer is an approximation since we have neglected terms $\geqslant \alpha^n$ where $n=3$ in the expansion (1).

6. $$\left(\frac{x+2}{x}\right)^{-1/2} = \left(1+\frac{2}{x}\right)^{-1/2}$$

$$= 1+(-\tfrac{1}{2})\left(\frac{2}{x}\right)+\frac{(-\frac{1}{2})(-\frac{3}{2})}{2\times 1}\left(\frac{2}{x}\right)^2+\frac{(-\frac{1}{2})(-\frac{3}{2})(-\frac{5}{2})}{3\times 2\times 1}\left(\frac{2}{x}\right)^3+\ldots$$

$$= 1-\frac{1}{x}+\frac{3}{2x^2}-\frac{5}{2x^3}+\ldots \qquad (1)$$

$$= a+\frac{b}{x}+\frac{c}{x^2}+\frac{d}{x^3}+\ldots \qquad (2)$$

Comparing (1) and (2)

$$a = 1 \qquad b = -1 \qquad c = \tfrac{3}{2} \qquad d = -\tfrac{5}{2}$$

$$\left(\frac{450}{51}\right)^{1/2} = \left(\frac{9\times 50}{51}\right)^{1/2}$$

$$= 3\left(\frac{50}{51}\right)^{1/2} = 3\left(\frac{51}{50}\right)^{-1/2}$$

$$= 3\left(1+\frac{2}{x}\right)^{-1/2} \qquad \text{when} \quad x = 100$$

$\therefore$ In (1)

$$\left(\frac{450}{51}\right)^{1/2} = 3\left(1-\frac{1}{100}+\frac{3}{20\,000}-\frac{5}{2\times 10^6}\right) = 3\times 0.990\,147\,5$$

$$= 2.970\,442\,5 = 2.9704 \qquad \text{(to 4 decimal places)}$$

EXERCISE

5 FUNCTIONS

MAPPINGS AND RELATIONS

In algebra a relation is a rule connecting one set of numbers with another. We say that the relation maps a number from its domain to an image set called the range. This concept is shown diagrammatically in Fig. 5.1.

Example

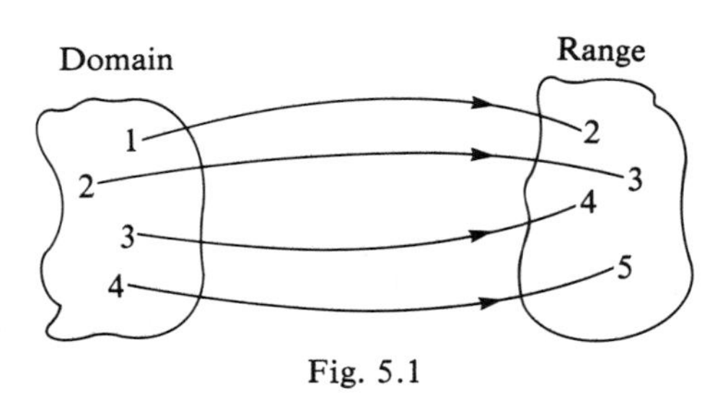

Fig. 5.1

If we let x denote the numbers in the domain and y those in the range, the connection between the two sets is that $y = x + 1$. In this case we say that x maps to $(x + 1)$, which is written as $x \to (x + 1)$.

FUNCTIONS

A function is a mapping that has the property that for each number in the domain there corresponds a unique value in the range. The function operates on the domain and maps it across uniquely to the range. The mapping in the example above satisfies this definition and is a function. The notation for this is $f: x \to x + 1$ or $y = f(x)$ where $f(x) = x + 1$. The first notation conveys the concept of a mapping, whereas the second suggests a graphical representation.

The graphical representation of a relation provides us with a useful method for selecting those relations that are also functions.

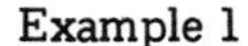

Example 1 $\quad f(x) = x + 1 \quad$ or $\quad f: x \to x + 1$

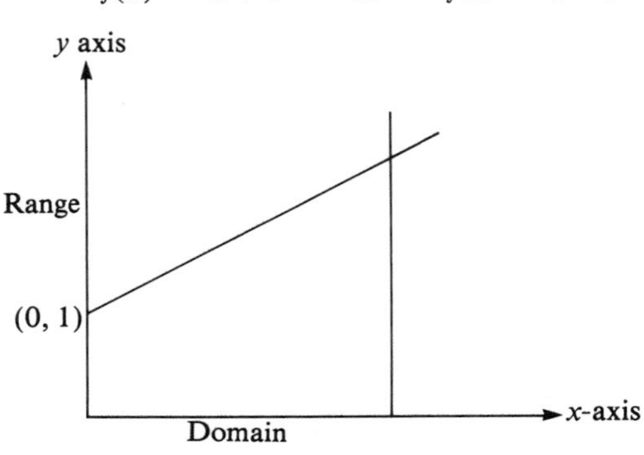

Fig. 5.2 One–one mapping.

It can be seen from the graph (Fig. 5.2) that each value of x corresponds to a unique value of y. A vertical line parallel to the y-axis cuts the graph once only. Since one value of x corresponds to only one value of y, it is referred to as a one–one mapping.

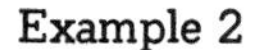

Example 2 $\qquad f{:}x \rightarrow x^2 \qquad$ or $\qquad y = x^2$

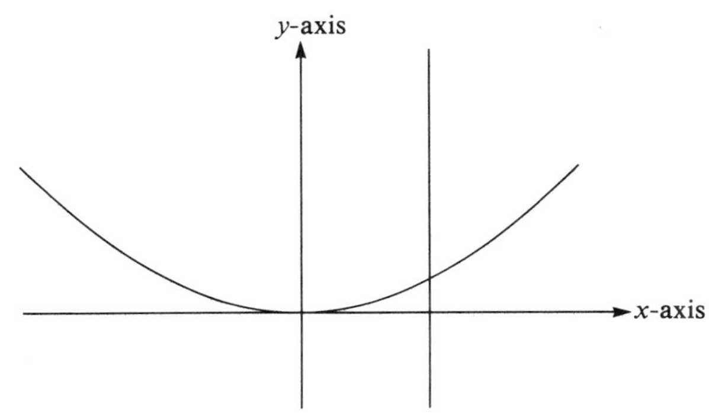

Fig. 5.3 Many–one mapping.

It can be seen from Fig. 5.3 that any arbitrary vertical line will intersect the curve at one point. Consequently, the mapping is a function. However, in this example, we note that $f(2) = 4$ and also $f(-2) = 4$. This is an example of a many–one mapping, since more than one value in the domain maps to the same value in the range.

Example 3 $\qquad f{:}x \rightarrow \sqrt{x} \qquad$ or $\qquad y^2 = x$

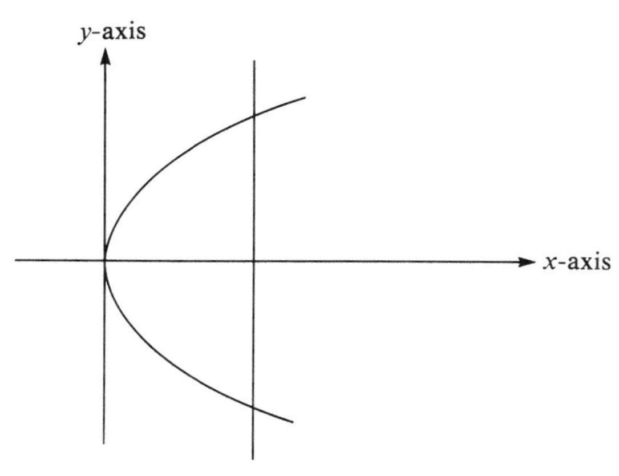

Fig. 5.4 One–many mapping.

In this case the curve is intersected twice by the vertical line with the result that one value of x corresponds to two values of y and the relation is not a function. This relation is an example of a one–many mapping.

THE INVERSE FUNCTION

A function maps the domain across to the range. The inverse function reverses the process and maps the range of the original function to the domain. If the function is $y = f(x)$ the inverse function is denoted by $x = f^{-1}(y)$ (see Fig. 5.5).

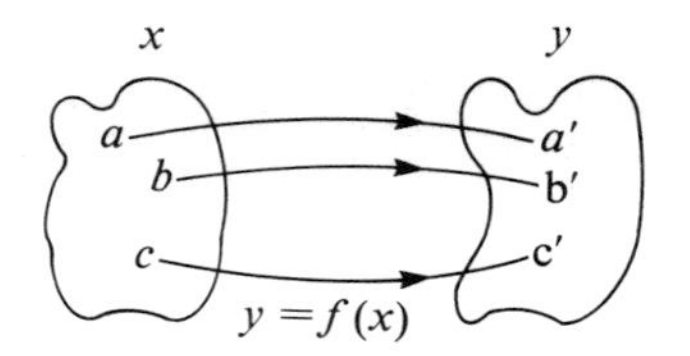

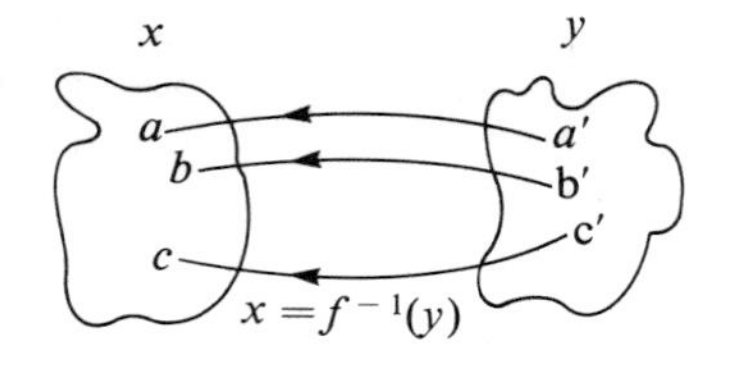

Fig. 5.5

The inverse function interchanges the role of the domain and range of the function. However, since a many–one mapping would then become a one–many mapping, which is not a function, the inverse function only exists for a one–one mapping. The method of determining the inverse function is shown in the following example.

Example

Find the inverse function of $f(x) = 3x + 1$.

Let $y = 3x + 1$

Since the inverse function interchanges the domain and range of the function, we replace x by y and y by x.

This gives $x = 3y + 1$

If we now make y the subject of the formula, we have

$$y = \frac{1}{3}(x - 1)$$

This is the inverse function. Hence

$$f^{-1}(x) = \frac{1}{3}(x - 1)$$

An important property of the inverse function is that it is the reflection in the straight line $y = x$ of $y = f(x)$.

SPECIAL FUNCTIONS

(1) **The Exponential Function $y = e^x$**

Any function of the form a^x where a is a constant and x is a variable is referred to as an exponential function. We define the exponential function to be the series given by

$$y = \underset{n\to\infty}{\text{Limit}} \left(1 + \frac{1}{n}\right)^{nx}$$

Expanding by the binomial series we have

$$\left(1 + \frac{1}{n}\right)^{nx} = 1 + nx\left(\frac{1}{n}\right) + \frac{nx(nx-1)}{2!}\left(\frac{1}{n}\right)^2 + \frac{nx(nx-1)(nx-2)}{3!}\left(\frac{1}{n}\right)^3 + \ldots$$

$$= 1 + x + \frac{x(x - 1/n)}{2!} + \frac{x(x-1/n)(x-2/n)}{3!} + \ldots$$

$$\underset{n\to\infty}{\text{Limit}} \left(1 + \frac{1}{n}\right)^{nx} = 1 + x + \frac{x^2}{2!} + \frac{x^3}{3!} + \ldots$$

Since, by definition, this series is the exponential function, we have

$$e^x = 1 + x + \frac{x^2}{2!} + \frac{x^3}{3!} + \ldots + \frac{x^r}{r!} + \ldots$$

If we put $x = 1$, we find that

$$e = 1 + 1 + \frac{1}{1!} + \frac{1}{2!} + \frac{1}{3!} + \frac{1}{4!} + \ldots \qquad \text{giving} \quad e \approx 2.718\,28$$

(2) **The Logarithmic Function $y = \ln x$**
If $y = e^x$, we interchange x and y in order to find the inverse function. This gives $x = e^y$. Taking the logarithm to base e of each side gives $\ln x = y$, where $\ln x = \log_e x$. If $f(x) = e^x$, $f^{-1}(x) = \ln x$.

The relationship between the two functions is shown in Fig. 5.6, which also shows that the inverse function $f^{-1}(x)$ is the reflection in $y = x$ of the function.

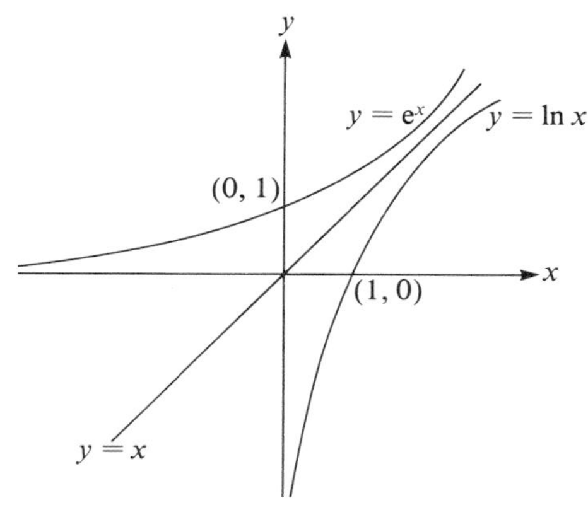

Fig. 5.6

COMPOSITE FUNCTIONS

Suppose we have two functions $y = f(x)$ and $u = g(x)$. The result of substituting the second function into the first to give $y = f(g(x))$ is called the composite or sometimes the product function. This composite function is usually denoted simply by $fg(x)$ or sometimes $f \circ g$. In general the order of the substitution is important and $fg(x) \neq gf(x)$ as shown in the following example.

Example

(i) Let $f(x) = e^x$ and $g(x) = x^2$.
The composite or product function fg is

$$fg(x) = e^{g(x)} = e^{x^2}$$

(ii) The product function gf is

$$gf(x) = f^2 = (e^x)^2 = e^{2x}$$

Note $gf(x)$ is not the same as $fg(x)$.

THE COMPOSITE FUNCTION $ff^{-1}(x)$

A function maps its domain across to its range. Since the inverse function, $f^{-1}(x)$, maps the range back to the domain, it follows that $ff^{-1}(x) = x$. This is shown in Fig. 5.7.

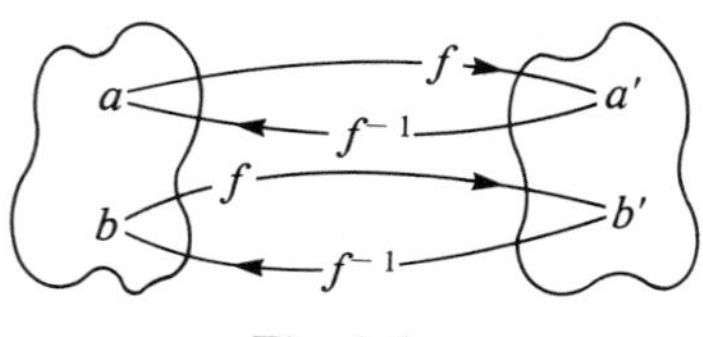

Fig. 5.7

Example

$$f(x) = e^x \quad \text{and} \quad f^{-1}(x) = \ln x$$
$$ff^{-1}(x) = e^{f^{-1}}$$
$$= e^{\ln x}$$
$$\therefore \quad ff^{-1(x)} = x$$

Worked Example

Given that $$f(x) = \frac{x^2+1}{2x^2+1} \quad (x \geqslant 2)$$

find an expression for $f^{-1}(x)$ and verify that $(f^{-1} \circ f)(x) = x$.

(WJEC 1982, part)

Solution

Let $$y = \frac{x^2+1}{2x^2+1}$$

Interchanging x and y gives

$$x = \frac{y^2+1}{2y^2+1}$$
$$x(2y^2+1) = y^2+1$$
$$2xy^2+x = y^2+1$$
$$y^2(2x-1) = 1-x$$
$$y^2 = \frac{1-x}{2x-1}$$
$$y = \sqrt{\frac{1-x}{2x-1}}$$
$$\therefore \quad f^{-1}(x) = \sqrt{\frac{1-x}{2x-1}}$$

hence $$(f^{-1} \circ f)(x) = \sqrt{\frac{1-f}{2f-1}}$$

$$= \sqrt{\frac{1-\dfrac{x^2+1}{2x^2+1}}{\dfrac{2x^2+2}{2x^2+1}-1}}$$

$$= \sqrt{\frac{(2x^2+1)-(x^2+1)}{2x^2+2-(2x^2+1)}}$$

$$= \sqrt{x^2}$$

$$\therefore \quad (f^{-1} \circ f)(x) = x \qquad \text{as required}$$

THE COMPOSITE FUNCTION $ff^{-1}(x)$

PROPERTIES OF FUNCTIONS

(1) **Odd Functions**
Functions that have the property that $f(-x) = -f(x)$ are called odd functions. All such functions have symmetry about the origin.

Example $y = x^3$
Since $(-x)^3 = -x^3$, this is an odd function. Fig. 5.8 shows the symmetry about the origin.

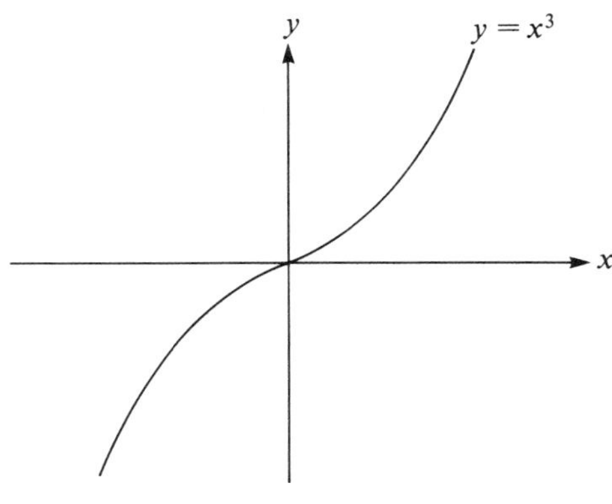

Fig. 5.8

(2) **Even Functions**
If a function has the property that $f(-x) = f(x)$ it is called an even function. All even functions have symmetry about the y-axis.

Example $y = x^2$ (see Fig. 5.9).

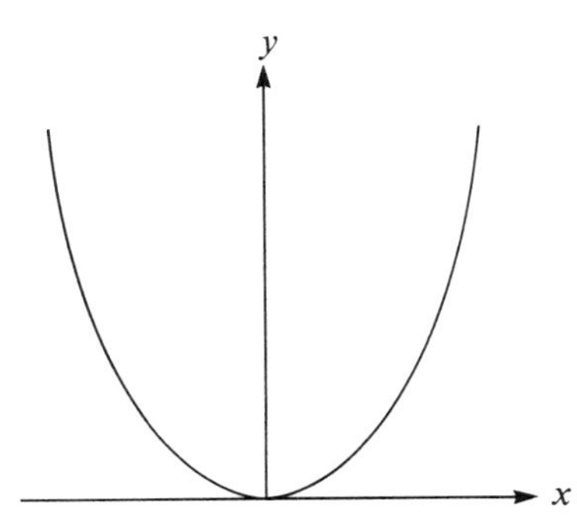

Fig. 5.9

Note $y = x^2$ is an even function because $(-x)^2 = x^2$.

EXERCISE

1. The functions f and g are defined by

$$f(x) = e^{2x} \quad g(x) = \sqrt{1-4x^2} \quad (-\tfrac{1}{2} \leqslant x \leqslant 0)$$

where $\sqrt{\ }$ denotes the positive square root. Find expressions for $f^{-1}(x)$ and $g^{-1}(x)$, and write down the domain and range of each of the two inverse functions. (WJEC 1980, part)

2. A function f with domain and range the interval $[0,3]$ is defined by

$$\begin{aligned} f(x) &= x+2 \quad \text{if} \quad x \in [0,1] \\ &= 3-x \quad \text{if} \quad x \in [1,3] \end{aligned}$$

Sketch the graphs of f, f^{-1}, $f \circ f$, and $(f \circ f) \circ (f \circ f)$, showing clearly the point of the graph at any discontinuity. (WJEC 1982, part)

3. (i) If $f(x) = 3^x$ show that

$$f(x+2) - f(x-1) = \tfrac{26}{3} f(x)$$

(ii) Obtain the inverse relation for $y = \dfrac{1-x}{2+x}$.

(iii) Show that the only linear functions $g(x) = ax + b$ (a, b constants) that satisfy $g(x+1) = g(x) + 1$ must be of the form $g(x) = x + k$, where k is a constant. (NI 1980)

4. (i) The functions f_1 and f_2, each with domain $D = \{x : x \in \mathbb{R}, x > -1\}$, are defined by $f_1(x) = \ln(x+1)$, $f_2(x) = x^2 + 1$.

For each function state the range. Show that an inverse function f_1^{-1} exists and, using the same axes, sketch the graphs of $y = f_1(x)$ and $y = f_1^{-1}(x)$. Show that an inverse function f_2^{-1} does not exist and suggest an interval such that f_2, restricted to this interval, will have an inverse function.

(ii) Functions g_1 and g_2, each with domain $\mathbb{R}$, are defined by

$$g_1(x) = \ln(1 + x^2), \quad g_2(x) = 1 + x$$

Given that $g_1 g_2$ and $g_2 g_1$ are the composite functions defined on $\mathbb{R}$, find expressions for $g_1 g_2(x)$ and $g_2 g_1(x)$ and state whether each of these composite functions is odd, even or neither. (LU 1981)

5. The functions f, g are defined by

$$f : x \to \frac{1}{x-1} \quad (x \in \mathbb{R}, x \neq 1)$$

$$g : x \to \frac{x}{x^2 - 1} \quad (x \in \mathbb{R}, x^2 \neq 1)$$

State whether f and g are odd functions, even functions or neither. Give a reason why there is no inverse to g. Find an expression for the inverse function to f in the form $f^{-1} : x \to \ldots$.

Sketch, on the same axes, the graph of f and the graph of the inverse to f, labelling your graphs clearly. (LU 1982)

Worked Solutions

1. For $f(x)$ let $\quad y = e^{2x}$

Interchanging x and y gives $\quad x = e^{2y}$

$$\begin{aligned} \ln x &= 2y \\ y &= \tfrac{1}{2} \ln x \end{aligned}$$

hence $\quad f^{-1}(x) = \tfrac{1}{2} \ln x$

For $g(x)$ let $\quad y = \sqrt{1 - 4x^2}$

EXERCISE

Interchanging x and y gives

$$\begin{aligned} x &= \sqrt{1-4y^2} \\ x^2 &= 1-4y^2 \\ y^2 &= \tfrac{1}{4}(1-x^2) \\ y &= \tfrac{1}{2}\sqrt{1-x^2} \\ g^{-1}(x) &= \tfrac{1}{2}\sqrt{1-x^2} \end{aligned}$$

The exponential function, $f(x) = e^{2x}$ is defined over the domain $-\infty < x < \infty$ and has a range given by $0 < f(x) < \infty$. Consequently, for the inverse function, $f^{-1}(x)$, the domain is $0 < x < \infty$ with range $-\infty < f^{-1} < \infty$.

Similarly, for $g(x)$ the domain is $-\frac{1}{2} \leqslant x \leqslant 0$, with range $0 \leqslant g(x) \leqslant 1$. The inverse function $g^{-1}(x)$ will have domain $0 \leqslant x \leqslant 1$ and range $\frac{1}{2} \leqslant g^{-1}(x) \leqslant 0$. These results can be summarised as

Function	*Domain*	*Range*
$f(x)$	$-\infty < x < \infty$	$0 < f(x) < \infty$
$f^{-1}(x)$	$0 \leqslant x < \infty$	$-\infty < f^{-1} < \infty$
$g(x)$	$-\frac{1}{2} \leqslant x \leqslant 0$	$0 \leqslant g(x) \leqslant 1$
$g^{-1}(x)$	$0 \leqslant x \leqslant 1$	$-\frac{1}{2} \leqslant g^{-1} \leqslant 0$

2. For $f(x)$ let $\quad y = x+2$

Interchanging x and y for the inverse function gives

$$\begin{aligned} x &= y+2 \\ y &= x-2 \end{aligned}$$

Hence, if $\quad f(x) = x+2, \quad f^{-1}(x) = x-2$

Let $\quad y = 3-x$

Interchanging x and y gives $\quad x = 3-y$

$$y = 3-x$$

Function	*Domain*	*Corresponding inverse function*	*Domain*
$f(x) = x+2$	$[0, 1]$	$f^{-1}(x) = x-2$	$[2, 3]$
$f(x) = 3-x$	$(1, 3]$	$f^{-1}(x) = 3-x$	$[0, 2)$

The composite function, $f \circ f$, is given by

$$\begin{aligned} f \circ f &= (x+2)+2 &\quad& \text{when } f(x) = x+2 \\ &= x+4 && x \in [0, 1] \end{aligned}$$

Also

$$\begin{aligned} f \circ f &= 3-(3-x) &\quad& \text{when } f(x) = 3-x \\ \therefore\ f \circ f &= x && x \in (1, 3] \\ \therefore\ (f \circ f) \circ (f \circ f) &= (x+4)+4 && \\ &= x+8 && x \in [0, 1] \end{aligned}$$

and $\quad (f \circ f) \circ (f \circ f) = x \qquad x \in (1, 3]$

The graphs are shown in Fig. 5.10.

EXERCISE

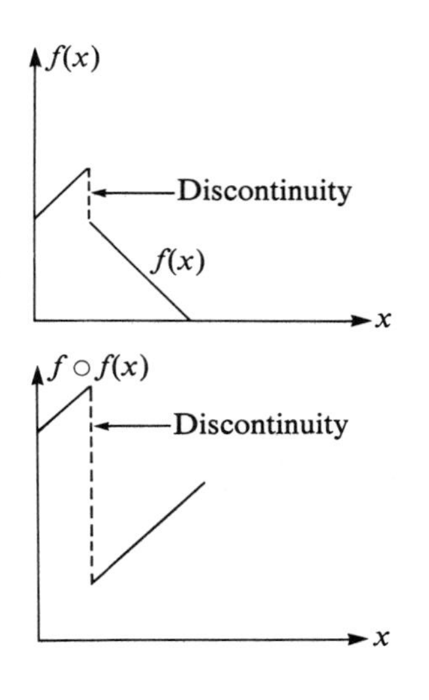

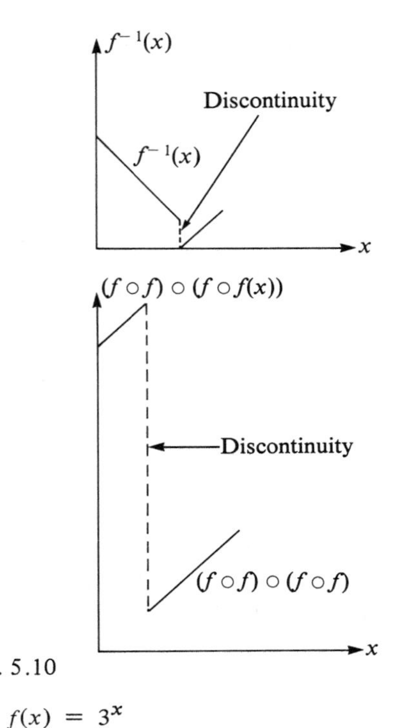

Fig. 5.10

3. (i) If

$$\begin{aligned} f(x) &= 3^x \\ f(x+2) &= 3^{x+2} \\ &= 3^2 \times 3^x \\ &= 9 \times 3^x \end{aligned}$$

Also

$$\begin{aligned} f(x-1) &= 3^{x-1} \\ &= 3^{-1} \times 3^x \\ &= \tfrac{1}{3} \times 3^x \end{aligned}$$

Hence

$$\begin{aligned} f(x+2)-f(x-1) &= 9 \times 3^x - \tfrac{1}{3} \times 3^x \\ &= (9-\tfrac{1}{3}) \times 3^x \\ &= \frac{26}{3} \times 3^x \end{aligned}$$

giving

$$f(x+2)-f(x-1) = \frac{26}{3} f(x)$$

(ii)

$$y = \frac{1-x}{2+x}$$

Interchanging x and y, we have

$$\begin{aligned} x &= \frac{1-y}{2+y} \\ x(2+y) &= (1-y) \\ 2x+xy &= 1-y \\ y+xy &= 1-2x \\ y(1+x) &= 1-2x \\ y &= \frac{1-2x}{1+x} \end{aligned}$$

which is the inverse relation

EXERCISE

(iii) If

$$g(x) = ax + b$$
$$g(x+1) = a(x+1) + b$$

i.e. $$g(x+1) = ax + a + b \quad (1)$$

and $$g(x) + 1 = ax + b + 1 \quad (2)$$

$$\therefore \quad g(x+1) = g(x) + 1 \quad \Rightarrow \quad a + b = b + 1$$
$$\Leftrightarrow \quad a = 1$$

Hence the only linear functions satisfying the condition $g(x+1) = g(x) + 1$ must be of the form $g(x) = x + k$, where k is a constant.

4. (i) For $f_1(x)$ the range is $\quad -\infty < f_1(x) < \infty$

For $f_2(x)$ the range is $\quad 1 < f_2(x) < \infty$

To find the inverse function, f_1^{-1}, we let

$$y = \ln(x+1)$$

Interchanging x and y gives

$$x = \ln(y+1)$$
$$\therefore \quad e^x = y + 1$$
$$y = e^x - 1$$

hence $\quad f_1^{-1}(x) = e^x - 1 \quad$ for $\quad -\infty < x < \infty$

To find the inverse relation, f_2^{-1}, again we let

$$y = x^2 + 1$$

Interchanging x and y gives

$$x = y^2 + 1$$
$$y^2 = x - 1$$
$$\therefore \quad y = \pm\sqrt{x-1} \quad \text{for} \quad 1 < x < \infty$$

This is a one–many relation. If, however, we restrict $f_2(x)$ to the domain $x > 1$ and define $f_2^{-1} = +\sqrt{x-1}$ the relation is now one–one and represents a function.

To sketch $f_1(x)$ we note that as $x \to -1$, $f_1(x) \to -\infty$ so that $x = -1$ is an asymptote to the curve. Also, for f_1^{-1} as $x \to -\infty$, $f_1^{-1} \to -1$, so that $y = -1$ is a horizontal asymptote to the curve. It is important that these features are shown clearly on the sketch (see Fig. 5.11) and that f_1^{-1} is the reflection of $f_1(x)$ in the straight line $y = x$.

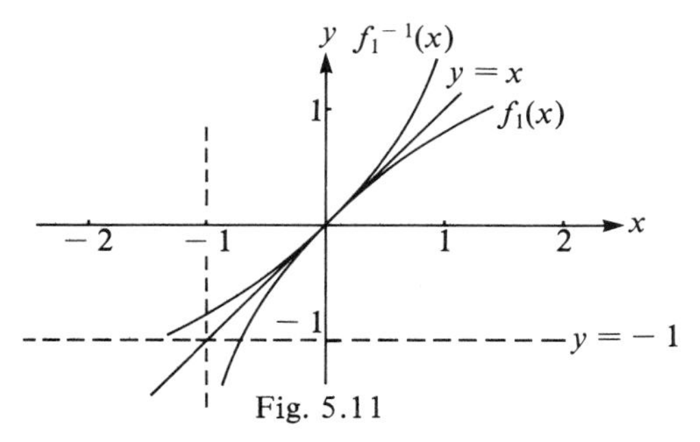

Fig. 5.11

(ii)

$$g_1g_2(x) = \ln(1 + g_2^2)$$
$$= \ln[1 + (1+x)^2]$$
$$= \ln[1 + 1 + 2x + x^2]$$
$$\therefore \quad g_1g_2(x) = \ln[2 + 2x + x^2] \quad (1)$$

EXERCISE

$$g_2g_1(x) = 1+g_1(x)$$
$$= 1+\ln(1+x^2) \qquad (2)$$
$$g_1g_2(-x) = \ln[2-2x+x^2] \neq g_1g_2 \quad \Rightarrow \quad \text{not even}$$

also $g_1g_2(-x) \neq -g_1g_2 \quad \Rightarrow$ not odd

hence $g_1g_2(x)$ is neither odd nor even.

$$g_2g_1(-x) = 1+\ln[1+(-x)^2]$$
$$= 1+\ln(1+x^2)$$
$$\therefore \quad g_2g_1(-x) = g_2g_1(x) \quad \Rightarrow \quad g_2g_1(x) \text{ is an even function}$$

5.

$$f:x \to \frac{1}{x-1}$$
$$f:-x \to \frac{1}{-x-1}$$

hence $\qquad f(-x) \neq f(x)$

and $\qquad f(-x) \neq -f(x)$

$\therefore \quad f:x$ is neither odd nor even

$$g:x \to \frac{x}{x^2-1}$$
$$g:-x \to \frac{-x}{(-x)^2-1} = \frac{-x}{x^2-1}$$

hence $\qquad g(x) \neq g(-x)$

but $\qquad g(x) = -g(-x)$

So $g:x$ is an odd function.

To investigate the inverse to $g:x$ we let

$$y = \frac{x}{x^2-1}$$

Interchanging x and y gives

$$x = \frac{y}{y^2-1}$$
$$x(y^2-1) = y$$
$$xy^2-y-x = 0$$

Solving for y

$$y = (1\pm\sqrt{1+4x^2})/2x$$

which shows that one value of x will generate two values for y. Hence this is a one–many relation and will not represent a function.

To find the inverse to f we let

$$y = \frac{1}{x-1}$$

Interchanging x and y gives

$$x = \frac{1}{y-1}$$
$$x(y-1) = 1$$
$$xy-x = 1$$

<u>EXERCISE</u>

$$xy = 1+x$$

$$y = \frac{1+x}{x}$$

hence $$f^{-1}: x \to \frac{1+x}{x}$$

In order to sketch $f(x)$ and $f^{-1}(x)$ we note the positions of the asymptotes. For $f(x)$, $x = 1$ is a vertical asymptote whereas for $f^{-1}(x)$ we note that as $x \to \infty$ $f^{-1}(x) \to 1$, giving $y = 1$ as a horizontal asymptote.

Also, as $x \to \pm\infty$, $f(x) \to 0$, giving the x-axis as a horizontal asymptote. Since $f(x)$ is not defined at $x = 1$, there is a break in the curve with one branch above the x-axis when $x > 1$ and the other branch underneath the x-axis when $x < 1$. Similarly, $f^{-1}(x)$ will have two branches, as shown in Fig. 5.12.

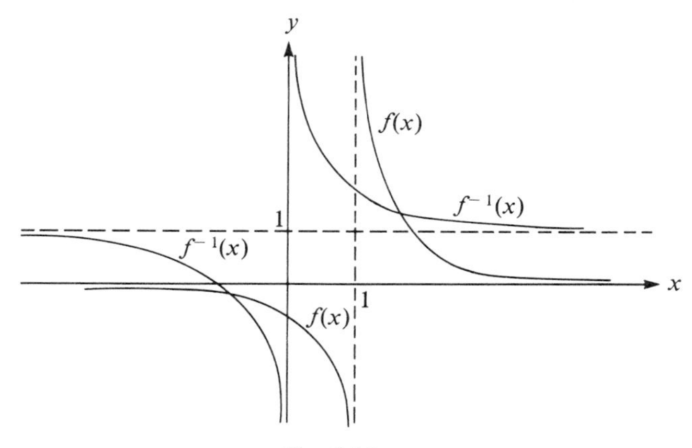

Fig. 5.12

EXERCISE

6 TRIGONOMETRY

BASIC DEFINITIONS

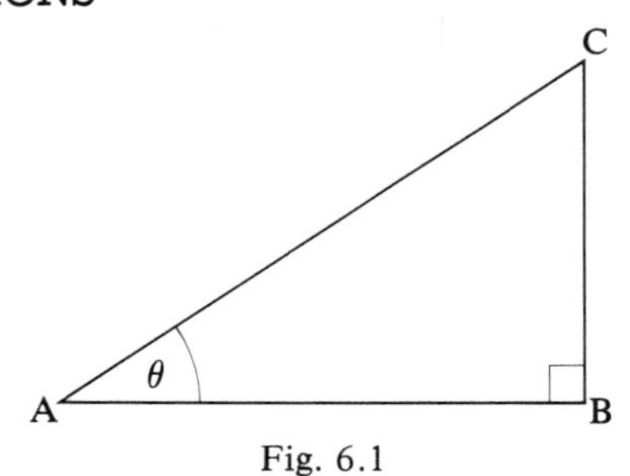

Fig. 6.1

In terms of the sides of the right-angled triangle ABC, we define the following trigonometric ratios:

$$\sin\theta = \frac{BC}{AC} \tag{6.1}$$

$$\cos\theta = \frac{AB}{AC} \tag{6.2}$$

$$\tan\theta = \frac{BC}{AB} \tag{6.3}$$

The reciprocals of these ratios are defined as

$$\operatorname{cosec}\theta = \frac{1}{\sin\theta} \tag{6.4}$$

$$\sec\theta = \frac{1}{\cos\theta} \tag{6.5}$$

$$\cot\theta = \frac{1}{\tan\theta} \tag{6.6}$$

IDENTITIES

From the definitions (6.1) and (6.2) we have

$$\frac{\sin\theta}{\cos\theta} = \frac{BC/AC}{AB/AC}$$

$$= \frac{BC}{AB}$$

$$= \tan\theta \qquad \text{[from (6.3)]}$$

which establishes the useful identity

$$\boxed{\tan\theta = \frac{\sin\theta}{\cos\theta}} \tag{6.7}$$

Further identities can be obtained by applying Pythagoras' theorem to the right-angled triangle ABC. We have

$$AB^2 + BC^2 = AC^2 \qquad (6.8)$$

Dividing throughout by AC^2 gives

$$\left(\frac{AB}{AC}\right)^2 + \left(\frac{BC}{AC}\right)^2 = 1$$

Using the definitions (6.1) and (6.2) we have

$$\boxed{\sin^2\theta + \cos^2\theta = 1} \qquad (6.9)$$

If we now divide (6.8) throughout by AB^2 we have

$$1 + \left(\frac{BC}{AB}\right)^2 = \left(\frac{AC}{AB}\right)^2$$

From the definitions (6.3) and (6.5) we can now establish the identity

$$\boxed{\sec^2\theta = 1 + \tan^2\theta} \qquad (6.10)$$

We can obtain a third identity by dividing (6.8) throughout by BC^2 to give

$$\left(\frac{AB}{BC}\right)^2 + 1 = \left(\frac{AC}{BC}\right)^2$$

From the definition of the reciprocal ratios this gives

$$\boxed{\operatorname{cosec}^2\theta = 1 + \cot^2\theta} \qquad (6.11)$$

All of these trigonometric identities are very useful and are used frequently in problems involving trigonometric analysis.

POSITIVE AND NEGATIVE ANGLES

Positive angles are measured in an anticlockwise direction (see Fig. 6.2).

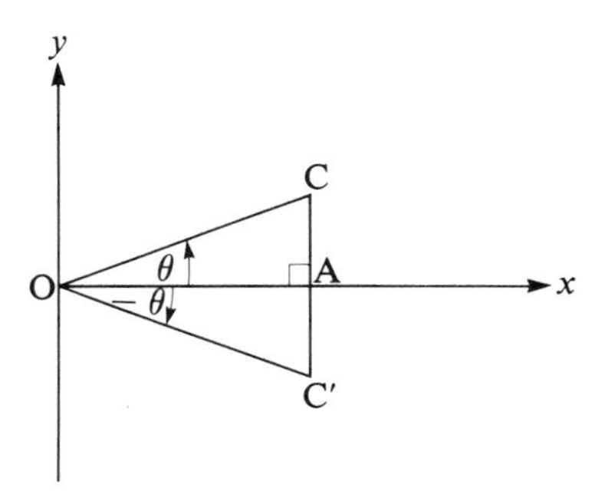

Fig. 6.2

Because C′ is below the x-axis in Fig. 6.2, we have $AC' = -AC$. From the definition of the trigonometric ratios we have

$$\sin\theta = \frac{AC}{OC}$$

or

$$\sin\theta = \frac{-AC'}{OC} \qquad (\text{since } AC = -AC')$$

The straight line connecting the origin to a point in any quadrant is, however, always positive by convention. Hence $OC = OC'$. Substituting gives

$$\sin\theta = -\frac{AC'}{OC'}$$

$$= -\sin(-\theta)$$

$$\therefore \quad \sin(-\theta) = -\sin\theta \qquad (6.12)$$

We can obtain a similar result for cos as follows

$$\cos\theta = \frac{OA}{OC}$$

$$= \frac{OA}{OC'}$$

$$\therefore \quad \cos\theta = \cos(-\theta) \qquad (6.13)$$

We see from these results that $\cos\theta$ is an even function while $\sin\theta$ is an odd function.

COMPLEMENTARY ANGLES

Two angles whose sum is 90° are said to be complementary. We will now derive a useful relationship between the trigonometric ratios of complementary angles. Consider the right-angled triangle ABC in Fig. 6.3, in which $\theta + \phi = 90°$.

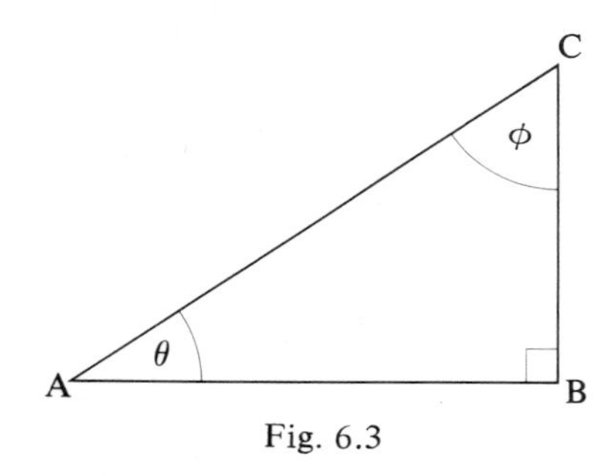

Fig. 6.3

From the definition of $\sin\theta$ we have

$$\sin\theta = \frac{BC}{AC}$$

But, also

$$\cos\phi = \frac{BC}{AC}$$

$$\therefore \quad \sin\theta = \cos\phi$$

However

$$\phi = 90° - \theta$$

$$\therefore \quad \sin\theta = \cos(90° - \theta) \qquad (6.14)$$

Similarly, we have

$$\cos\theta = \frac{AB}{AC}$$

and

$$\sin\phi = \frac{AB}{AC}$$

$$\therefore \quad \sin\phi = \cos\theta$$

and

$$\sin(90° - \theta) = \cos\theta \qquad (6.15)$$

From (6.14) and (6.15) we find

$$\tan(90° - \theta) = \cot\theta \qquad (6.16)$$

SUPPLEMENTARY ANGLE RESULTS

Supplementary angles have the property that their sum is 180°. In order to derive similar results for supplementary angles to those already obtained for complementary angles, we will let $\theta = \phi - 90^\circ$ in the relationship $\sin(90^\circ - \theta) = \cos\theta$.

$$\sin(90^\circ - \theta) = \cos(\phi - 90^\circ)$$

$$\sin[90^\circ - (\phi - 90^\circ)] = \cos(90^\circ - \phi) \qquad [\cos(-x) = \cos x]$$

$$\sin(180^\circ - \phi) = \sin\phi \qquad [\text{from } (6.14)] \qquad (6.17)$$

Similarly, if we let $\theta = \phi - 90^\circ$ in the relationship $\sin\theta = \cos(90^\circ - \theta)$, we have

$$\cos(90^\circ - \theta) = \sin(\phi - 90^\circ)$$

$$\cos[90^\circ - (\phi - 90^\circ)] = -\sin(90^\circ - \phi)$$

$$\therefore \quad \cos(180^\circ - \phi) = -\cos\phi \qquad (6.18)$$

Dividing (6.17) by (6.18) gives

$$\tan(180^\circ - \phi) = -\tan\phi \qquad (6.19)$$

RADIANS

Radians provide an alternative method of measuring angles. The radian is defined to be the angle subtended at the centre of a circle of radius r by the arc of a circle of length r (see Fig. 6.4).

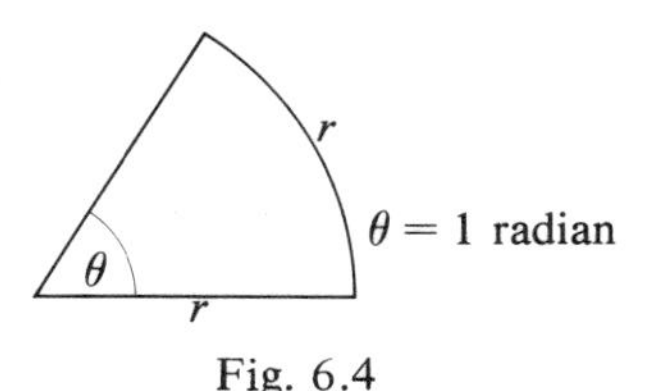

Fig. 6.4

Since the circumference of a circle is given by $C = 2\pi r$, the number of radians subtended at the centre of the circle by the circumference is 2π. The angle subtended by the circumference at the centre of the circle is 360°. Consequently, the relationship between these two methods of measuring angles must be such that $360^\circ = 2\pi$ radians. If θ denotes the angle in radians and d the same angle in degrees, we have

$$\frac{\theta}{\pi} = \frac{d}{180^\circ} \qquad (6.20)$$

In order to convert from degrees to radians, we make θ the subject of this formula

$$\theta = \frac{\pi d}{180} \qquad (6.21)$$

To convert from radians to degrees we make d the subject of the formula, so that

$$d = \frac{180^\circ\theta}{\pi} \qquad (6.22)$$

These two conversion formulae enable us easily to express an angle either in terms of radians or degrees. In the table below we summarise the most frequently used angles in degrees and their corresponding value in radians.

Angle in degrees	Angle in radians
30°	$\pi/6$
45°	$\pi/4$
60°	$\pi/3$
90°	$\pi/2$
180°	π
360°	2π

THE TRIGONOMETRIC ADDITION FORMULAE

We state without proof the following results:

$$\sin(A+B) = \sin A \cos B + \cos A \sin B \tag{6.23}$$

$$\sin(A-B) = \sin A \cos B - \cos A \sin B \tag{6.24}$$

$$\cos(A+B) = \cos A \cos B - \sin A \sin B \tag{6.25}$$

$$\cos(A-B) = \cos A \cos B + \sin A \sin B \tag{6.26}$$

$$\tan(A+B) = \frac{\tan A + \tan B}{1 - \tan A \tan B} \tag{6.27}$$

$$\tan(A-B) = \frac{\tan A - \tan B}{1 + \tan A \tan B} \tag{6.28}$$

DOUBLE-ANGLE FORMULAE

The double-angle formulae can be obtained directly from the addition formulae (6.23), (6.25) and (6.27) by putting $B = A$. We then find

$$\sin 2A = 2 \sin A \cos A \tag{6.29}$$

$$\cos 2A = \cos^2 A - \sin^2 A \tag{6.30}$$

$$\tan 2A = \frac{2 \tan A}{1 - \tan^2 A} \tag{6.31}$$

If we use the identity (6.9) the following alternative formulae may be obtained for $\cos 2A$

$$\cos 2A = 1 - 2\sin^2 A \tag{6.32}$$

$$\cos 2A = 2\cos^2 A - 1 \tag{6.33}$$

THE HALF-ANGLE FORMULAE

Similar results to those already obtained for double angles may be found for half-angles by the simple technique of relabelling. In this case we let $A = \frac{x}{2}$. The double-angle formulae then become

$$\sin x = 2 \sin\frac{x}{2} \cos\frac{x}{2} \tag{6.34}$$

$$\cos x = \cos^2\frac{x}{2} - \sin^2\frac{x}{2} \tag{6.35}$$

$$\cos x = 1 - 2\sin^2\frac{x}{2} \tag{6.36}$$

$$\cos x = 2\cos^2\frac{x}{2} - 1 \tag{6.37}$$

$$\tan x = \frac{2\tan\dfrac{x}{2}}{1-\tan^2\dfrac{x}{2}} \qquad (6.38)$$

THE FACTOR FORMULAE

From the addition formulae (6.23) and (6.24) we have

$$\sin(A+B)+\sin(A-B) = 2\sin A\cos B$$

Now let $S = A+B$ and $T = A-B$. It follows that $A = \dfrac{S+T}{2}$ and $B = \dfrac{S-T}{2}$.

Substituting gives

$$\sin S + \sin T = 2\sin\left(\frac{S+T}{2}\right)\cos\left(\frac{S-T}{2}\right) \qquad (6.39)$$

Similar results may be obtained from the other addition formulae and these are summarised below:

$$\sin S - \sin T = 2\cos\left(\frac{S+T}{2}\right)\sin\left(\frac{S-T}{2}\right) \qquad (6.40)$$

$$\cos S + \cos T = 2\cos\left(\frac{S+T}{2}\right)\cos\left(\frac{S-T}{2}\right) \qquad (6.41)$$

$$\cos S - \cos T = -2\sin\left(\frac{S+T}{2}\right)\sin\left(\frac{S-T}{2}\right) \qquad (6.42)$$

Worked Example

Prove that $\tan\frac{1}{2}(A+B)+\tan\frac{1}{2}(A-B) = \dfrac{2\sin A}{\cos A+\cos B}$ (WJEC 1980, part)

Solution

$$\tan\tfrac{1}{2}(A+B)+\tan\tfrac{1}{2}(A-B)$$

$$= \frac{\sin\frac{1}{2}(A+B)}{\cos\frac{1}{2}(A+B)} + \frac{\sin\frac{1}{2}(A-B)}{\cos\frac{1}{2}(A-B)}$$

$$= \frac{\sin\frac{1}{2}(A+B)\cos\frac{1}{2}(A-B)+\sin\frac{1}{2}(A-B)\cos\frac{1}{2}(A+B)}{\cos\frac{1}{2}(A+B)\cos\frac{1}{2}(A-B)}$$

The numerator can be simplified by using the addition formula (6.23) and the denominator by using (6.41). This gives

$$\tan\tfrac{1}{2}(A+B)+\tan\tfrac{1}{2}(A-B) = \frac{\sin A}{\frac{1}{2}(\cos A+\cos B)}$$

$$\therefore\quad \tan\tfrac{1}{2}(A+B)+\tan\tfrac{1}{2}(A-B) = \frac{2\sin A}{\cos A+\cos B}$$

EXERCISE

1. If $\cos(x+\alpha) = p$ and $\sin(x+\beta) = q$, express $\cos x$ and $\sin x$ in terms of α, β, p and q.

Deduce that

$$p^2+q^2+2pq\sin(\alpha-\beta) = \cos^2(\alpha-\beta) \quad \text{(NI 1980, part)}$$

2. Simplify $\dfrac{\sin 4\theta(1-\cos 2\theta)}{\cos 2\theta(1-\cos 4\theta)}$, where $\cos 2\theta(1-\cos 4\theta) \neq 0$. (LU 1981)

3. If $\tan(x+y)=a$ and $\tan(x-y)=b$, express

$$\frac{\sin 2x+\sin 2y}{\sin 2x-\sin 2y}$$

in terms of a and b.

Show that $\tan 2y = \dfrac{a-b}{1+ab}$ and by using this result, or otherwise, obtain an expression for $\tan(x+3y)$ in terms of a and b. (AEB 1980)

4. Given that $A+B+C=2\pi$, prove that

(i) $\sin\frac{1}{2}A = \sin\frac{1}{2}(B+C)$

(ii) $\cos\frac{1}{2}A = -\cos\frac{1}{2}(B+C)$

(iii) $\sin A+\sin B+\sin C = 4\sin\dfrac{A}{2}\sin\dfrac{B}{2}\sin\dfrac{C}{2}$ (AEB 1982)

Worked Solutions

1. From the addition formulae we have

$$\cos(x+\alpha) = \cos x\cos\alpha-\sin\alpha\sin x = p \quad (1)$$

$$\sin(x+\beta) = \sin x\cos\beta+\sin\beta\cos x = q \quad (2)$$

$$(1)\times\sin\beta \quad \cos x\cos\alpha\sin\beta-\sin\alpha\sin\beta\sin x = p\sin\beta \quad (3)$$

$$(2)\times\cos\alpha \quad \sin x\cos\beta\cos\alpha+\sin\beta\cos\alpha\cos x = q\cos\alpha \quad (4)$$

$$(4)-(3) \quad \sin x(\cos\beta\cos\alpha+\sin\alpha\sin\beta) = q\cos\alpha-p\sin\beta$$

$$\sin x\cos(\alpha-\beta) = q\cos\alpha-p\sin\beta$$

$$\therefore \quad \sin x = \frac{q\cos\alpha-p\sin\beta}{\cos(\alpha-\beta)} \quad (5)$$

$$(1)\times\cos\beta \quad \cos x\cos\alpha\cos\beta-\sin\alpha\cos\beta\sin x = p\cos\beta \quad (6)$$

$$(2)\times\sin\alpha \quad \sin x\cos\beta\sin\alpha+\sin\beta\sin\alpha\cos x = q\sin\alpha \quad (7)$$

$$(6)+(7) \quad \cos x(\cos\alpha\cos\beta+\sin\beta\sin\alpha) = p\cos\beta+q\sin\alpha$$

$$\cos x\cos(\alpha-\beta) = p\cos\beta+q\sin\alpha$$

$$\therefore \quad \cos x = \frac{p\cos\beta+q\sin\alpha}{\cos(\alpha-\beta)} \quad (8)$$

Substituting in the identity $\cos^2 x = 1-\sin^2 x$ gives

$$\frac{(p\cos\beta+q\sin\alpha)^2}{\cos^2(\alpha-\beta)} = 1-\frac{(q\cos\alpha-p\sin\beta)^2}{\cos^2(\alpha-\beta)}$$

$$(p\cos\beta+q\sin\alpha)^2 = \cos^2(\alpha-\beta)-(q\cos\alpha-p\sin\beta)^2$$

$$(p\cos\beta+q\sin\alpha)^2+(q\cos\alpha-p\sin\beta)^2 = \cos^2(\alpha-\beta)$$

This can be simplified by using the identity (6.9) and the addition formula (6.24). This gives

$$p^2+q^2+2pq\sin(\alpha-\beta) = \cos^2(\alpha-\beta)$$

EXERCISE

2.

$$\frac{\sin 4\theta(1-\cos 2\theta)}{\cos 2\theta(1-\cos 4\theta)} = \frac{2\sin 2\theta\ \cos 2\theta\,[1-(1-2\sin^2\theta)]}{\cos 2\theta\,[1-(1-2\sin^2 2\theta)]}$$

$$= \frac{2\sin 2\theta \times 2\sin^2\theta}{2\sin^2 2\theta}$$

$$= \frac{2\sin^2\theta}{\sin 2\theta}$$

$$= \frac{2\sin^2\theta}{2\sin\theta\ \cos\theta}$$

$$= \frac{\sin\theta}{\cos\theta}$$

$$\therefore\quad \frac{\sin 4\theta(1-\cos 2\theta)}{\cos 2\theta(1-\cos 4\theta)} = \tan\theta$$

3.

$$\sin 2x+\sin 2y = 2\sin(x+y)\cos(x-y) \qquad \text{(factor formula)}$$

$$\sin 2x-\sin 2y = 2\cos(x+y)\sin(x-y) \qquad \text{(factor formula)}$$

$$\frac{\sin 2x+\sin 2y}{\sin 2x-\sin 2y} = \frac{\sin(x+y)\cos(x-y)}{\cos(x+y)\sin(x-y)}$$

$$= \frac{\tan(x+y)}{\tan(x-y)}$$

$$\therefore\quad \frac{\sin 2x+\sin 2y}{\sin 2x-\sin 2y} = \frac{a}{b}$$

$$\frac{a-b}{1+ab} = \frac{\tan(x+y)-\tan(x-y)}{1+\tan(x+y)\tan(x-y)}$$

$$= \frac{\sin(x+y)\cos(x-y)-\sin(x-y)\cos(x+y)}{\cos(x+y)\cos(x-y)+\sin(x+y)\sin(x-y)}$$

$$= \frac{\sin 2y}{\cos 2y} \qquad \text{(using the addition formulae to simplify)}$$

$$= \tan 2y$$

$$\tan(x+3y) = \tan[(x+y)+2y]$$

$$= \frac{\tan(x+y)+\tan 2y}{1-\tan(x+y)\tan 2y}$$

$$= \frac{a+\dfrac{a-b}{1+ab}}{1-\dfrac{a(a-b)}{1+ab}}$$

$$= \frac{a(1+ab)+a-b}{1+ab-a(a-b)}$$

$$\therefore\quad \tan(x+3y) = \frac{2a+a^2b-b}{1+2ab-a^2}$$

4. (i) If $A+B+C=2\pi$

$$\frac{A}{2} = \pi-\tfrac{1}{2}(B+C)$$

$$\therefore \quad \sin\frac{A}{2} = \sin\left[\pi-\tfrac{1}{2}(B+C)\right]$$

$$\therefore \quad \sin\frac{A}{2} = \sin\tfrac{1}{2}(B+C) \qquad [\sin(\pi-\theta)=\sin\theta]$$

(ii)

$$\cos\frac{A}{2} = \cos\left[\pi-\tfrac{1}{2}(B+C)\right]$$

$$\therefore \quad \cos\frac{A}{2} = -\cos\tfrac{1}{2}(B+C) \qquad [\cos(\pi-\theta)=-\cos\theta]$$

(iii)

$$\begin{aligned}
\sin A+\sin B+\sin C &= \sin A + 2\sin\left(\frac{B+C}{2}\right)\cos\left(\frac{B-C}{2}\right)\\
&= 2\sin\frac{A}{2}\cos\frac{A}{2} + 2\sin\frac{A}{2}\cos\left(\frac{B-C}{2}\right)\\
&= 2\sin\frac{A}{2}\left[\cos\frac{A}{2}+\cos\left(\frac{B-C}{2}\right)\right]\\
&= 2\sin\frac{A}{2}\left[2\cos\left(\frac{A+B-C}{2\cdot 2}\right)\cos\left(\frac{A-B+C}{4}\right)\right]
\end{aligned}$$

(using 6.41)

$$= 2\sin\frac{A}{2}\left[2\cos\frac{(2\pi-2C)}{4}\cos\frac{(2\pi-2B)}{4}\right]$$

(since $A+B+C=2\pi$)

$$= 4\sin\frac{A}{2}\cos\left(\frac{\pi}{2}-\frac{C}{2}\right)\cos\left(\frac{\pi}{2}-\frac{B}{2}\right)$$

$$\therefore \quad \sin A+\sin B+\sin C = 4\sin\frac{A}{2}\sin\frac{B}{2}\sin\frac{C}{2}$$

THE PERIODICITY OF $\sin\theta$, $\cos\theta$ and $\tan\theta$

The graphs of the sine, cosine and tangent functions are shown in Figs. 6.5, 6.6 and 6.7. An important feature of both the sine and cosine graphs is that they oscillate between ± 1 with a period of 2π. However, the tangent function is not so restricted in its range and varies between $\pm\infty$ with a period of π.

The periodicity of $\sin\theta$ may be verified by using the addition formula (6.23), which gives

$$\sin(2\pi+\theta) = \sin 2\pi\cos\theta+\sin\theta\cos 2\pi$$

$$\therefore \quad \sin(2\pi+\theta) = \sin\theta \qquad (\text{since } \sin 2\pi = 0 \text{ and } \cos 2\pi = 1)$$

Similarly, by using the addition formulae (6.25) and (6.27), it may be shown that

$$\cos(2\pi+\theta) = \cos\theta$$

and

$$\tan(\pi+\theta) = \tan\theta$$

EXERCISE/THE PERIODICITY OF $\sin\theta$, $\cos\theta$ and $\tan\theta$

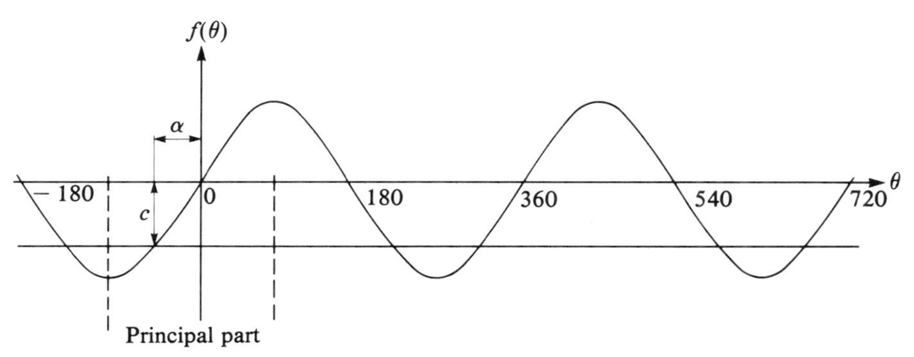

Fig. 6.5 $\sin\theta$

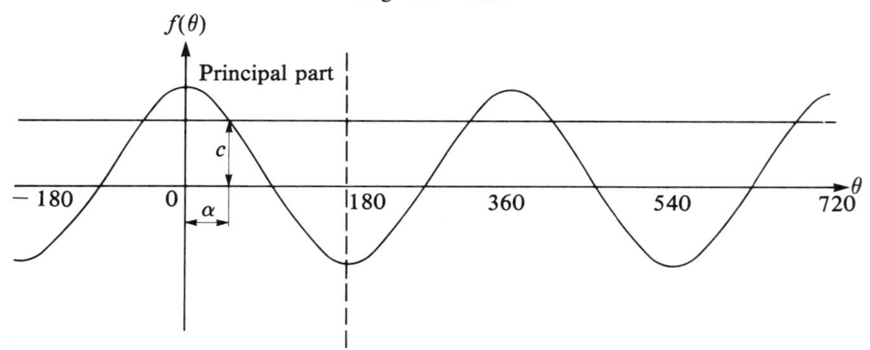

Fig. 6.6 $\cos\theta$

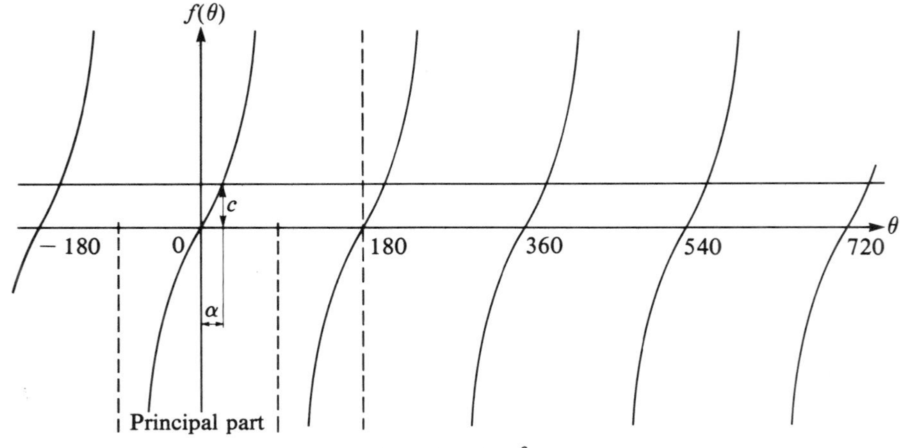

Fig. 6.7 $\tan\theta$

PRINCIPAL PARTS

It is seen from Fig. 6.5 that $\sin\theta$ takes on all values between ± 1 for θ such that $-\frac{\pi}{2} \leqslant \theta \leqslant \frac{\pi}{2}$. Consequently, this will be referred to as the principal part of the sine function. Similarly, the principal part for $\tan\theta$ is $-\frac{\pi}{2} \leqslant \theta \leqslant \frac{\pi}{2}$ and the principal part for $\cos\theta$ is $0 \leqslant \theta \leqslant \pi$.

INVERSE FUNCTIONS

We have seen in Chapter 5 that only one–one relationships have an inverse function. If we consider the equation $\sin\theta = c \quad (|c| \leqslant 1)$, it is apparent from the periodicity of $\sin\theta$ that there will be an infinite number of values of θ satisfying this equation. If, however, we restrict θ to values in the principal part of $\sin\theta$ the relationship will now be one–one and an inverse function will exist which, following the notation of Chapter 5, will be denoted by $\sin^{-1}\theta$. An alternative notation that is sometimes used for this inverse function is $\arcsin\theta$.

Corresponding inverse functions also exist for $\cos\theta$ and $\tan\theta$ when θ is restricted to the principal part and these are denoted by $\cos^{-1}\theta$ and $\tan^{-1}\theta$ respectively (or $\arccos\theta$, $\arctan\theta$).

SOLUTION OF $\sin\theta = c$

The equation $\sin\theta = c$ must have a solution which is contained in the principal part of the sine curve. If α denotes this value it is called the principal value of θ. From Fig. 6.5 it is seen that the general solution of $\sin\theta = c$ is given by

$$\theta = n \times 180^\circ + (-1)^n\alpha \qquad (n \in \mathbb{Z}) \qquad (6.43)$$

SOLUTION OF $\cos\theta = c$

$\cos\theta = c \Rightarrow \theta = \cos^{-1}c$. This equation must have, by definition, a solution contained in the principal part of the cosine curve. We will let α denote the principal value of θ. From Fig. 6.6 it is seen that the general solution of $\cos\theta = c$ is given by

$$\theta = n \times 360^\circ \pm \alpha \qquad (n \in \mathbb{Z}) \qquad (6.44)$$

SOLUTION OF $\tan\theta = c$

The solutions to this equation are given by $\theta = \tan^{-1}c$. If α denotes the principal value of θ, it is seen from Fig. 6.6 that the general solution to this equation is

$$\theta = n \times 180^\circ + \alpha \qquad (n \in \mathbb{Z}) \qquad (6.45)$$

THE EQUATION $a\cos\theta + b\sin\theta = c$

This equation may be solved by two different methods which are shown below.

First Method (Auxiliary Angle)

$$a\cos\theta + b\sin\theta = \sqrt{a^2+b^2}\left[\frac{a\cos\theta}{\sqrt{a^2+b^2}} + \frac{b\sin\theta}{\sqrt{a^2+b^2}}\right] \qquad (6.46)$$

Since multiplication and division by $\sqrt{a^2+b^2}$ leaves the value of the LHS unchanged. If we let $R^2 = a^2 + b^2$ it follows that R represents the hypotenuse of a right-angled triangle with sides a and b. In order to ensure that R is positive the positive root of (a^2+b^2) is always taken. This enables us to introduce an acute angle α such that $\sin\alpha = a/R$ and $\cos\alpha = b/R$ as shown in the right-angled triangle ABC in Fig. 6.8.

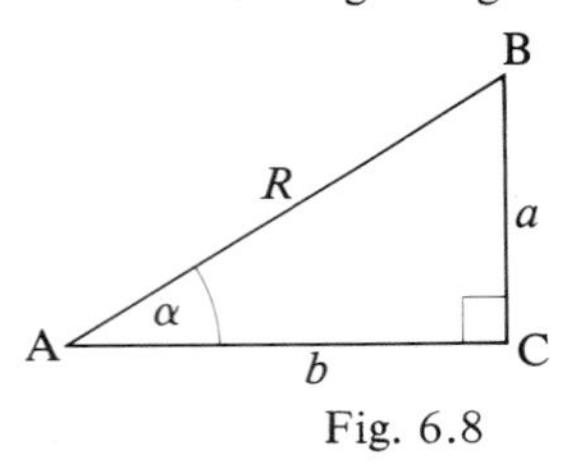

Fig. 6.8

Using the auxiliary angle α we can rewrite (6.46) as

$$a\cos\theta + b\sin\theta = R(\sin\alpha\cos\theta + \cos\alpha\sin\theta)$$

The addition formula (6.23) may be used to simplify this and gives

$$a\cos\theta + b\sin\theta = R\sin(\alpha+\theta) \qquad (6.47)$$

The relationship (6.47) shows that the maximum value of $a\cos\theta + b\sin\theta$ is R, while the minimum value is $-R$. We can rewrite the equation $a\cos\theta + b\sin\theta = c$ as

$$R\sin(\alpha+\theta) = c$$

$$\sin(\alpha+\theta) = \frac{c}{R}$$

$$\alpha+\theta = \sin^{-1}\frac{c}{R}$$

$$\alpha+\theta = n\times 180^\circ + (-1)^n PV$$

where $PV = \sin^{-1} c/R$ and denotes the principal value in the range -90° up to $+90^\circ$. This gives

$$\theta = n\times 180^\circ + (-1)^n PV - \alpha \qquad (n\in\mathbb{Z})$$

as the general solution.

Worked Example

Express $4\sin 2x + 3\cos 2x$ in the form $R\sin(2x+\alpha)$ where R is positive and α is an acute angle measured in degrees.

Hence find the values of x, between 0° and 360°, for which $4\sin 2x + 3\cos 2x = 2.49$. (AEB 1981)

Solution

If $R^2 = 4^2 + 3^2$ $\qquad R = 5$

Hence $\qquad 4\sin 2x + 3\cos 2x = 5[\frac{4}{5}\sin 2x + \frac{3}{5}\cos 2x]$

To express this in the form $R\sin(2x+\alpha)$ we introduce the angle α of the right-angled triangle ABC (Fig. 6.9) such that $\cos\alpha = \frac{4}{5}$ and $\sin\alpha = \frac{3}{5}$.

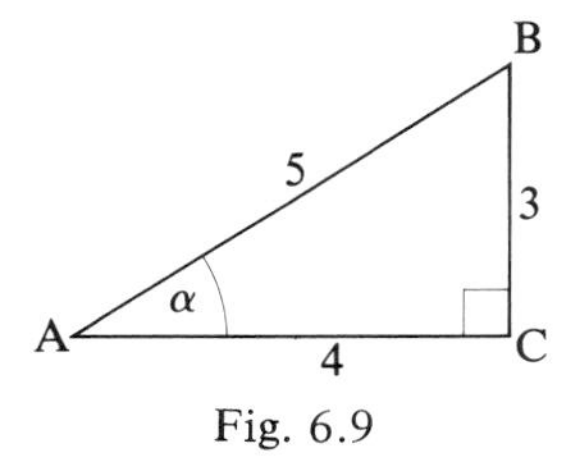

Fig. 6.9

This gives

$$4\sin 2x + 3\cos 2x = 5(\sin 2x\cos\alpha + \sin\alpha\cos 2x)$$
$$= 5\sin(2x+\alpha)$$

The equation is

$$4\sin 2x + 3\cos 2x = 2.49$$
$$5\sin(2x+\alpha) = 2.49$$
$$\sin(2x+\alpha) = 0.498$$
$$2x+\alpha = \sin^{-1} 0.498$$

giving $\qquad 2x+\alpha = 29.87^\circ \qquad$ (principal value)

General solution is $2x+\alpha = n\times 180^\circ+(-1)^n 29.87^\circ \quad (n\in\mathbb{Z})$

where $\alpha = \cos^{-1}\frac{4}{5} = 36.87^\circ$

$2x = n\times 180^\circ+(-1)^n 29.87^\circ-36.87^\circ$

$n=1$ $\quad 2x = 113.26^\circ$

giving $\quad x = 56.63^\circ$

$n=2$ $\quad 2x = 353^\circ$

giving $\quad x = 176.5^\circ$

$n=3$ $\quad 2x = 473.26^\circ$

giving $\quad x = 236.63^\circ$

$n=4$ $\quad 2x = 713^\circ$

giving $\quad x = 356.5^\circ$

Therefore the complete solution set is

$$\{x : x = 56.63^\circ, 176.5^\circ, 236.63^\circ, 356.5^\circ\}$$

Second Method (t Substitutions)

If $t = \tan\frac{\theta}{2}$ it is easily verified that

$$\sin\theta = \frac{2t}{1+t^2} \tag{6.48}$$

and

$$\cos\theta = \frac{1-t^2}{1+t^2} \tag{6.49}$$

These results are referred to as the t substitutions. The effect of using the t substitutions on the linear equation $a\cos\theta+b\sin\theta = c$ is to obtain a quadratic equation in t. Substituting gives

$$a\cos\theta+b\sin\theta = a\left(\frac{1-t^2}{1+t^2}\right)+b\left(\frac{2t}{1+t^2}\right) = c$$

Multiplication throughout by $(1+t^2)$ gives

$$a(1-t^2)+2bt = c(1+t^2)$$

which simplifies to $\quad (a+c)t^2-2bt+(c-a) = 0$

This equation may be solved either by factorisation or by using the formula. The general solution is then obtained by solving the equation

$$\frac{\theta}{2} = \tan^{-1} t$$

Worked Example

Express $4\cos x+\sin x$ in terms of t, where $t = \tan\frac{x}{2}$, and hence solve the equation $4\cos x+\sin x = 1$ for values of x between 0° and 360°.

(LU 1980, part)

Solution

The appropriate substitutions are given by (6.48) and (6.49). Substituting in the given equation gives

$$4\left(\frac{1-t^2}{1+t^2}\right)+\frac{2t}{1+t^2} = 1$$

$$4(1-t^2)+2t = 1+t^2$$

Simplifying to

$$5t^2-2t-3 = 0$$
$$(5t+3)(t-1) = 0$$
$$t = -\tfrac{3}{5} \quad \text{or} \quad t = 1$$

First solution:

If $t = \dfrac{-3}{5}$ $\qquad \tan\dfrac{x}{2} = \dfrac{-3}{5}$

$$\frac{x}{2} = -30.96^\circ \qquad \text{(principal value)}$$

General solution $\qquad \dfrac{x}{2} = n\times 180^\circ - 30.96^\circ$

$$x = n\times 360^\circ - 61.92^\circ$$

$n = 1$ gives $\qquad x = 298.08^\circ$

Second solution:

If $t = 1$ $\qquad \tan\dfrac{x}{2} = 1$

$$\frac{x}{2} = 45 \qquad \text{(principal value)}$$

General solution $\qquad \dfrac{x}{2} = n\times 180^\circ + 45^\circ$

$$x = n\times 360^\circ + 90^\circ$$

$n = 0$ gives $\qquad x = 90^\circ$

All other values of n give solutions outside the range 0° to 360°.

The complete solution set is $\{x : x = 90^\circ, 298.08^\circ\}$.

TRIGONOMETRIC EQUATIONS BASED ON IDENTITIES

Some trigonometric equations require the use of the trigonometric identities or the factor formulae for their solution. This type of problem is shown below.

Worked Example

Solve the following equations, giving your answers in the range 0° to 360°.

(i) $\sec^2\theta - 3\tan\theta - 5 = 0$

(ii) $\cos 4x + \cos 2x - \sin 4x + \sin 2x = 0$ (AEB 1982)

Solution

(i)

$$\sec^2\theta - 3\tan\theta - 5 = 0$$
$$(1+\tan^2\theta) - 3\tan\theta - 5 = 0$$
$$\tan^2\theta - 3\tan\theta - 4 = 0$$
$$(\tan\theta + 1)(\tan\theta - 4) = 0$$
$$\tan\theta = -1 \quad \text{or} \quad \tan\theta = 4$$

First solution:

If $\tan\theta = -1$ $\qquad \theta = -45^\circ$ (principal value)

General solution $\qquad \theta = n\times 180^\circ - 45^\circ$

$n = 1$ gives $\qquad \theta = 135^\circ$

$n = 2$ gives $\qquad \theta = 315^\circ$

Second solution:

If $\tan\theta = 4$ $\qquad \theta = 75.96^\circ$ (principal value)

General solution $\qquad \theta = n \times 180^\circ + 75.96^\circ$

$n = 1$ gives $\qquad \theta = 255.96^\circ$

The solution set is $\{\theta : \theta = 75.96^\circ, 135^\circ, 255.96^\circ, 315^\circ\}$.

(ii) $\cos 4x + \cos 2x - \sin 4x + \sin 2x = 0$

$2\cos 3x \cos x + 2\cos 3x \sin(-x) = 0$ (using the factor formulae)

$2\cos 3x(\cos x - \sin x) = 0 \, [\sin(-x) = -\sin x]$

First solution:

$\cos 3x = 0$ $\qquad 3x = 90^\circ$ (principal value)

General solution $\qquad 3x = n \times 360^\circ \pm 90^\circ$

$x = n \times 120^\circ \pm 30^\circ$

$n = 0$ gives $\qquad x = 30^\circ$

$n = 1$ gives $\qquad x = 90^\circ, 150^\circ$

$n = 2$ gives $\qquad x = 210^\circ, 270^\circ$

$n = 3$ gives $\qquad x = 330^\circ$

Second solution:

If $\cos x - \sin x = 0$

$\tan x = 1$

$x = 45^\circ$ (principal value)

General solution $\qquad x = n \times 180^\circ + 45^\circ$

$n = 0$ gives $\qquad x = 45^\circ$

$n = 1$ gives $\qquad x = 225^\circ$

The complete solution set is $\{x : x = 30^\circ, 45^\circ, 90^\circ, 150^\circ, 210^\circ, 225^\circ, 270^\circ, 330^\circ\}$.

THE AREA AND ARC LENGTH OF A SECTOR

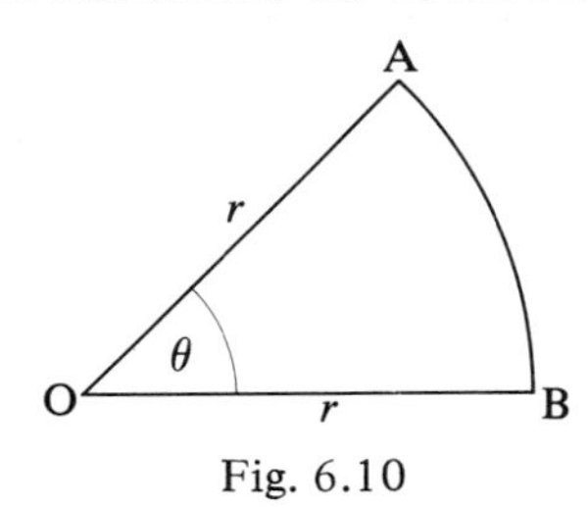

Fig. 6.10

Consider the sector AOB of a circle of radius r (Fig. 6.10). The area of AOB is a fraction of the total area of the circle and is proportional to the $\angle$AOB. Consequently, the ratio of the area of the sector to the area of the circle is given by the ratio of $\angle$AOB to 360°. This gives

$$\frac{\text{area AOB}}{\pi r^2} = \frac{\angle \text{AOB}}{360^\circ}$$

If θ is measured in radians the angle subtended by the circumference at the centre of the circle is 2π. We then have

$$\frac{\text{area AOB}}{\pi r^2} = \frac{\theta}{2\pi}$$

$$\therefore \quad \text{area AOB} = \tfrac{1}{2}r^2\theta$$

THE AREA AND ARC LENGTH OF A SECTOR

The arc length AB is also proportional to the angle θ. The angle θ determines the fraction of the circumference which represents the arc length AB. We have

$$\frac{\text{AB}}{2\pi r} = \frac{\theta}{2\pi}$$

$$\therefore \quad \text{AB} = r\theta$$

EXERCISE

1. For x in the range $0 < x < 2\pi$, solve the equations

(i) $\sin 2x = \tan x$

(ii) $3\sin^4 x + 2\sin^2 x - 1 = 0$. (NI 1980, part)

2. Solve the simultaneous equations

$$\tan\alpha + \tan\beta = 1$$
$$\cot\alpha + \cot\beta = -1$$

giving all values of α between 0° and 180°, together with the corresponding value of β. (NI 1981, part)

3. Prove that one of (i) and (ii) below is an identity and find the solution of the other as an equation in θ, giving only the smallest positive root.

(i) $\sin^6\theta + \cos^6\theta = \sin 2\theta \cos 2\theta$

(ii) $\sin^6\theta + \cos^6\theta = \frac{5}{8} + \frac{3}{8}\cos 4\theta$. (WJEC 1982, part)

4. Express $4\cos\theta + 3\sin\theta$ in the form $r\cos(\theta - \alpha)$ where $r > 0$ and $0^\circ < \alpha < 360^\circ$, giving the values of r and α.

Find values of θ between 0° and 360° for which

$$4\cos\theta + 3\sin\theta = 2$$

Find the range of values of θ between 0° and 360° for which

$$|4\cos\theta + 3\sin\theta| \leqslant 2$$ (O 1979)

5. Express $\sin x - 2\cos x$ in the form $R\sin(x - \alpha)$, where R is positive and α is acute. Hence, or otherwise

(i) find the set of possible values of $\sin x - 2\cos x$

(ii) solve the equation

$$\sin x - 2\cos x = 1 \quad \text{for} \quad 0^\circ \leqslant x \leqslant 360^\circ$$ (AEB 1981)

6. (i) Solve the equation $2\tan\theta - 4\cot\theta = \operatorname{cosec}\theta$, giving your answers in radians in the range $-\pi < \theta < \pi$.

(ii) Prove that the area of the minor segment cut off by a chord subtending an angle of θ radians at the centre of a circle of radius r is $\frac{1}{2}r^2(\theta - \sin\theta)$. A chord which subtends an angle α at the centre of a circle divides the area into two segments in the ratio 1 : 5.

Prove that $\sin\alpha = \alpha - \pi/3$.

Plot the graphs of $y = \sin\alpha$ and $y = \alpha - \pi/3$ for values of α between 0 and π using the same axes. Hence find the value of α. (SUJB 1981)

7. (i) Solve the following equations, giving all solutions in the range 0° to 360° inclusive.

(a) $2\cos^2 x + 5\sin x + 1 = 0$

(b) $3\sin x + 4\cos x = 5$.

(ii) A sector containing an angle $\pi/3$ radians is cut from a circular piece of cardboard of radius r. The straight edges of the remaining cardboard are then brought together (without overlapping) to form a cone. Calculate the semi-vertical angle of this cone, giving your answer to the nearest degree. (SUJB 1979)

Worked Solutions

1. (i)

$$\sin 2x = \tan x$$
$$2\sin x\cos x = \frac{\sin x}{\cos x}$$
$$2\sin x\cos^2 x - \sin x = 0$$
$$\sin x(2\cos^2 x - 1) = 0$$
$$\therefore \quad \sin x = 0 \quad \text{or} \quad 2\cos^2 x = 1$$

First solution:

If $\sin x = 0$

$x = \pi$ (solutions must be in the range $0 < x < 2\pi$)

Second solution:

$$2\cos^2 x = 1$$
$$\cos x = \frac{\pm 1}{\sqrt{2}}$$

If $\cos x = \frac{1}{\sqrt{2}}$ $\qquad x = \frac{\pi}{4}$ (principal value)

Corresponding to this principal value the general solution is

$$x = 2n\pi \pm \frac{\pi}{4}$$

$n = 0$ gives $\qquad x = \frac{\pi}{4}$

$n = 1$ gives $\qquad x = 2\pi - \frac{\pi}{4} = \frac{7\pi}{4}$

All other values of n give solutions outside the range $0 < x < 2\pi$.

If $\cos x = \frac{-1}{\sqrt{2}}$ $\qquad x = \frac{3\pi}{4}$ (principal value)

The general solution is

$$x = 2n\pi \pm \frac{3\pi}{4}$$

$n = 0$ gives $\qquad x = \frac{3\pi}{4}$

$n = 1$ gives $\qquad x = 2\pi - \frac{3\pi}{4} = \frac{5\pi}{4}$

All other values of n give solutions outside the range. Hence the solution set is

$$\left\{x : x = \frac{\pi}{4}, \frac{3\pi}{4}, \pi, \frac{5\pi}{4}, \frac{7\pi}{4}\right\}$$

(ii)

$$3\sin^4 x + 2\sin^2 x - 1 = 0$$
$$(3\sin^2 x - 1)(\sin^2 x + 1) = 0$$
$$3\sin^2 x = 1 \quad (\sin^2 x \neq -1 \text{ since } \sin x \text{ must be real})$$
$$\therefore \quad \sin x = \frac{\pm 1}{\sqrt{3}}$$

EXERCISE

First solution:

$$\sin x = \frac{1}{\sqrt{3}}$$
$$x = 0.615^c$$

where the c denotes radian measure.

The general solution is

$$x = n\pi + (-1)^n 0.615^c$$

$n = 0$ gives $x = 0.615^c$

$n = 1$ gives $x = \pi - 0.615^c$

$$x = 2.526^c$$

Second solution:

$$\sin x = -\frac{1}{\sqrt{3}}$$
$$x = -0.615^c \qquad \text{(principal value)}$$

Corresponding to this principal value the general solution is

$$x = n\pi + (-1)^n(-0.615^c)$$

$n = 1$ gives $x = \pi + 0.615^c$

$$x = 3.757^c$$

$n = 2$ gives $x = 2\pi - 0.615^c$

$$x = 5.668^c$$

The solution set is

$$\{x : x = 0.615^c, 2.526^c, 3.757^c, 5.668^c\}$$

2.

$$\tan\alpha + \tan\beta = 1 \qquad (1)$$
$$\cot\alpha + \cot\beta = -1 \qquad (2)$$

From (2)

$$\frac{1}{\tan\alpha} + \frac{1}{\tan\beta} = -1$$
$$\therefore \quad \frac{\tan\alpha + \tan\beta}{\tan\alpha \tan\beta} = -1$$

Using (1) this gives

$$\frac{1}{\tan\alpha \tan\beta} = -1$$
$$\tan\beta = \frac{-1}{\tan\alpha} \qquad (3)$$

Substituting (3) in (1) gives

$$\tan\alpha - \frac{1}{\tan\alpha} = 1$$

Multiplication throughout by $\tan\alpha$ gives

$$\tan^2\alpha - 1 = \tan\alpha$$
$$\tan^2\alpha - \tan\alpha - 1 = 0$$
$$\tan\alpha = \frac{1 \pm \sqrt{5}}{2}$$

First solution:

If $\tan\alpha = \frac{1}{2}(1+\sqrt{5})$ $\qquad \alpha = 58.28°$

$$\therefore \quad \tan\beta = \frac{-2}{1+\sqrt{5}}$$

$$\beta = -31.72°$$

General solution: $\qquad \beta = n\times 180° - 31.72°$

$n = 1$ gives $\qquad \beta = 180° - 31.72°$

$$\beta = 148.28°$$

Second solution:

If $\tan\alpha = \frac{1}{2}(1-\sqrt{5})$

$$\alpha = -31.72° \qquad \text{(principal value)}$$

In the range 0° to 180°, this gives

$$\alpha = 148.28°$$

From (3) we have

$$\tan\beta = \frac{-2}{1-\sqrt{5}}$$

$$\therefore \quad \beta = 58.28°$$

The required solutions are

$$\alpha = 58.28°, \quad \beta = 148.28°; \qquad \alpha = 148.28°, \quad \beta = 58.28°$$

3. Using the factorisation

$$x^3+y^3 = (x+y)(x^2-xy+y^2)$$

with $x = \sin^2\theta$ and $y = \cos^2\theta$

$$\sin^6+\cos^6 = (\sin^2\theta+\cos^2\theta)(\sin^4\theta-\sin^2\theta\cos^2\theta+\cos^4\theta)$$

but $\quad \sin^2\theta+\cos^2\theta = 1$

$$\therefore \quad \sin^6\theta+\cos^6\theta = \sin^4\theta-\sin^2\theta(1-\sin^2\theta)+(1-\sin^2\theta)^2$$

$$= 3\sin^4\theta - 3\sin^2\theta + 1 \qquad (1)$$

From the double-angle formula

$$\cos 4\theta = \cos^2 2\theta - \sin^2 2\theta$$

$$= (1-2\sin^2\theta)^2 - 4\sin^2\theta\cos^2\theta$$

$$= 1-4\sin^2\theta+4\sin^4\theta-4\sin^2\theta(1-\sin^2\theta)$$

$$= 1-8\sin^2\theta+8\sin^4\theta \qquad (2)$$

From (2) $\qquad \frac{3}{8}\cos 4\theta + \frac{5}{8} = 1-3\sin^2\theta+3\sin^4\theta \qquad (3)$

Comparing (1) and (3) establishes the identity

$$\sin^6\theta+\cos^6\theta = \frac{3}{8}\cos 4\theta+\frac{5}{8} \qquad (4)$$

We now need to solve the equation

$$\sin^6\theta+\cos^6\theta = \sin 2\theta\cos 2\theta$$

Substituting (4) on the LHS gives

$$\frac{3}{8}\cos 4\theta+\frac{5}{8} = \frac{1}{2}\sin 4\theta \qquad (\sin 4\theta = 2\sin 2\theta\cos 2\theta)$$

$$3\cos 4\theta + 5 = 4\sin 4\theta$$

$$4\sin 4\theta - 3\cos 4\theta = 5$$

EXERCISE

Using the auxiliary angle method of solution this gives

$$5\left[\tfrac{4}{5}\sin 4\theta - \tfrac{3}{5}\cos 4\theta\right] = 5$$
$$\tfrac{4}{5}\sin 4\theta - \tfrac{3}{5}\cos 4\theta = 1$$

If we let $\cos\alpha = \frac{4}{5}$ and $\sin\alpha = \frac{3}{5}$ this gives

$$\sin(4\theta - \alpha) = 1$$
$$4\theta - \alpha = 90^\circ$$
$$4\theta = 90^\circ + \alpha$$

but $\alpha = \cos^{-1}\frac{4}{5}$ $\quad\therefore\ \alpha = 36.87^\circ$

hence $\quad 4\theta = 126.87^\circ$

$$\therefore\ \theta = 31.72^\circ$$

4.

$$4\cos\theta + 3\sin\theta = 5\left(\tfrac{4}{5}\cos\theta + \tfrac{3}{5}\sin\theta\right)$$

Introducing the auxiliary angle α such that $\cos\alpha = \frac{4}{5}$ and $\sin\alpha = \frac{3}{5}$, gives

$$4\cos\theta + 3\sin\theta = 5(\cos\alpha\cos\theta + \sin\alpha\sin\theta)$$
$$= 5\cos(\theta - \alpha)$$

where $\quad \alpha = 36.87^\circ$

hence $\quad 4\cos\theta + 3\sin\theta = r\cos(\theta - \alpha)$

where $r = 5$ and $\alpha = 36.87^\circ$

$$4\cos\theta + 3\sin\theta = 2 \Rightarrow 5\cos(\theta - 36.87^\circ) = 2$$
$$\cos(\theta - 36.87^\circ) = \tfrac{2}{5}$$
$$\theta - 36.87^\circ = \cos^{-1}\tfrac{2}{5}$$
$$= 66.42^\circ \quad \text{(principal value)}$$

General solution is $\quad \theta - 36.87^\circ = n \times 360^\circ \pm 66.42^\circ$

$n = 0$ gives $\quad \theta = 103.29^\circ$

$n = 1$ gives $\quad \theta = 330.45^\circ$

$$|4\cos\theta + 3\sin\theta| = 2 \Rightarrow 4\cos\theta + 3\sin\theta = 2$$

or $\quad 4\cos\theta + 3\sin\theta = -2$

The first equation has already been solved. We now investigate the solutions of the second equation.

If $4\cos\theta + 3\sin\theta = -2$

$$5\cos(\theta - 36.87^\circ) = -2$$
$$\theta - 36.87^\circ = \cos^{-1}\left(\frac{-2}{5}\right)$$
$$= 113.58^\circ \quad \text{(principal value)}$$

General solution is

$$\theta - 36.87^\circ = n \times 360^\circ \pm 113.58^\circ$$

$n = 0$ gives $\quad \theta = 150.45^\circ$

$n = 1$ gives $\quad \theta = 283.29^\circ$

Combining these results

$$|4\cos\theta + 3\sin\theta| \leqslant 2$$

for $\quad 103.29^\circ < \theta < 150.45^\circ$

and $\quad 283.29^\circ < \theta < 330.45^\circ$

EXERCISE

5.

$$\sin x - 2\cos x = \sqrt{5}\left[\frac{1}{\sqrt{5}}\sin x - \frac{2}{\sqrt{5}}\cos x\right]$$

If we now introduce the auxiliary angle α such that $\cos\alpha = \frac{1}{\sqrt{5}}$ and $\sin\alpha = \frac{2}{\sqrt{5}}$, we have

$$\sin x - 2\cos x = \sqrt{5}(\sin x\cos\alpha - \sin\alpha\cos x)$$

$$\therefore \quad \sin x - 2\cos x = \sqrt{5}\sin(x-\alpha) \qquad (1)$$

where $\alpha = \cos^{-1}\frac{1}{5}$

$$\therefore \quad \alpha = 63.435^\circ$$

(i) The maximum value of $\sin(x-\alpha)$ is $+1$, while the minimum value of $\sin(x-\alpha)$ is -1. From (1) it is seen that the range of values of $\sin x - 2\cos x$ is $-\sqrt{5}$ to $+\sqrt{5}$.

(ii)

$$\sin x - 2\cos x = 1 \Rightarrow \sqrt{5}\sin(x - 63.435^\circ) = 1$$

$$\sin(x-63.435^\circ) = \frac{1}{\sqrt{5}}$$

$$x - 63.435^\circ = \sin^{-1}\frac{1}{\sqrt{5}}$$

$$= 26.565^\circ \quad \text{(principal value)}$$

General solution $\quad x - 63.435^\circ = n\times180^\circ + (-1)^n 26.565^\circ$

$n = 0$ gives $\quad x = 90^\circ$

$n = 1$ gives $\quad x = 216.87^\circ$

Therefore the solution set is

$$\{x : x = 90^\circ, 216.87^\circ\}$$

6. (i)

$$2\tan\theta - 4\cot\theta = \operatorname{cosec}\theta$$

$$\frac{2\sin\theta}{\cos\theta} - \frac{4\cos\theta}{\sin\theta} = \frac{1}{\sin\theta}$$

Multiplying throughout by $\sin\theta\cos\theta$ gives

$$2\sin^2\theta - 4\cos^2\theta = \cos\theta$$

$$2(1-\cos^2\theta) - 4\cos^2\theta = \cos\theta$$

$$6\cos^2\theta + \cos\theta - 2 = 0$$

$$(3\cos\theta + 2)(2\cos\theta - 1) = 0$$

$$\therefore \quad \cos\theta = -\tfrac{2}{3} \quad \text{or} \quad \cos\theta = \tfrac{1}{2}$$

First solution:

$$\cos\theta = -\tfrac{2}{3}$$

$$\theta = 2.3^c \qquad \text{(principal value)}$$

General solution $\quad \theta = 2n\pi \pm 2.3^c$

$n = 0$ gives $\quad \theta = 2.3^c$ or $\theta = -2.3^c$

EXERCISE

Second solution:

$$\cos\theta = \tfrac{1}{2}$$
$$\theta = 1.047^c$$

General solution $\theta = 2n\pi \pm 1.047^c$

$n = 0$ gives $\theta = 1.047^c$ or $\theta = -1.047^c$

The complete solution set is

$$\{\theta : \theta = -2.3^c, \; -1.047^c, \; 1.047^c, \; 2.3^c\}$$

(ii)

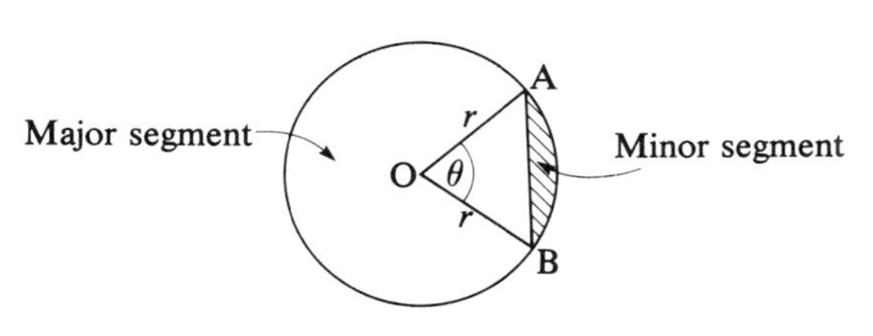

Fig. 6.11

The area of the sector OAB $= \tfrac{1}{2}r^2\theta$

$$\text{the area of } \triangle\text{AOB} = \tfrac{1}{2}r^2\sin\theta$$

$$\therefore \quad \text{area of minor segment} = \tfrac{1}{2}r^2\theta - \tfrac{1}{2}r^2\sin\theta$$
$$= \tfrac{1}{2}r^2(\theta - \sin\theta) \qquad (1)$$

$$\therefore \quad \text{area of major segment} = \pi r^2 - \tfrac{1}{2}r^2(\theta - \sin\theta)$$
$$= r^2\left(\pi - \frac{\theta}{2} + \frac{\sin\theta}{2}\right) \qquad (2)$$

We require

$$\frac{\text{area of minor segment}}{\text{area of major segment}} = \frac{1}{5}$$

If the chord subtends an angle α at the centre of the circle, we have from (1) and (2)

$$\frac{\tfrac{1}{2}(\alpha - \sin\alpha)}{\left(\pi - \frac{\alpha}{2} + \frac{\sin\alpha}{2}\right)} = \frac{1}{5}$$

$$\tfrac{5}{2}(\alpha - \sin\alpha) = \pi - \frac{\alpha}{2} + \frac{\sin\alpha}{2}$$

which simplifies to $\sin\alpha = \alpha - \dfrac{\pi}{3}$

As this question cannot be directly solved by algebraic or trigonometrical methods we will attempt a graphical solution.

In order to plot $y = \sin\alpha$ and $y = \alpha - \frac{\pi}{3}$ we construct the following tables.

α	$\frac{\pi}{6}$	$\frac{\pi}{3}$	$\frac{\pi}{2}$	$\frac{2\pi}{3}$	$\frac{5\pi}{6}$	π
$\sin\alpha$	0.5	0.87	1	0.87	0.5	0

α	$\frac{\pi}{3}$	$\frac{5\pi}{6}$
$\alpha - \frac{\pi}{3}$	0	$\frac{\pi}{2}$

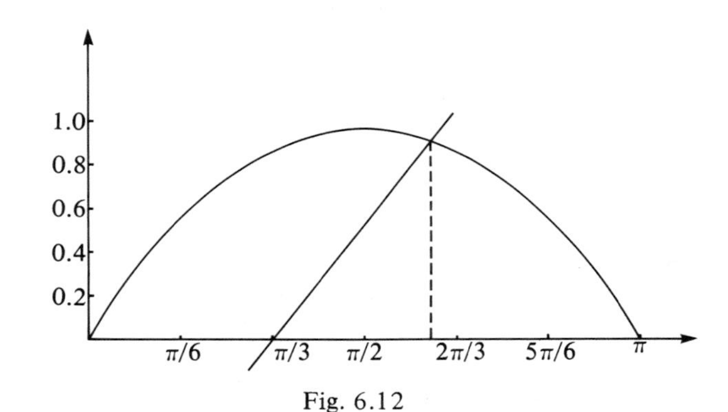

Fig. 6.12

From the graph in Fig. 6.12, the point of intersection of $y = \sin\alpha$ and $y = \alpha - \frac{\pi}{3}$ is approximately $\alpha = 1.97^c$.

7. (i)

(a)

$$\begin{aligned}
2\cos^2 x + 5\sin x + 1 &= 0 \\
2(1 - \sin^2 x) + 5\sin x + 1 &= 0 \\
2\sin^2 x - 5\sin x - 3 &= 0 \\
(2\sin x + 1)(\sin x - 3) &= 0 \\
\sin x &= -\tfrac{1}{2} \qquad (\text{since } \sin x \neq 3) \\
\therefore \quad x &= -30^\circ \qquad (\text{principal value})
\end{aligned}$$

General solution $\quad x = n \times 180^\circ + (-1)^n(-30^\circ)$

$n = 1$ gives $\quad x = 210^\circ$

$n = 2$ gives $\quad x = 330^\circ$

Therefore the solution set is

$$\{x : x = 210^\circ, 330^\circ\}$$

EXERCISE

(b) $$3 \sin x + 4 \cos x = 5$$

The t substitutions $\sin x = \dfrac{2t}{1+t^2}$ and $\cos x = \dfrac{1-t^2}{1+t^2}$ where $t = \tan\dfrac{x}{2}$, give

$$3\left(\frac{2t}{1+t^2}\right)+4\left(\frac{1-t^2}{1+t^2}\right) = 5$$
$$6t+4(1-t^2) = 5(1+t^2)$$
$$9t^2-6t+1 = 0$$
$$(3t-1)^2 = 0$$
$$\therefore \quad t = \tfrac{1}{3} \qquad \text{(repeated root)}$$
$$\tan\frac{x}{2} = \frac{1}{3}$$
$$\therefore \quad \frac{x}{2} = \tan^{-1}\tfrac{1}{3}$$

giving $$\frac{x}{2} = 18.43^\circ \qquad \text{(principal value)}$$

The general solution is

$$\frac{x}{2} = n \times 180^\circ + 18.43^\circ$$

$n = 0$ gives $$x = 36.87^\circ$$

This is the only solution in the range 0° to 360° inclusive.

(ii)

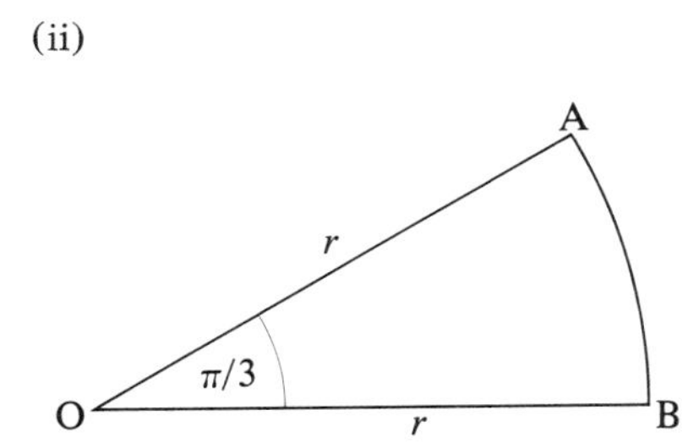

Fig. 6.13

See Fig. 6.13. The arc length AB is given by $AB = \pi r/3$. The slant height of the cone is the radius of the sector AOB. The radius, r', of the cone is given by $2\pi r' = AB$. This gives

$$2\pi r' = \frac{\pi r}{3}$$
$$r' = \frac{r}{6}$$

For the cone

$$\sin\theta = \frac{r'}{r}$$
$$= \tfrac{1}{6}$$
$$\therefore \quad \theta = 10^\circ \qquad \text{(to the nearest degree)}$$

7 DIFFERENTIATION

BASIC CONCEPTS

If we have a function of the form $y = f(x)$, we define the dependent variable to be y and the independent variable to be x. The independent variable is free to take on all values in its domain, while the dependent variable has its value determined by the function and the independent variable.

Differentiation establishes the rate of change of the dependent variable with respect to the independent variable. The result of differentiation is denoted by $\mathrm{d}y/\mathrm{d}x$ or sometimes $f'(x)$. An alternative notation emphasising that differentiation is an operation applied to a function is to write $\dfrac{\mathrm{d}}{\mathrm{d}x}[f(x)]$, indicating that the function enclosed in the square brackets has to be differentiated with respect to x (from now on this will be abbreviated to w.r.t. x).

From the definition given above, differentiation determines the ratio of the instantaneous change in the dependent variable to the change in the independent variable. This process can be usefully viewed geometrically and can be applied to the investigation of conditions for turning points, which is dealt with in the next chapter.

Consider two points A and B on the curve $y = f(x)$ with coordinates (x, y) and $(x + h, y + k)$ respectively (Fig. 7.1).

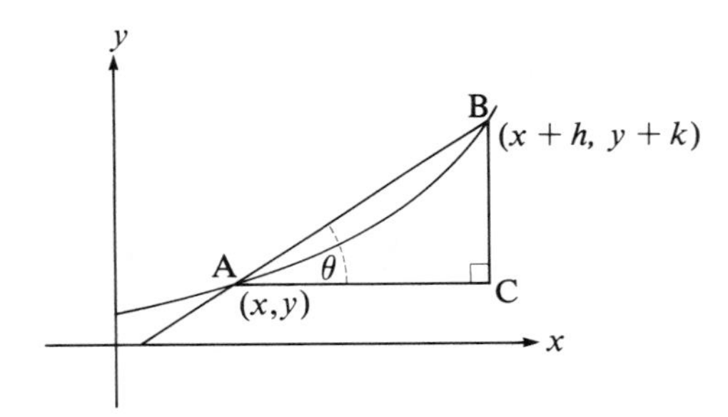

Fig. 7.1

The gradient of the chord AB is given by BC/AC. However, BC represents the change in y between A and B, while AC represents the equivalent change in x. The ratio BC : AC is given by

$$\frac{\mathrm{BC}}{\mathrm{AC}} = \frac{\text{change in } y}{\text{change in } x}$$

From Fig. 7.1 it follows that

$$\frac{\mathrm{BC}}{\mathrm{AC}} = \frac{(y+k)-y}{(x+h)-x}$$

giving

$$\frac{\mathrm{BC}}{\mathrm{AC}} = \frac{k}{h}$$

Applying simple trigonometry to the right-angled triangle ABC, we have

$$\frac{k}{h} = \tan\theta$$

If we let $h \to 0$ the increase in y must also decrease with the result that $k \to 0$. However, as both h and k approach zero, the point B will move round on the curve to coincide with A. The chord AB then becomes the tangent to the curve at A. This limiting position is shown in Fig. 7.2.

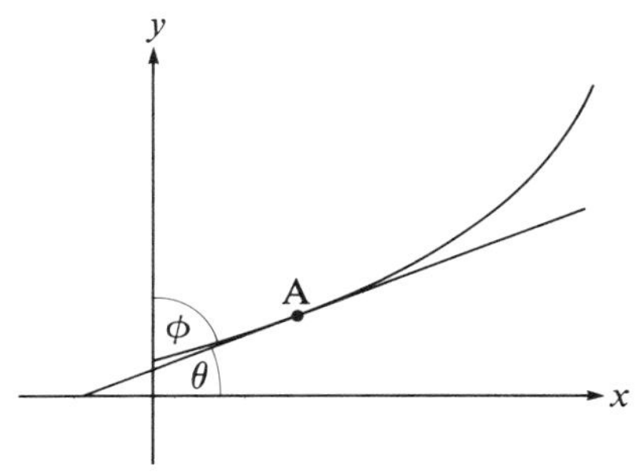

Fig. 7.2 The limiting position when A and B coincide at A.

As both h and $k \to 0$, it follows that the gradient of the tangent measures the ratio of the instantaneous change in y to the corresponding change in x. This quantity is defined to be $\mathrm{d}y/\mathrm{d}x$. Consequently, in the limiting position when the chord AB becomes the tangent at A, we have

$$\frac{\mathrm{d}y}{\mathrm{d}x} = \tan\theta$$

where θ is the angle that the tangent makes with the x-axis in the positive direction of increasing x.

We will now suppose that instead of $\mathrm{d}y/\mathrm{d}x$, we wish to find $\mathrm{d}x/\mathrm{d}y$. Since $\mathrm{d}y/\mathrm{d}x = \tan\theta$ where θ is the angle that the tangent makes with the x-axis, it follows that $\mathrm{d}x/\mathrm{d}y = \tan\phi$ where ϕ is the angle between the y-axis and the tangent. The connection between these two angles is

$$\phi = 90^\circ - \theta$$

However

$$\tan\phi = \cot\theta$$

$$\tan\phi = \frac{1}{\tan\theta}$$

$$\therefore \quad \frac{\mathrm{d}x}{\mathrm{d}y} = \frac{1}{\dfrac{\mathrm{d}y}{\mathrm{d}x}}$$

which is a useful result in some problems.

DIFFERENTIATION OF POWERS OF x

Given $y = ax^n$, where a is a constant and n is a fixed power, the result of differentiating y w.r.t. x is

$$\frac{\mathrm{d}y}{\mathrm{d}x} = nax^{n-1}$$

Since differentiation is distributive this rule can be applied to a sum or difference of any number of expressions such as

$$\frac{\mathrm{d}}{\mathrm{d}x}(f+g) = \frac{\mathrm{d}f}{\mathrm{d}x} + \frac{\mathrm{d}g}{\mathrm{d}x}$$

Example

If $y = 2x^3+\frac{1}{x}$, find $\frac{dy}{dx}$.

In order to apply the basic rule for differentiating powers of x, we express y in index form as

$$y = 2x^3+x^{-1}$$

$$\frac{dy}{dx} = 2\times 3x^{3-1}+(-1)x^{-1-1}$$

$$= 6x^2-x^{-2}$$

$$\therefore \quad \frac{dy}{dx} = 6x^2-\frac{1}{x^2}$$

DIFFERENTIATION OF THE EXPONENTIAL FUNCTION

The exponential function, e^x, is defined by the series

$$e^x = 1+x+\frac{x^2}{2!}+\frac{x^3}{3!}+\ldots+\frac{x^n}{n!}+\ldots$$

Differentiating each side w.r.t. x gives

$$\frac{d}{dx}(e^x) = 0+1+x+\frac{x^2}{2!}+\ldots+\frac{nx^{n-1}}{n!}+\ldots$$

$$= 1+x+\frac{x^2}{2!}+\frac{x^3}{3!}+\ldots+\frac{x^{n-1}}{(n-1)!}+\ldots$$

$$\therefore \quad \frac{d}{dx}(e^x) = e^x$$

If $y = e^x$ $\qquad \frac{dy}{dx} = e^x$

DIFFERENTIATION OF THE LOGARITHMIC FUNCTION

$$y = \ln x \quad \Rightarrow \quad x = e^y$$

$$\therefore \quad \frac{dx}{dy} = e^y$$

$$\frac{dy}{dx} = \frac{1}{e^y} \qquad \left(\text{using } \frac{dy}{dx} = \frac{1}{\frac{dx}{dy}}\right)$$

giving $\qquad \frac{dy}{dx} = \frac{1}{x}$

If $y = \ln x$ $\qquad \frac{dy}{dx} = \frac{1}{x}$

STANDARD DIFFERENTIATION RESULTS

For convenience we summarise the derivatives of several standard functions. The list is not exhaustive, and it is recommended that students check the standard results available to them in the formulae booklet (if any) of the appropriate examination board.

DIFFERENTIATION OF e^x AND $\ln x$

Function $f(x)$	*Derived function* $f'(x)$
ax^n	nax^{n-1}
e^x	e^x
$\ln x$	$\dfrac{1}{x}$
$\sin x$	$\cos x$
$\cos x$	$-\sin x$
$\tan x$	$\sec^2 x$
$\cot x$	$-\operatorname{cosec}^2 x$
$\sec x$	$\sec x \tan x$
$\operatorname{cosec} x$	$-\operatorname{cosec} x \cot x$
$\sin^{-1} x$	$\dfrac{1}{\sqrt{1-x^2}}$
$\cos^{-1} x$	$-\dfrac{1}{\sqrt{1-x^2}}$
$\tan^{-1} x$	$\dfrac{1}{1+x^2}$

THE QUOTIENT RULE FOR DIFFERENTIATION

If
$$y = \frac{u}{v}$$
where both u and v are functions of x, the quotient rule for differentiation states that

$$\frac{dy}{dx} = \frac{v\dfrac{du}{dx} - u\dfrac{dv}{dx}}{v^2}$$

THE PRODUCT RULE FOR DIFFERENTIATION

If $y = uv$

where both u and v are functions of x, the product rule for differentiation is

$$\frac{dy}{dx} = u\frac{dv}{dx} + v\frac{du}{dx}$$

PARAMETRIC DIFFERENTIATION

Suppose we have two equations of the form $y = f(t)$ and $x = g(t)$. It is sometimes possible to eliminate t between them and express y as a function of x. The two equations are said to provide a parametric representation of the function. They enable us to identify a point on the graph of the function by the value of t alone, instead of the two coordinates x and y.

The process of eliminating t may be complicated and time-consuming. Moreover, in order to obtain dy/dx, it is unnecessary since we can differentiate the parametric equations separately and then use the result

$$\frac{dy}{dx} = \frac{dy/dt}{dx/dt}$$

DIFFERENTIATION OF COMPOSITE FUNCTIONS

Given two functions $y = f(u)$ and $u = g(x)$, differentiation may be applied to the product function $fg(x)$ which is solely a function of x. The rule for calculating the rate of change w.r.t. x is

$$\frac{dy}{dx} = \frac{dy}{du} \times \frac{du}{dx}$$

This result may be extended to apply to the product function of any number of functions. Suppose $y = f(u)$, $u = g(v)$ and $v = h(x)$ then

$$\frac{dy}{dx} = \frac{dy}{du} \times \frac{du}{dv} \times \frac{dv}{dx}$$

IMPLICIT DIFFERENTIATION

An example of an explicit relationship between y and x is $y = x^2$, since it provides a direct connection between the dependent and the independent variable. In the case of an implicit relationship it is not always possible or easy to find the direct connection between the dependent and the independent variable. The process of implicit differentiation is shown below.

Example

If $x^2 + 2xy + y^3 = 0$, find $\frac{dy}{dx}$.

If $x^2 + 2xy + y^3 = 0$

$$\frac{d}{dx}(x^2 + 2xy + y^3) = 0$$

$$\frac{d}{dx}(x^2) + \frac{d}{dx}(2xy) + \frac{d}{dx}(y^3) = 0$$

$$2x + 2y + 2x\frac{dy}{dx} + \frac{d}{dy}(y^3)\frac{dy}{dx} = 0$$

$$2x + 2y + 2x\frac{dy}{dx} + 3y^2\frac{dy}{dx} = 0$$

Factorising

$$(2x + 3y^2)\frac{dy}{dx} = -(2x + 2y)$$

$$\frac{dy}{dx} = -\frac{(2x + 2y)}{(2x + 3y^2)}$$

HIGHER DERIVATIVES

The result of differentiating dy/dx w.r.t. x is denoted by d^2y/dx^2. In general the nth derivative of y w.r.t. x is written as d^ny/dx^n.

Worked Example

(i) Differentiate $\log_e[\tan(3x + 5)]$, $0 < 3x + 5 < \pi/2$.

(ii) Given $y = x\tan^{-1}x$, show that

$$\frac{d^2y}{dx^2} = \frac{2}{(1 + x^2)^2}$$

(WJEC 1982, part)

Solution

(i) Let $y = \log_e[\tan(3x + 5)]$

This is a composite function obtained from the three functions

$y = \log_e u$, $u = \tan v$ and $v = 3x + 5$. The rule for differentiating functions like this is

$$\frac{dy}{dx} = \frac{dy}{du} \times \frac{du}{dv} \times \frac{dv}{dx} \qquad (1)$$

To evaluate dy/dx we need to find three separate rates of change.

$$\frac{dy}{du} = \frac{d}{du}(\log_e u) = \frac{1}{u}$$
$$= \frac{1}{\tan(3x+5)}$$
$$\frac{du}{dv} = \frac{d}{dv}(\tan v)$$
$$= \sec^2 v$$
$$= \sec^2(3x+5)$$
$$\frac{dv}{dx} = \frac{d}{dx}(3x+5)$$
$$= 3$$

Substituting these results in (1) gives

$$\frac{dy}{dx} = \frac{3\sec^2(3x+5)}{\tan(3x+5)}$$
$$= \frac{3[1+\tan^2(3x+5)]}{\tan(3x+5)}$$
$$= 3[\cot(3x+5) + \tan(3x+5)]$$

(ii) If $y = x\tan^{-1}x$

$$\frac{dy}{dx} = \tan^{-1}x + \frac{xd}{dx}(\tan^{-1}x) \qquad \text{(product rule for differentiation)}$$
$$= \tan^{-1}x + \frac{x}{1+x^2}$$

Differentiating again

$$\frac{d^2y}{dx^2} = \frac{1}{1+x^2} + \frac{(1+x^2) - 2x \times x}{(1+x^2)^2} \qquad \text{(quotient rule)}$$
$$= \frac{1}{1+x^2} + \frac{1-x^2}{(1+x^2)^2}$$
$$= \frac{1+x^2+1-x^2}{(1+x^2)^2}$$
$$\therefore \quad \frac{d^2y}{dx^2} = \frac{2}{(1+x^2)^2}$$

EXERCISE

1. (i) Differentiate $\log_e \cos x$, $0 \leqslant x < \pi/2$

   (ii) Find d^2y/dx^2 when $y = \sin^{-1}x - x\sqrt{1-x^2}$, expressing your answer as simply as possible. (WJEC 1981, part)

2. (i) Differentiate with respect to x

(a) $e^{\tan x}$ (b) $x^3 \log_e x$ (c) $\dfrac{\sin x}{x}$

(ii) The function ϕ is defined by

$$\phi(x) = x^3 + 2x - 1$$

and the inverse function ϕ^{-1} is denoted by ψ. Find the values of $\psi(2)$ and $\psi'(2)$. (WJEC 1980)

3. (i) If $y = x + \sqrt{1+x^2}$, find dy/dx and hence prove that

$$\sqrt{1+x^2}\,\frac{dy}{dx} = y$$

(ii) If $x = t^2 \sin 3t$ and $y = t^2 \cos 3t$, find dy/dx in terms of t, and show that the curve defined by these parametric equations is parallel to the x-axis at points where $\tan 3t = \dfrac{2}{3t}$. (SUJB 1981)

4. Given that $y = e^{2t}\cos 3t$ and $\log_e x = \sin 3t$, where t is a parameter, prove that

(i) $\dfrac{dy}{dx} = (\tfrac{2}{3} - \tan 3t)\, e^{(2t - \sin 3t)}$

(ii) if $\dfrac{dy}{dx} = 0$ then $x = e^{2/\sqrt{13}}$ or $x = e^{-2/\sqrt{13}}$. (AEB 1982)

5. Determine $\dfrac{dy}{dx}$ in each of the following cases:

(i) $y = \left(\dfrac{1+2x}{1+x}\right)^2$

(ii) $y = \sin 3x \cos^2 x$

(iii) $y + \cos y = x + \cos x$ (NI 1982)

6. (i) Evaluate $\dfrac{dy}{dx}$ at the point $(1, 2)$ on the curve

$$x^2 + 2xy - 3y^2 + 4x - y + 5 = 0$$

(ii) Determine $\dfrac{dy}{dx}$ if $y = x^a a^x$, where a is a constant. (NI 1981)

7. (i) Express in their simplest form the derivatives, with respect to x, of the following expressions:

(a) $\dfrac{1+\sin x}{1+\cos x}$

(b) $\log_e x^2\sqrt{1+x^2}$

(ii) If $y = x^n \log_e x$, where n is a constant, verify that

$$x^2\frac{d^2y}{dx^2} - (2n-1)x\frac{dy}{dx} + n^2 y = 0$$ (NI 1980)

8. (i) Differentiate with respect to x

$$y = \frac{\ln \sin x}{(1+x)^2}$$

(Note $\ln z \equiv \log_e z$)

EXERCISE

(ii) Find $\frac{dy}{dx}$ in terms of x and y where

$$xy^2 + y\cos(2x+1) = 2x$$ (NI 1980)

Worked Solutions

1. (i) Let $u = \cos x$ and $y = \log_e u$.

The rule for differentiating composite functions is

$$\frac{dy}{dx} = \frac{dy}{du} \times \frac{du}{dx}$$

$y = \log_e u$ $\quad \therefore \quad \frac{dy}{du} = \frac{1}{u}$

and $\quad \frac{du}{dx} = \frac{d}{dx}(\cos x) = -\sin x$

hence $\quad \frac{dy}{dx} = \frac{1}{u} \times (-\sin x)$

$$= \frac{1}{\cos x} \times (-\sin x)$$

$$\therefore \quad \frac{dy}{dx} = -\tan x$$

(ii) $y = \sin^{-1}x - x\sqrt{1-x^2}$

$$\frac{dy}{dx} = \frac{1}{\sqrt{1-x^2}} - \sqrt{1-x^2} + \frac{x^2}{\sqrt{1-x^2}}$$ (using the product rule)

Simplifying

$$\frac{dy}{dx} = \frac{1-(1-x^2)+x^2}{\sqrt{1-x^2}}$$

giving

$$\frac{dy}{dx} = \frac{2x^2}{\sqrt{1-x^2}}$$

Differentiating again and multiplying both numerator and denominator by $\sqrt{1-x^2}$ gives

$$\frac{d^2y}{dx^2} = \frac{4x(1-x^2)+2x^3}{(1-x^2)^{3/2}}$$

$$= \frac{2x(2-x^2)}{(1-x^2)^{3/2}}$$

2. (i) (a) Let $y = e^u$ where $u = \tan x$

$$\frac{dy}{du} = e^u$$

or, in terms of x

$$\frac{dy}{du} = e^{\tan x}$$

$$\frac{du}{dx} = \frac{d}{dx}(\tan x) = \sec^2 x$$

$$\frac{dy}{dx} = \frac{dy}{du} \times \frac{du}{dx}$$

$$\therefore \quad \frac{dy}{dx} = e^{\tan x} \times \sec^2 x$$
$$= \sec^2 x \, e^{\tan x}$$

(b) Let $y = x^3 \log_e x$

Using the product rule for differentiating

$$\frac{dy}{dx} = 3x^2 \log_e x + x^3 \times \frac{1}{x}$$
$$= 3x^2 \log_e x + x^2$$
$$\therefore \quad \frac{dy}{dx} = x^2(3 \log_e x + 1)$$

(c) Let $y = \dfrac{\sin x}{x}$

Applying the quotient rule for differentiation

$$\frac{dy}{dx} = \frac{x \cos x - \sin x}{x^2}$$

(ii) Let $y = x^3 + 2x - 1$

Interchanging x and y gives

$$x = y^3 + 2y - 1$$
$$y^3 + 2y = x + 1 \qquad (1)$$

This implicit relationship defines the function ψ.

When $x = 2$, we have

$$y^3 + 2y - 3 = 0$$
$$(y-1)(y^2 + y + 3) = 0$$

Now $y^2 + y + 3 = 0$ has no real solutions. The only real solution is when $y - 1 = 0$.

Hence $y = 1$ $\qquad \therefore \quad \psi(2) = 1 \qquad (2)$

Differentiating (1) implicitly

$$3y^2 \frac{dy}{dx} + 2y \frac{dy}{dx} = 1$$

When $x = 2$, $y = 1$ which gives

$$5 \frac{dy}{dx} = 1$$
$$\therefore \quad \frac{dy}{dx} = \frac{1}{5} \quad \text{or} \quad \psi'(2) = \frac{1}{5}$$

3. (i)

$$y = x + \sqrt{1 + x^2}$$
$$\frac{dy}{dx} = 1 + \tfrac{1}{2}(1 + x^2)^{-1/2} \times 2x$$
$$\frac{dy}{dx} = 1 + \frac{x}{\sqrt{1 + x^2}}$$
$$\sqrt{1 + x^2}\,\frac{dy}{dx} = \sqrt{1 + x^2} + x$$

hence
$$\sqrt{1 + x^2}\,\frac{dy}{dx} = y$$

EXERCISE

(ii) $$\frac{dy}{dx} = \frac{dy/dt}{dx/dt} \quad \text{(the rule for parametric differentiation)}$$

$$\frac{dy}{dt} = 2t\cos 3t - 3t^2 \sin 3t$$

$$\frac{dx}{dt} = 2t\sin 3t + 3t^2\cos 3t$$

Substituting

$$\frac{dy}{dx} = \frac{2t\cos 3t - 3t^2\sin 3t}{2t\sin 3t + 3t^2\cos 3t}$$

$$= \frac{t(2\cos 3t - 3t\sin 3t)}{t(2\sin 3t + 3t\cos 3t)}$$

$$\therefore \quad \frac{dy}{dx} = \frac{2\cos 3t - 3t\sin 3t}{2\sin 3t + 3t\cos 3t}$$

The curve is parallel to the x-axis when the tangent to the curve is also parallel to the x-axis. This can only occur when $\frac{dy}{dx} = 0$.

$$\frac{dy}{dx} = 0 \quad \Rightarrow \quad 2\cos 3t - 3t\sin 3t = 0$$

$$\therefore \quad \tan 3t = \frac{2}{3t}$$

4. (i) $$\frac{dy}{dt} = 2e^{2t}\cos 3t - 3\sin 3t\, e^{2t} \quad \text{(using the product rule)}$$

$$\therefore \quad \frac{dy}{dt} = e^{2t}(2\cos 3t - 3\sin 3t)$$

$$\log_e x = \sin 3t \quad \Rightarrow \quad x = e^{\sin 3t}$$

$$\therefore \quad \frac{dx}{dt} = e^{\sin 3t} \times \frac{d}{dt}(\sin 3t)$$

$$= 3\cos 3t\, e^{\sin 3t}$$

but

$$\frac{dy}{dx} = \frac{\frac{dy}{dt}}{\frac{dx}{dt}}$$

$$\therefore \quad \frac{dy}{dx} = \frac{e^{2t}(2\cos 3t - 3\sin 3t)}{3\cos 3t\, e^{\sin 3t}}$$

$$= \left(\frac{2}{3} - \tan 3t\right) e^{2t} \times e^{-\sin 3t}$$

giving

$$\frac{dy}{dx} = \left(\frac{2}{3} - \tan 3t\right) e^{(2t - \sin 3t)}$$

EXERCISE

(ii) $$\frac{dy}{dx} = 0 \Rightarrow \left(\frac{2}{3} - \tan 3t\right) e^{(2t - \sin 3t)} = 0$$

Since the exponential function is non-zero for finite values of t, the only solution is given by

$$\frac{2}{3} - \tan 3t = 0$$

$$\therefore \quad \tan 3t = \frac{2}{3}$$

Constructing a right-angled triangle (Fig. 7.3) we have a hypotenuse of length $\sqrt{13}$.

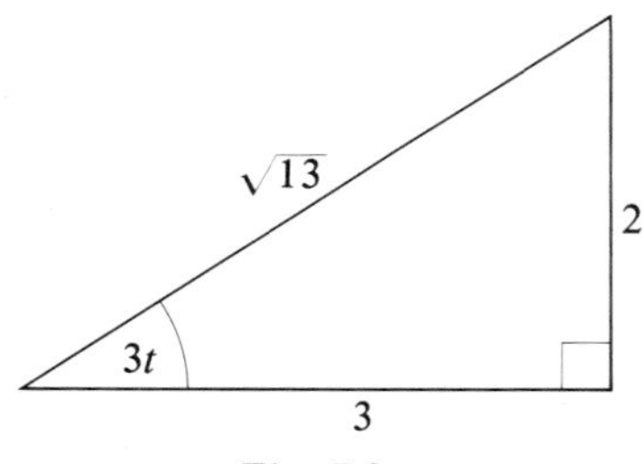

Fig. 7.3

From this triangle it follows that $\sin 3t = \frac{2}{\sqrt{13}}$ or $\sin 3t = \frac{-2}{\sqrt{13}}$, since the angle could be in either the first or third quadrants.

$$\therefore \quad \log_e x = \frac{2}{\sqrt{13}} \quad \text{or} \quad \log_e x = \frac{-2}{\sqrt{13}}$$

Taking antilogs:

$$x = e^{2/\sqrt{13}} \quad \text{or} \quad x = e^{-2/\sqrt{13}}$$

5. (i) $$y = \left(\frac{1+2x}{1+x}\right)^2$$

Let $$y = u^2 \quad \text{where} \quad u = \frac{1+2x}{1+x}$$

$$\frac{dy}{du} = 2u$$

In terms of x $$\frac{dy}{du} = \frac{2(1+2x)}{1+x}$$

$$\frac{du}{dx} = \frac{2(1+x)-(1+2x)}{(1+x)^2}$$

$$= \frac{1}{(1+x)^2}$$

$$\frac{dy}{dx} = \frac{2(1+2x)}{(1+x)} \times \frac{1}{(1+x)^2}$$

$$= \frac{2(1+2x)}{(1+x)^3}$$

<u>EXERCISE</u>

(ii) $$y = \sin 3x \cos^2 x$$

Applying the product rule for differentiation gives

$$\frac{dy}{dx} = 3\cos 3x \cos^2 x - 2\cos x \sin x (\sin 3x)$$

$$= \cos x (3\cos 3x \cos x - 2\sin x \sin 3x)$$

(iii) $$y + \cos y = x + \cos x$$

Differentiating implicitly

$$\frac{dy}{dx} - \sin y \frac{dy}{dx} = 1 - \sin x$$

Factorising $$\frac{dy}{dx}(1 - \sin y) = 1 - \sin x$$

$$\therefore \quad \frac{dy}{dx} = \frac{1 - \sin x}{1 - \sin y}$$

6. (i) $$x^2 + 2xy - 3y^2 + 4x - y + 5 = 0$$

Differentiating implicitly

$$2x + 2y + 2x\frac{dy}{dx} - 6y\frac{dy}{dx} + 4 - \frac{dy}{dx} = 0$$

Putting $x = 1$ and $y = 2$, gives

$$2 + 4 + 2\frac{dy}{dx} - 12\frac{dy}{dx} + 4 - \frac{dy}{dx} = 0$$

$$\therefore \quad -11\frac{dy}{dx} + 10 = 0$$

giving $$\frac{dy}{dx} = \frac{10}{11}$$

(ii) $$y = x^a \times a^x$$

$$\frac{dy}{dx} = ax^{a-1} \times a^x + x^a \frac{d}{dx}(a^x)$$

Now $$a^x = (e^{\ln a})^x$$

$$= e^{x \ln a}$$

$$\therefore \quad \frac{d}{dx}(a^x) = \ln a \times e^{x \ln a}$$

$$= \ln a \times a^x$$

hence $$\frac{dy}{dx} = x^{a-1} \times a^{x+1} + x^a \times \ln a \times a^x$$

$$= x^a \times a^x \left(\frac{a}{x} + \ln a\right)$$

7. (i) (a) $$y = \frac{1 + \sin x}{1 + \cos x}$$

$$\frac{dy}{dx} = \frac{\cos x(1 + \cos x) - (-\sin x)(1 + \sin x)}{(1 + \cos x)^2}$$

$$= \frac{\cos x + \cos^2 x + \sin x + \sin^2 x}{(1+\cos x)^2}$$

$$\therefore \quad \frac{dy}{dx} = \frac{1+\cos x + \sin x}{(1+\cos x)^2} \qquad (\text{since } \sin^2 x + \cos^2 x = 1)$$

(b) Let $y = \log_e u$ where $u = x^2\sqrt{1+x^2}$

$$\frac{dy}{du} = \frac{1}{u}$$

$$= \frac{1}{x^2\sqrt{1+x^2}}$$

Also

$$\frac{du}{dx} = 2x\sqrt{1+x^2} + x^2 \tfrac{1}{2}(1+x^2)^{-1/2}\,2x$$

$$= 2x\sqrt{1+x^2} + \frac{x^3}{\sqrt{1+x^2}}$$

$$= \frac{2x(1+x^2)+x^3}{\sqrt{1+x^2}}$$

$$\therefore \quad \frac{du}{dx} = \frac{2x+3x^3}{\sqrt{1+x^2}}$$

Since

$$\frac{dy}{dx} = \frac{dy}{du} \times \frac{du}{dx}$$

$$\frac{dy}{dx} = \frac{1}{x^2\sqrt{1+x^2}} \times \frac{x(2+3x^2)}{\sqrt{1+x^2}}$$

giving

$$\frac{dy}{dx} = \frac{(2+3x^2)}{x(1+x^2)}$$

(ii)

$$y = x^n \log_e x$$

$$\frac{dy}{dx} = nx^{n-1}\log_e x + x^n \times \frac{1}{x}$$

$$= nx^{n-1}\log_e x + x^{n-1}$$

$$\frac{d^2y}{dx^2} = n(n-1)x^{n-2}\log_e x + nx^{n-1}\left(\frac{1}{x}\right) + (n-1)x^{n-2}$$

giving

$$\frac{d^2y}{dx^2} = n(n-1)x^{n-2}\log_e x + (2n-1)x^{n-2}$$

Multiplying throughout by x^2 gives the result

$$x^2\frac{d^2y}{dx^2} = n(n-1)x^n\log_e x + (2n-1)x^n$$

Also

$$(2n-1)x\frac{dy}{dx} - n^2 y = (2n-1)nx^n\log_e x + (2n-1)x^n - n^2x^n\log_e x$$

Hence

$$x^2\frac{d^2y}{dx^2} - (2n-1)x\frac{dy}{dx} + n^2 y = x^n\log_e x[n(n-1)-(2n-1)n+n^2]$$

$$= 0 \qquad \text{as required}$$

EXERCISE

8. (i)
$$y = \frac{\ln \sin x}{(1+x)^2}$$

Using the quotient rule for differentiation gives

$$\frac{dy}{dx} = \frac{\frac{\cos x}{\sin x}(1+x)^2 - 2(1+x)\ln \sin x}{(1+x)^4}$$

$$\therefore \quad \frac{dy}{dx} = \frac{(1+x)\cot x - 2\ln \sin x}{(1+x)^3}$$

(ii)
$$xy^2 + y\cos(2x+1) = 2x$$

Implicit differentiation gives

$$y^2 + 2xy\frac{dy}{dx} + \cos(2x+1)\frac{dy}{dx} - 2\sin(2x+1)\,y = 2$$

$$[2xy + \cos(2x+1)]\frac{dy}{dx} = 2 + 2y\sin(2x+1) - y^2$$

$$\therefore \quad \frac{dy}{dx} = \frac{2 + 2y\sin(2x+1) - y^2}{2xy + \cos(2x+1)}$$

8 APPLICATIONS OF DIFFERENTIATION

TURNING POINTS, STATIONARY POINTS AND POINTS OF INFLECTION

The changes in direction on the graph of $y = f(x)$ occur at points of maximum or minimum value of the function. Such points are called turning points. If, for example, the function attains a maximum value it will subsequently decrease with increasing values of x, resulting in a change of direction on the curve. Conversely, for a minimum value the curve decreases with increasing values of x and then increases with increasing values of x. In each case the maximum and minimum values correspond to points at which the curve changes direction, and for this reason they are referred to as turning points.

We can illustrate this by reference to the graph of $y = f(x)$ shown in Fig. 8.1. The points A and C correspond to changes in the direction of the curve and are, respectively, points of maximum or minimum value. Consequently, A and C are turning points on the curve. An important characteristic of the points A and C is that the tangents at these points are parallel to the x-axis. The angle θ that the tangents make with the x-axis is such that $\theta = 0$. However, since $\mathrm{d}y/\mathrm{d}x = \tan\theta$, we have $\mathrm{d}y/\mathrm{d}x = 0$ at both A and C.

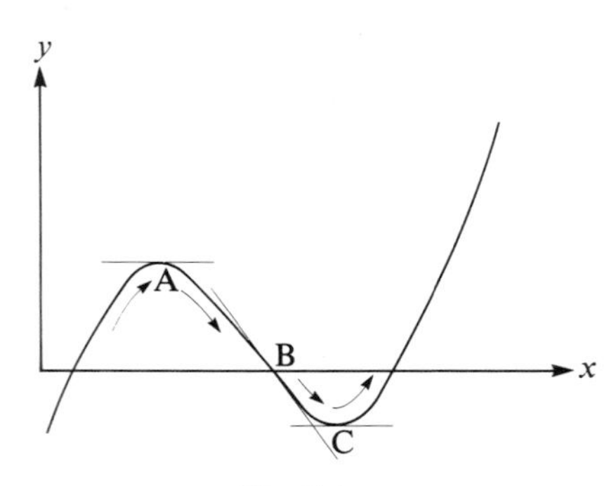

Fig. 8.1

We now consider the graph of $y = x^3$ (see Fig. 8.2). For this function, $\mathrm{d}y/\mathrm{d}x = 3x^2$ and $\mathrm{d}^2y/\mathrm{d}x^2 = 6x$. At the point $x = 0$, both $\mathrm{d}y/\mathrm{d}x = 0$ and $\mathrm{d}^2y/\mathrm{d}x^2 = 0$.

However, although $\mathrm{d}y/\mathrm{d}x = 0$, the point $x = 0$ is not a turning point because the direction of the curve remains unchanged. The value of the function at this point is neither increasing nor decreasing and it is referred to as a stationary point. The points A and C in Fig. 8.1 are also stationary points, but they have the additional property of being turning points. It follows that all turning points are stationary points, but not all stationary points are turning points. The condition for stationary points is that $\mathrm{d}y/\mathrm{d}x = 0$.

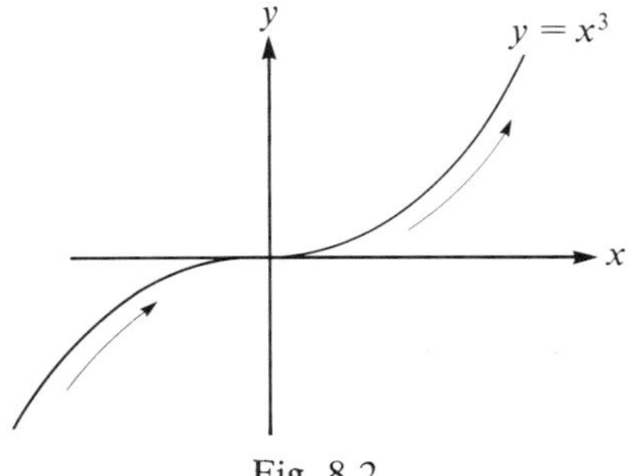

Fig. 8.2

We also note that at the origin the curvature of $y = x^3$ changes from concave downwards to concave upwards. This change in curvature causes the curve to cross its own tangent at $x = 0$, which is the x-axis. The point $x = 0$ is a special point which is referred to as a point of inflection. Referring to Fig. 8.1, it is seen that the point B is also a point of inflection. Points of inflection can occur either with (as in Fig. 8.2) or without $dy/dx = 0$ (as in Fig. 8.1). If $dy/dx = 0$ it is also a stationary point. We conclude that points of inflection are determined by the second derivative vanishing and the direction of the curve remaining unchanged on either side of the point.

We may summarise these results as follows

at stationary points	$dy/dx = 0$
at turning points	$dy/dx = 0$ and the direction of the curve changes, i.e. dy/dx has different signs on either side of the point
at points of inflection	$d^2y/dx^2 = 0$ and the direction of the curve is unchanged, i.e. dy/dx has the same sign on either side of the point.

CONDITIONS FOR MAXIMUM AND MINIMUM VALUES

The condition $dy/dx = 0$ is a characteristic of all turning points. We now need a method for determining if a turning point is a maximum or minimum value.

The maximum value at point A in Fig. 8.1 has increasing values of y to the left of A and decreasing values of y to the right of A. Consequently, the gradient changes from positive to negative values. Hence dy/dx is decreasing as it passes through the point A with the result that d^2y/dx^2 will be negative at the point A.

Examining the behaviour of the curve at point C in Fig. 8.1, we arrive at similar conclusions for minimum values. To the left of C, y is decreasing, it subsequently increases to the right of C. The gradient changes from negative to positive values. Hence dy/dx is increasing as it passes through the point C with the result that d^2y/dx^2 will be positive at this point.

The sign of the second derivative is a useful test for discriminating between maximum or minimum values. If, however, the second derivative vanishes at a stationary point it is inconclusive, and the sign of the first derivative before and after the turning point must be used to distinguish between maximum and minimum values. These results may be summarised as follows.

First set of conditions: $dy/dx = 0$

(i) $\dfrac{d^2y}{dx^2} < 0 \Rightarrow$ Turning point is a maximum value

(ii) $\dfrac{d^2y}{dx^2} > 0 \Rightarrow$ Turning point is a minimum value

Second set of conditions: $dy/dx = d^2y/dx^2 = 0$

(i) $\dfrac{dy}{dx} > 0$ on the left of the stationary point, changing to $dy/dx < 0$ on the right of the stationary point
$\Rightarrow$ Turning point is a maximum value

(ii) $\dfrac{dy}{dx} < 0$ on the left of the stationary point, changing to $dy/dx > 0$ on the right of the stationary point
$\Rightarrow$ Turning point is a minimum value

(iii) $\dfrac{dy}{dx} > 0$ to the left and to the right of the stationary point
$\Rightarrow$ Stationary point is a point of inflection

(iv) $\dfrac{dy}{dx} < 0$ to the left and to the right of the stationary point
$\Rightarrow$ Stationary point is a point of inflection

The first set of conditions are the most useful and the most widely used in applications of differentiation to problems.

Worked Example

Investigate the function f defined by

$$f(x) = 3x^5 - 10x^3 + 10$$

for local maxima, minima and points of inflection. Sketch the graph of the function, showing clearly the stationary points and any points of inflection. (WJEC 1981, part)

Solution

$$f(x) = 3x^5 - 10x^3 + 10$$
$$f'(x) = 15x^4 - 30x^2$$
$$f''(x) = 60x^3 - 60x$$

For stationary points we require $f'(x) = 0$.

Hence $$15x^2(x^2 - 2) = 0$$

$$\therefore \quad x = 0 \quad \text{or} \quad x = \sqrt{2} \quad \text{or} \quad x = -\sqrt{2}$$

We now examine each of these stationary points in turn. When $x = 0$ we have $f''(x) = 0$. This is a point of inflection if the direction of the curve is the same, the direction of the curve remains unchanged. Hence $x = 0$ is a $f'(x)$ when $x = -1$ and $x = 1$, which are convenient integer values of x between $x = \pm\sqrt{2}$.

Now $f'(1) = -15$ and $f'(-1) = -15$. Since the sign of these gradients is the same, the direction of the curve remains unchanged. Hence $x = 0$ is a stationary point which is also a point of inflection.

We now investigate the points $x = \pm\sqrt{2}$.

$$f''(\sqrt{2}) = 60 \times (\sqrt{2})^3 - 60\sqrt{2}$$
$$= 120\sqrt{2} - 60\sqrt{2}$$
$$\therefore \quad f''(\sqrt{2}) = 60\sqrt{2} > 0 \quad \text{i.e.} \quad x = \sqrt{2} \quad \text{is a minimum point}$$
$$f''(-\sqrt{2}) = -120\sqrt{2} + 60\sqrt{2}$$
$$= -60\sqrt{2} < 0 \quad \text{i.e.} \quad x = -\sqrt{2} \quad \text{is a maximum point}$$
$$f(\sqrt{2}) = 3 \times 4\sqrt{2} - 20\sqrt{2} + 10$$
$$= 10 - 8\sqrt{2}$$

giving $f(\sqrt{2}) \approx -1.3$

$f(-\sqrt{2}) = 10+8\sqrt{2}$

$f(-\sqrt{2}) \approx 21.3$

This completes the investigation of the stationary points. In order to find the points of inflection we put $f''(x) = 0$. This gives

$$60x(x^2-1) = 0$$

$$\therefore \quad x = 0 \quad \text{or} \quad x = -1 \quad \text{or} \quad x = 1$$

The point $x = 0$ has already been examined since it was a stationary point. We now look at the sign of the gradients at $x = -0.9$ and $x = -1.1$, which are points on either side of $x = -1$.

$$f'(-0.9) = 15\times(-0.9)^4 - 30\times(-0.9)^2$$

giving $f'(-0.9) = -14.4585$

$$f'(-1.1) = 15\times(-1.1)^4 - 30\times(-1.1)^2$$

giving $f'(-1.1) = -14.3385$

We observe that the sign of the gradients is the same on either side of the point $x = -1$ which is, therefore, a point of inflection. When $x = -1$ we have $f(-1) = 17$.

Since $f'(x)$ is an even function of x it will have the same signs and values at the points $x = \pm 0.9$ and $x = \pm 1.1$. Hence, since the gradient has the same sign on either side of $x = -1$ it will also have the same sign on either side of $x = 1$, which is, therefore, also a point of inflection. When $x = 1$, we have $f(1) = 3$.

These results are sufficient to produce a sketch of the graph of $f(x)$ (Fig. 8.3), and may be summarised as

$(-\sqrt{2}, 21.3)$ is a maximum point

$(\sqrt{2}, -1.3)$ is a minimum point

$(0,10)$ is a stationary point that is also a point of inflection

$(-1,17)$ is a point of inflection

$(1,3)$ is a point of inflection

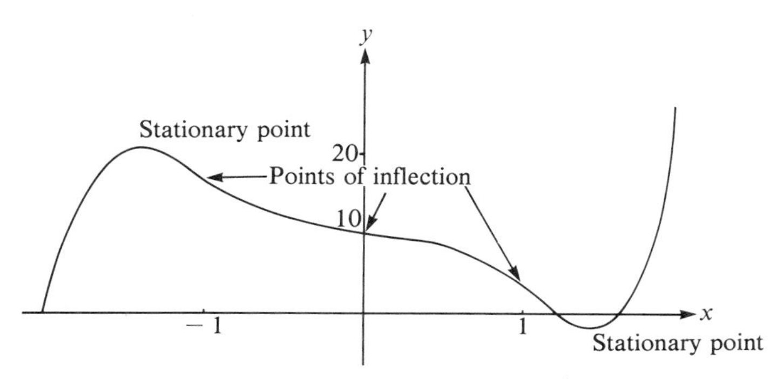

Fig. 8.3 The curve $y = 3x^5 - 10x^3 + 10$

EXERCISE

1. Differentiate $e^{2x}(x^2 - 6x + 7)$ with respect to x. Hence find the value of x for which the function has maximum and minimum values, distinguishing between them. (O 1977)

2. A curve has the equation $y = \dfrac{a}{b + e^{-cx}}$ $(a \neq 0, b > 0, c > 0)$. Show that it has one point of inflection, and that the value of y at the point of inflection is half the limiting value of y as $x \to \infty$. (O 1977)

3. If y is defined in terms of x by the equation $x^3 + y^3 - 3xy = 0$, show that the graph of y has a turning point at $(2^{1/3}, 2^{2/3})$.
Determine whether this gives a maximum or minimum value of y. (O 1979)

4. Differentiate the function $\dfrac{x+3}{\sqrt{1+x^2}}$ with respect to x. Find the value of x at which the function has a maximum or minimum, and determine which of these it is. (O 1982)

5. Show that if $f(x) = \dfrac{(x-4)^2}{x-3}$ then $f'(x) = \dfrac{(x-4)(x-2)}{(x-3)^2}$. Find the local maxima or minima of the function f and show that it has no points of inflection. Sketch the graph of f. (WJEC 1982, part)

6. The parametric equations of a curve are $x = \log_e(1+t)$, $y = e^{t^2}$ for $t > -1$. Find dy/dx and d^2y/dx^2 in terms of t.
Prove that the curve has only one turning point and that it must be a minimum. (AEB 1982)

Worked Solutions

1.
$$y = e^{2x}(x^2 - 6x + 7)$$
$$\frac{dy}{dx} = 2e^{2x}(x^2 - 6x + 7) + e^{2x}(2x - 6)$$

Factorising
$$\frac{dy}{dx} = 2e^{2x}(x^2 - 5x + 4)$$
$$= 2e^{2x}(x-4)(x-1)$$

For turning points $dy/dx = 0$
$$\Rightarrow \quad 2e^{2x}(x-4)(x-1) = 0$$
$$\therefore \quad x = 4 \quad \text{or} \quad x = 1 \qquad (\text{since } e^{2x} \neq 0)$$

Differentiating again
$$\frac{d^2y}{dx^2} = 4e^{2x}(x-4)(x-1) + 2e^{2x}(x-1) + 2e^{2x}(x-4)$$

When $x = 4$
$$\frac{d^2y}{dx^2} = 6e^8 > 0$$

Therefore $x = 4$ is a minimum point

When $x = 1$ $\quad \dfrac{d^2y}{dx^2} = -6e^2 < 0$

Therefore $x = 1$ is a maximum point

2.
$$y = \frac{a}{b + e^{-cx}} \qquad (1)$$
$$\frac{dy}{dx} = \frac{ace^{-cx}}{(b + e^{-cx})^2} \qquad (2)$$

also $$\frac{d^2y}{dx^2} = \frac{-ac^2e^{-cx}(b+e^{-cx})+2ac^2e^{-2cx}}{(b+e^{-cx})^3}$$

Factorising to

$$\frac{d^2y}{dx^2} = \frac{ac^2e^{-cx}(2e^{-cx}-b-e^{-cx})}{(b+e^{-cx})^3}$$

Simplifying $$\frac{d^2y}{dx^2} = \frac{ac^2e^{-cx}(e^{-cx}-b)}{(b+e^{-cx})^3}$$

A necessary condition for a point of inflection is $d^2y/dx^2 = 0$

$$\Rightarrow \quad e^{-cx} = b \qquad (\text{since } e^{-cx} \neq 0)$$

Substituting this value of b in (1) gives

$$y = \frac{a}{2b} \tag{3}$$

This will only be a point of inflection if the sign of dy/dx is the same on either side of the point. To investigate this we note that the sign of dy/dx is determined solely by the sign of a, since all the other quantities involved in (2) are positive. Hence the sign of dy/dx will be the same on either side of the point. Therefore $b = e^{-cx}$ corresponds to a point of inflection. Now as $x \to \infty$, $e^{-cx} \to 0$ as $c > 0$.

$$\therefore \lim_{x\to\infty} \frac{a}{b+e^{-cx}} = \frac{a}{b} \tag{4}$$

Comparing (3) and (4) we see that the value at the point of inflection is half the limiting value of y as $x \to \infty$.

3. $$x^3+y^3-3xy = 0 \tag{1}$$

Differentiating implicitly

$$3x^2+3y^2\frac{dy}{dx}-3y-3x\frac{dy}{dx} = 0$$

$$(3y^2-3x)\frac{dy}{dx} = 3y-3x^2 \tag{2}$$

$$\therefore \quad \frac{dy}{dx} = \frac{y-x^2}{y^2-x}$$

If $\dfrac{dy}{dx} = 0$, $y = x^2$. Substituting in (1) gives

$$x^6-2x^3 = 0$$

Factorising $$x^3(x^3-2) = 0$$

$$\therefore \quad x = 0, \quad y = 0 \qquad \text{or} \qquad x = 2^{1/3}, \quad y = 2^{2/3}$$

hence there is a turning point at $(2^{1/3}, 2^{2/3})$.

Differentiating (2) implicitly

$$(3y^2-3x)\frac{d^2y}{dx^2}+\left(6y\frac{dy}{dx}-3\right)\frac{dy}{dx} = 3\frac{dy}{dx}-6x$$

Since $\dfrac{dy}{dx} = 0$ this gives

$$(3y^2-3x)\frac{d^2y}{dx^2} = -6x$$

Substituting $y = x^2$ gives

$$(3x^4 - 3x)\frac{d^2y}{dx^2} = -6x$$

$$\frac{d^2y}{dx^2} = \frac{-2}{(x^3 - 1)}$$

When $x = 2^{1/3}$

$$\frac{d^2y}{dx^2} = -2$$

$\therefore \quad (2^{1/3}, 2^{2/3})$ is a maximum value

4. Let

$$y = \frac{x+3}{\sqrt{1+x^2}}$$

$$\frac{dy}{dx} = \frac{(1+x^2)^{1/2} - x(1+x^2)^{-1/2}(x+3)}{1+x^2}$$

Simplifying to

$$\frac{dy}{dx} = \frac{1-3x}{(1+x^2)^{3/2}} \qquad (1)$$

Differentiating again

$$\frac{d^2y}{dx^2} = \frac{-3(1+x^2)^{3/2} - \frac{3}{2}(1+x^2)^{1/2}\, 2x(1-3x)}{(1+x^2)^3}$$

Simplifying to

$$\frac{d^2y}{dx^2} = \frac{3(2x^4 - x^3 + x^2 - x - 1)}{(1+x^2)^{7/2}} \qquad (2)$$

For a maximum or minimum value $dy/dx = 0$.

$$\therefore \quad 1 - 3x = 0$$

$$x = \tfrac{1}{3}$$

We only need to establish the sign of the numerator of d^2y/dx^2, since the denominator is positive.

Substituting $x = \frac{1}{3}$ in $(2x^4 - x^3 + x^2 - x - 1)$ gives

$$2(\tfrac{1}{3})^4 - (\tfrac{1}{3})^3 + (\tfrac{1}{3})^2 - \tfrac{1}{3} - 1 < 0$$

Consequently at $x = \frac{1}{3}$, $d^2y/dx^2 < 0 \Rightarrow x = \frac{1}{3}$ is a maximum point.

5. If

$$f(x) = \frac{(x-4)^2}{x-3}$$

$$f'(x) = \frac{2(x-4)(x-3) - (x-4)^2}{(x-3)^2}$$

$$= \frac{(2x^2 - 14x + 24) - (x^2 - 8x + 16)}{(x-3)^2}$$

giving

$$f'(x) = \frac{x^2 - 6x + 8}{(x-3)^2}$$

Factorising to

$$f'(x) = \frac{(x-4)(x-2)}{(x-3)^2} \qquad \text{(as required)}$$

EXERCISE

Local maxima or minima occur when $f'(x) = 0$.

If $f'(x) = 0$ $\qquad (x-4)(x-2) = 0$

$$\therefore \quad x = 4 \quad \text{or} \quad x = 2$$

$$f''(x) = \frac{(2x-6)(x-3)^2 - 2(x-3)(x^2-6x+8)}{(x-3)^4}$$

Simplifying

$$f''(x) = \frac{(2x-6)(x-3) - 2(x^2-6x+8)}{(x-3)^3}$$

giving $\qquad f''(x) = \dfrac{2}{(x-3)^3}$

Hence $f''(x) \neq 0$, since the numerator never vanishes. There is therefore no point of inflection.

When $x = 4$, $f''(4) = 2 > 0$; hence $x = 4$ is a minimum point.

When $x = 2$, $f''(2) = -2 < 0$; hence $x = 2$ is a maximum point.

The minimum value is $f(4) = 0$

The maximum value is $f(2) = -4$

The denominator of $f(x)$ vanishes when $x = 3$ so that the straight line $x = 3$ corresponds to a vertical asymptote of the curve. Moreover, when $x < 3$, $f(x) < 0$ and when $x > 3$, $f(x) > 0$. These results enable us to sketch the graph of $f(x)$ (Fig. 8.4).

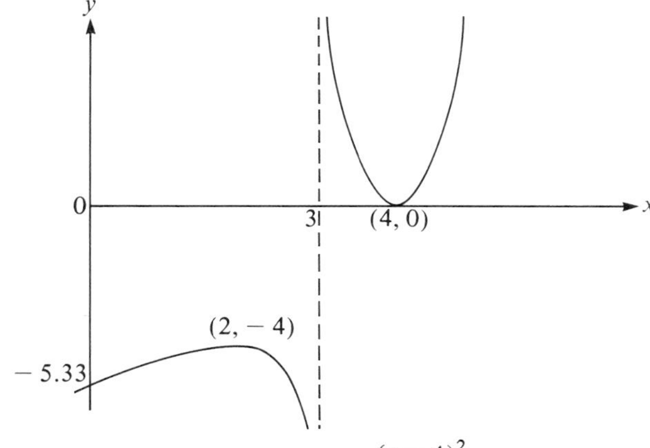

Fig. 8.4 $\quad f(x) = \dfrac{(x-4)^2}{x-3}$

6. Parametric differentiation gives

$$\frac{dy}{dt} = 2te^{t^2}$$

$$\frac{dx}{dt} = \frac{1}{1+t}$$

$$\frac{dy}{dx} = \frac{dy/dt}{dx/dt} = \frac{2te^{t^2}}{\left(\dfrac{1}{1+t}\right)}$$

giving $\qquad \dfrac{dy}{dx} = 2t(1+t)e^{t^2} \qquad (1)$

EXERCISE

$$\frac{d^2y}{dx^2} = \frac{d}{dx}[2t(1+t)e^{t^2}]$$
$$= \frac{d}{dt}[2t(1+t)e^{t^2}]\frac{dt}{dx}$$
$$= [2(1+t)e^{t^2} + 2te^{t^2} + 4t^2(1+t)e^{t^2}]\frac{dt}{dx}$$

but $$\frac{dt}{dx} = \frac{1}{dx/dt} = 1+t$$

$$\therefore \quad \frac{d^2y}{dx^2} = (1+t)[2(1+t)e^{t^2} + 2te^{t^2} + 4t^2(1+t)e^{t^2}]$$
$$= 2e^{t^2}(1+t)(2t^3+2t^2+2t+1) \qquad (2)$$

For a turning point $dy/dx = 0$

$$\therefore \quad 2t(1+t)e^{t^2} = 0$$
$$\therefore \quad t = 0 \qquad (\text{since } t \neq -1 \text{ and } e^{t^2} \neq 0)$$

$\therefore$ there is only one turning point

Substituting $t = 0$ in (2) $\quad \dfrac{d^2y}{dx^2} = 2$

$\therefore$ $t = 0$ is a minimum point

EXERCISE

9 INTEGRATION

INTRODUCTION

Integration is the reverse process to differentiation. Suppose we are given the derivative, $f'(x)$, of some function. The process of recovering $f(x)$ from $f'(x)$ is called integration. The symbol $\int$ inserted before an expression is used to denote that it is to be integrated. Furthermore, if the integration is with respect to x, we write dx after the expression which is to be integrated. The expression which is to be integrated is usually referred to as the integrand.

We may summarise the relationship between $f(x)$ and $f'(x)$ as

$$\int f'(x)\,dx = f(x) + c$$

where c is an arbitrary constant. Because the derivative of a constant is zero, the reverse process of integration must introduce an unknown constant, c, whose value can be determined if additional information is supplied.

Example

$$f(x) = x^2 + 2 \quad \Rightarrow \quad f'(x) = 2x$$

$$f(x) = \int f'(x)\,dx \quad \Rightarrow \quad f(x) = \int 2x\,dx$$

$$\therefore \quad f(x) = x^2 + c$$

The value of c in this case is obviously 2. In practice, however, the original function is unknown initially and extra information is required in order to find its value.

PROPERTIES OF INTEGRATION

We assume without proof the validity of the following properties

(i) $\int af(x)\,dx = a\int f(x)\,dx$ where a is a constant

(ii) $\int [f(x)+g(x)]\,dx = \int f(x)\,dx + \int g(x)\,dx$

INTEGRATING POWERS OF x

If $f(x) = x^{n+1}$

$$f'(x) = (n+1)x^n$$

$$\therefore \quad x^n = \frac{1}{n+1}f'(x)$$

$$\int x^n\,dx = \frac{1}{n+1}\int f'(x)\,dx$$

$$= \frac{1}{n+1}f(x) + c$$

giving

$$\int x^n\,dx = \frac{1}{n+1}x^{n+1} + c \qquad (n \neq -1) \tag{9.1}$$

DEFINITE INTEGRALS

Suppose $F'(x) = f(x)$. The relationship between the function and its derivative may be written as

$$\int f(x)\,\mathrm{d}x = F(x) + c$$

This is called an indefinite integral because the RHS cannot be uniquely determined without additional information.

We define the definite integral of $f(x)$ to be given by

$$\int_a^b f(x)\,\mathrm{d}x = F(b) - F(a)$$

b is called the upper limit and a the lower limit of integration. This is referred to as a definite integral because there is no unknown constant introduced as a result of the integration.

Example

Find
$$\int_2^5 x^2\,\mathrm{d}x$$

Using the rule for integrating powers of x, we have

$$\int_2^5 x^2\,\mathrm{d}x = \left[\frac{x^3}{3}\right]_2^5$$

Note that the result of integrating is enclosed in square brackets with the limits of integration inserted to their right. To evaluate this we put $x = 5$ into the expression enclosed by the square brackets and subtract its value when $x = 2$.

$$\begin{aligned}\int_2^5 x^2\,\mathrm{d}x &= \frac{5^3}{3} - \frac{2^3}{3}\\ &= \frac{1}{3}(125 - 8)\\ &= 39\end{aligned}$$

USEFUL INTEGRALS

(1)
$$y = \ln x \quad \Rightarrow \quad \frac{\mathrm{d}y}{\mathrm{d}x} = \frac{1}{x}$$

If we now reverse this process and integrate, we have

$$\int \frac{\mathrm{d}x}{x} = \ln x + c \qquad (9.2)$$

Suppose now $y = \ln f(x)$. If we let $u = f(x)$ and use the differentiation rule for composite functions we have

$$\frac{\mathrm{d}y}{\mathrm{d}x} = \frac{\mathrm{d}y}{\mathrm{d}u} \times \frac{\mathrm{d}u}{\mathrm{d}x}$$

$$\frac{\mathrm{d}y}{\mathrm{d}u} = \frac{\mathrm{d}}{\mathrm{d}u}(\ln u) = \frac{1}{u}$$

$$\frac{\mathrm{d}u}{\mathrm{d}x} = f'(x)$$

$$\frac{dy}{dx} = \frac{f'(x)}{f(x)}$$

$$\therefore \quad \int \frac{f'(x)}{f(x)}\,dx = \ln|f(x)| + c \qquad (9.3)$$

The modulus sign is included to ensure that the logarithm of a positive number is taken.

(2) If $y = e^{ax}$ $\qquad \frac{dy}{dx} = ae^{ax}$

$$\int e^{ax}\,dx = \frac{1}{a}e^{ax} + c \qquad (9.4)$$

If $y = e^{f(x)}$ and we let $u = f(x)$, differentiation using the composite function rule gives

$$\frac{dy}{dx} = f'(x)e^{f(x)}$$

Reversing this process by using integration gives

$$\int f'(x)e^{f(x)}\,dx = e^{f(x)} + c \qquad (9.5)$$

(3) If $y = [f(x)]^n$ $\qquad \frac{dy}{dx} = nf'(x)[f(x)]^{n-1}$

$$\int f'(x)[f(x)]^{n-1}\,dx = \frac{1}{n}[f(x)]^n + c \qquad (9.6)$$

STANDARD INTEGRALS

A number of standard integrals are provided by the examining boards and for reference some of these are summarised below.

$$\int \sin x\,dx = -\cos x + c$$

$$\int \cos x\,dx = \sin x + c$$

$$\int \tan x\,dx = \log_e \sec x + c$$

$$\int \cot x\,dx = \log_e \sin x + c$$

$$\int \sec x\,dx = \log_e(\sec x + \tan x) + c$$

$$\int \operatorname{cosec} x\,dx = \log_e\left(\tan\frac{x}{2}\right) + c$$

$$\int \frac{dx}{\sqrt{a^2 - x^2}} = \sin^{-1}\frac{x}{a} + c$$

$$\int \frac{dx}{a^2 + x^2} = \frac{1}{a}\tan^{-1}\frac{x}{a} + c$$

$$\int \frac{dx}{\sqrt{a^2 + x^2}} = \log_e\left(\frac{x + \sqrt{x^2 + a^2}}{a}\right) + c$$

INTEGRATION BY PARTIAL FRACTIONS

If the denominator of an algebraic fraction can be resolved into factors, it may be broken down into partial fractions. The integral of the fraction may then be found by integrating the partial fractions.

Worked Example

Given that $$y = \frac{(2x-1)}{(x-2)(5-x)}$$

(i) express y in partial fractions.

(ii) evaluate $\int_3^4 y\,\mathrm{d}x$ (AEB 1980)

Solution

(i) $$\frac{2x-1}{(x-2)(5-x)} = \frac{A}{x-2}+\frac{B}{5-x}$$

$$\therefore\quad 2x-1 = A(5-x)+B(x-2)$$

Putting $x = 2$ $\quad 3 = 3A \quad \therefore\quad A = 1$

Putting $x = 5$ $\quad 9 = 3B \quad \therefore\quad B = 3$

giving $$\frac{2x-1}{(x-2)(5-x)} = \frac{1}{x-2}+\frac{3}{5-x}$$

(ii) $$\therefore\quad \int_3^4 y\,\mathrm{d}x = \int_3^4 \frac{\mathrm{d}x}{(x-2)}+\int_3^4 \frac{3\,\mathrm{d}x}{(5-x)}$$

Note that $\frac{\mathrm{d}}{\mathrm{d}x}(x-2) = 1$ with the result that the first integral on the RHS is immediately integrable as the logarithm of the denominator. However, $\frac{\mathrm{d}}{\mathrm{d}x}(5-x) = -1$, so that some adjustment must be made to the sign in the numerator before it fits into the standard logarithmic form (9.3). This may be done as follows

$$\int_3^4 y\,\mathrm{d}x = \int_3^4 \frac{\mathrm{d}x}{x-2} - 3\int_3^4 \frac{-\mathrm{d}x}{5-x}$$

In both integrals we now have $\frac{\mathrm{d}}{\mathrm{d}x}$(denominator) = numerator.

Consequently

$$\int_3^4 y\,\mathrm{d}x = \Big[\ln(x-2)\Big]_3^4 - 3\Big[\ln(5-x)\Big]_3^4$$
$$= (\ln 2-\ln 1)-3(\ln 1-\ln 2)$$
$$= \ln 2+3\ln 2$$
$$= 4\ln 2$$

INTEGRATION BY SUBSTITUTION

This is one of the most useful methods of integration. The method is to introduce a substitution which reduces an integral into a standard form which is immediately integrable. In many A-level problems the appropriate substitution is given. It must be remembered when applying integration by substitution that the entire integral must be expressed in terms of the new variable, including the limits of integration (if any).

INTEGRATION BY PARTIAL FRACTIONS AND BY SUBSTITUTION

Worked Example

Using the substitution $t = \sin x$, evaluate to two decimal places the integral

$$\int_{\pi/6}^{\pi/2} \frac{4\cos x\,dx}{3+\cos^2 x} \qquad \text{(AEB 1983)}$$

Solution

Let $t = \sin x$ $\qquad \therefore \quad \dfrac{dt}{dx} = \cos x$

$$dt = \cos x\,dx$$

We now calculate the new limits of integration. When $x = \pi/2$, we have

$$t = \sin\frac{\pi}{2} \qquad \therefore \quad t = 1$$

When $x = \pi/6$

$$t = \sin\frac{\pi}{6} = \frac{1}{2}$$

Hence

$$\begin{aligned}\int_{x=\pi/6}^{x=\pi/2} \frac{4\cos x\,dx}{3+\cos^2 x} &= \int_{t=1/2}^{t=1} \frac{4dt}{3+(1-t^2)} \\ &= \int_{1/2}^{1} \frac{4dt}{4-t^2} \\ &= \int_{1/2}^{1} \frac{4dt}{(2-t)(2+t)}\end{aligned}$$

This can now be integrated by the method of partial fractions.

Let

$$\frac{4}{(2-t)(2+t)} = \frac{A}{2-t}+\frac{B}{2+t}$$

$$\therefore \quad 4 = A(2+t)+B(2-t)$$

Putting $t = 2$ $\qquad 4 = 4A \qquad \therefore \quad A = 1$

Putting $t = -2$ $\qquad 4 = 4B \qquad \therefore \quad B = 1$

Hence

$$\begin{aligned}\int_{1/2}^{1} \frac{4dt}{(2-t)(2+t)} &= \int_{1/2}^{1} \frac{dt}{2-t} + \int_{1/2}^{1} \frac{dt}{2+t} \\ &= \Big[-\ln(2-t)\Big]_{1/2}^{1} + \Big[\ln(2+t)\Big]_{1/2}^{1} \\ &= -\ln 1 + \ln\tfrac{3}{2} + \ln 3 - \ln 2\tfrac{1}{2} \\ &= \ln\tfrac{9}{5} \\ &= 0.59 \qquad \text{(correct to two decimal places)}\end{aligned}$$

EXERCISE

1. Use the method of partial fractions to obtain

$$\int \frac{(1-2x^2)dx}{(x-1)^2(3-4x)} \qquad \text{(NI 1982)}$$

2. Express
$$\frac{1}{(2-x)(1+x)}$$
in partial fractions and hence, or otherwise, evaluate
$$\int_0^1 \frac{dx}{(2-x)(1+x)}$$
(O 1978)

3. Find
$$\int \frac{(3x^2+1)\,dx}{x^2(x^2+1)}$$
(WJEC 1982, part)

4. Find
$$\int \frac{(x-4)\,dx}{(x-1)^2(2x+1)}$$
(WJEC 1980, part)

5. (i) Resolve the expression
$$\frac{9-10x}{(1-x)(2-x)}$$
into partial fractions.

(ii) Evaluate $I = \int_0^t \frac{(9-10x)\,dx}{(1-x)(2-x)}$ (where $0<t<1$)

(iii) Deduce that, if t is small, then
$$I \approx \tfrac{9}{2}t + \tfrac{7}{8}t^2 + \tfrac{1}{8}t^3$$
(NI 1980)

6. By using the substitution $u^2 = 4 - x^2$, or otherwise, show that
$$\int_0^1 \frac{x^3\,dx}{\sqrt{4-x^2}} = \frac{16}{3} - 3\sqrt{3}$$
(NI 1980, part)

7. By means of the substitution $u = 1 + \cos\theta$, or otherwise, evaluate
$$\int_0^{\pi/2} \frac{\sin^3\theta\,d\theta}{(1+\cos\theta)^{3/2}}$$
(NI 1981, part)

8. By suitable substitution, or otherwise, evaluate the integrals
$$\int_0^{1/4} \frac{dx}{\sqrt{1-4x^2}} \quad \text{and} \quad \int_0^{1/4} \frac{x\,dx}{\sqrt{1-4x^2}}$$
(O 1982)

9. Using the substitution $x = \sin\theta$, or otherwise, show that
$$\int_0^{1/2} \frac{x^2\,dx}{1-x^2} = \frac{\pi}{12} - \frac{\sqrt{3}}{8}$$
(WJEC 1982, part)

10. Using the change of variable $\tan\frac{x}{2} = t$, or otherwise, show that
$$\int_0^{\pi/2} \frac{dx}{2+\cos x} = \frac{\pi}{3\sqrt{3}}$$
(WJEC 1981, part)

Worked Solutions

1. Let
$$\frac{1-2x^2}{(x-1)^2(3-4x)} = \frac{A}{(3-4x)} + \frac{B}{(x-1)} + \frac{C}{(x-1)^2}$$
$$\therefore\quad 1-2x^2 = A(x-1)^2 + B(x-1)(3-4x) + C(3-4x) \qquad (1)$$
Putting $x = 1$ $\quad -1 = -C \quad \therefore\ C = 1$

Putting $x = \frac{3}{4}$ $\quad \frac{-1}{8} = \frac{A}{16} \quad \therefore\ A = -2$

EXERCISE

To find B we need to equate coefficients of like powers of x. Multiplying out the brackets in (1) gives

$$1-2x^2 = A(x^2-2x+1)+B(7x-4x^2-3)+C(3-4x)$$

Collecting like terms together

$$1-2x^2 = (A-4B)x^2+(7B-2A-4C)x+(A-3B+3C)$$

Equating coefficients of x^2

$$-2 = A-4B$$

Substituting for A

$$-2 = -2-4B \quad \Rightarrow \quad B = 0$$

hence

$$\frac{1-2x^2}{(x-1)^2(3-4x)} = \frac{-2}{(3-4x)}+\frac{1}{(x-1)^2}$$

$$\therefore \quad \int\frac{(1-2x^2)\,dx}{(x-1)^2(3-4x)} = \int\frac{-2\,dx}{(3-4x)}+\int\frac{dx}{(x-1)^2}$$

We deal with each of these integrals separately.

First integral $\displaystyle\int\frac{-2\,dx}{(3-4x)}$

This can be arranged in the standard logarithmic integral form by multiplying the numerator of the integrand by 2 and multiplying by $\frac{1}{2}$ on the other side of the integral sign. Since $2\times\frac{1}{2}=1$, this will leave the value of the integral unchanged.

i.e.
$$\int\frac{-2\,dx}{(3-4x)} = \frac{1}{2}\int\frac{-4\,dx}{(3-4x)}$$

$$= \frac{1}{2}\ln(3-4x)+c_1 \qquad \left[\text{since } \frac{d}{dx}(3-4x) = -4\right]$$

Second integral $\displaystyle\int\frac{dx}{(x-1)^2}$

To find this integral we substitute $u=x-1$, $du\equiv dx$

$$\int\frac{dx}{(x-1)^2} = \int\frac{du}{u^2}$$

$$= \int u^{-2}\,du$$

$$= -u^{-1}+c_2$$

$$\therefore \quad \int\frac{dx}{(x-1)^2} = -\frac{1}{(x-1)}+c_2$$

Using both these results, we have

$$\int\frac{(1-2x^2)dx}{(x-1)^2(3-4x)} = \frac{1}{2}\ln(3-4x)-\frac{1}{(x-1)}+c \qquad (\text{where } c=c_1+c_2)$$

2. Let

$$\frac{1}{(2-x)(1+x)} = \frac{A}{(2-x)}+\frac{B}{(1+x)}$$

$$\therefore \quad 1 = A(1+x)+B(2-x)$$

Putting $x = 2$ $\qquad 1 = 3A \qquad \therefore \quad A = \frac{1}{3}$

Putting $x = -1$ $\qquad 1 = 3B \qquad \therefore \quad B = \frac{1}{3}$

hence
$$\frac{1}{(2-x)(1+x)} = \frac{1}{3(2-x)} + \frac{1}{3(1+x)}$$

$$\therefore \int_0^1 \frac{dx}{(2-x)(1+x)} = \frac{1}{3}\int_0^1 \frac{dx}{(2-x)} + \frac{1}{3}\int_0^1 \frac{dx}{(1+x)}$$

$$= -\frac{1}{3}\int_0^1 \frac{-dx}{(2-x)} + \frac{1}{3}\int_0^1 \frac{dx}{(1+x)}$$

$$= -\frac{1}{3}\Big[\ln(2-x)\Big]_0^1 + \frac{1}{3}\Big[\ln(1+x)\Big]_0^1$$

$$= \frac{1}{3}\ln 2 + \frac{1}{3}\ln 2$$

$$= \frac{2}{3}\ln 2$$

3. Let
$$\frac{3x^2+1}{x^2(x^2+1)} = \frac{A}{x} + \frac{B}{x^2} + \frac{Cx+D}{x^2+1}$$

$$3x^2+1 = Ax(x^2+1) + B(x^2+1) + x^2(Cx+D)$$

Multiplying out the brackets and collecting like terms together

$$3x^2+1 = (A+C)x^3 + (B+D)x^2 + Ax + B$$

Equating coefficients of like powers of x

$x^3 \qquad A+C = 0 \qquad (1)$

$x^2 \qquad B+D = 3 \qquad (2)$

$x \qquad A = 0 \qquad (3)$

$x^0 \qquad 1 = B \qquad (4)$

Substituting (4) in (2)

$$1+D = 3 \qquad \therefore \quad D = 2$$

Substituting (3) in (1)

$$0+C = 0 \qquad \therefore \quad C = 0$$

$$\therefore \int \frac{(3x^2+1)\,dx}{x^2(x^2+1)} = \int \frac{dx}{x^2} + \int \frac{2dx}{x^2+1}$$

$$= -\frac{1}{x} + 2\arctan x + c$$

4. Let
$$\frac{x-4}{(x-1)^2(2x+1)} = \frac{A}{(x-1)} + \frac{B}{(x-1)^2} + \frac{C}{(2x+1)}$$

$$\therefore \quad x-4 = A(x-1)(2x+1) + B(2x+1) + C(x-1)^2$$

Putting $x = 1$ $\qquad -3 = 3B \qquad \therefore \quad B = -1$

Multiplying out the brackets gives

$$x-4 = (2A+C)x^2 + (2B-2C-A)x + (C+B-A)$$

We now equate coefficients of like powers of x

$x^2 \qquad 0 = 2A + C \qquad (1)$

$$x \qquad 1 = 2B - 2C - A \qquad (2)$$

$$x^0 \qquad -4 = C + B - A \qquad (3)$$

Substituting for B in (2) and (3)

$$1 = -2 - 2C - A \qquad (4)$$

$$-4 = C - 1 - A \qquad (5)$$

$$(4)-(5) \qquad 5 = -1 - 3C \qquad \therefore \quad C = -2$$

Substituting for C in (5) gives

$$-4 = -2 - 1 - A \quad \Rightarrow \quad A = 1$$

hence $$\int \frac{(x-4)\,dx}{(x-1)^2(2x+1)} = \int \frac{dx}{(x-1)} - \int \frac{dx}{(x-1)^2} - \int \frac{2dx}{2x+1}$$

giving $$\int \frac{(x-4)\,dx}{(x-1)^2(2x+1)} = \ln(x-1) + \frac{1}{(x-1)} - \ln(2x+1) + c$$

5. (i) Let $$\frac{9-10x}{(1-x)(2-x)} = \frac{A}{(1-x)} + \frac{B}{(2-x)}$$

$$\therefore \quad 9 - 10x = A(2-x) + B(1-x)$$

Putting $x = 2$ $\qquad -11 = -B \qquad \therefore \quad B = 11$

Putting $x = 1$ $\qquad -1 = A \qquad \therefore \quad A = -1$

hence $$\frac{9-10x}{(1-x)(2-x)} = -\frac{1}{(1-x)} + \frac{11}{(2-x)}$$

(ii) $$\int_0^t \frac{(9-10x)}{(1-x)(2-x)}\,dx = -\int_0^t \frac{dx}{(1-x)} + \int_0^t \frac{11dx}{(2-x)}$$

$$= \Big[\ln(1-x)\Big]_0^t - 11\Big[\ln(2-x)\Big]_0^t$$

$$= \ln(1-t) - 11[\ln(2-t) - \ln 2]$$

$$= \ln(1-t) - 11\ln\left(\frac{2-t}{2}\right)$$

$$= \ln(1-t) - 11\ln(1-t/2) \qquad (1)$$

The standard expansion for $\ln(1+x)$ is sometimes provided by the different examining boards and is

$$\ln(1+x) = x - \frac{x^2}{2} + \frac{x^3}{3} + \ldots + (-1)^{r-1}\frac{x^r}{r} + \ldots$$

(iii) Replacing x by $-t$ gives

$$\ln(1-t) = -t - \frac{t^2}{2} - \frac{t^3}{3} - \ldots \qquad (2)$$

Replacing x by $-t/2$ gives

$$\ln(1-t/2) = \frac{-t}{2} - \frac{t^2}{8} - \frac{t^3}{24} - \ldots \qquad (3)$$

Substituting (2) and (3) in (1) gives

$$\int_0^t \frac{9-10x}{(1-x)(2-x)}\,dx = -t - \frac{t^2}{2} - \frac{t^3}{3} - 11\left(-\frac{t}{2} - \frac{t^2}{8} - \frac{t^3}{24}\right)$$

$$\approx \frac{9}{2}t + \frac{7}{8}t^2 + \frac{1}{8}t^3$$

6. Let $u^2 = 4-x^2$

Differentiating implicitly $2u\dfrac{du}{dx} = -2x$

$\therefore$ $\therefore\ \dfrac{u}{x}du \equiv -dx$

Substituting for x gives $\dfrac{u\,du}{\sqrt{4-u^2}} \equiv -dx$

When $x = 1$, $u = \sqrt{3}$ and when $x = 0$, $u = 2$.

Hence $\displaystyle\int_0^1 \frac{x^3 dx}{4-x^2} = \int_0^{\sqrt{3}} \frac{-u(4-u^2)^{3/2}}{u(4-u^2)^{1/2}} du$

$$= -\int_2^{\sqrt{3}} (4-u^2)\,du$$

$$= \left[\frac{u^3}{3} - 4u\right]_2^{\sqrt{3}}$$

$$= (\sqrt{3}-4\sqrt{3}) - \left(\frac{8}{3}-8\right)$$

$$= \frac{16}{3} - 3\sqrt{3}$$

7. If $u = 1+\cos\theta$

$$\frac{du}{d\theta} = -\sin\theta$$

$$\therefore\ du \equiv -\sin\theta\ d\theta$$

$$\sin^2\theta = 1-\cos^2\theta$$

$$= 1-(u-1)^2$$

giving $\sin^2\theta = 2u-u^2$

When $\theta = 0$, $u = 2$. When $\theta = \pi/2$, $u = 1$ (since $\cos\pi/2 = 0$).

Substituting

$$\int_0^{\pi/2} \frac{\sin^3\theta\,d\theta}{(1+\cos\theta)^{3/2}} = \int_0^{\pi/2} \frac{\sin^2\theta\,(\sin\theta)\,d\theta}{(1+\cos\theta)^{3/2}}$$

$$= -\int_2^1 \frac{(2u-u^2)}{u^{3/2}} du$$

$$= -\int_2^1 \left(\frac{2}{u^{1/2}} - u^{1/2}\right) du$$

$$= -\left[4u^{1/2} - \frac{2}{3}u^{3/2}\right]_2^1$$

$$= -\left(4-\frac{2}{3}\right) + \left(4\sqrt{2} - \frac{4\sqrt{2}}{3}\right)$$

$$= \frac{8\sqrt{2}}{3} - \frac{10}{3}$$

<u>EXERCISE</u>

8. The integral $\int_0^{1/4} \frac{dx}{\sqrt{1-4x^2}}$ can be put into a standard form by putting $u = 2x$.

If $u = 2x$ $\qquad du \equiv 2\,dx$

i.e. $\qquad dx \equiv \frac{du}{2}$

When $x = \frac{1}{4}$, $u = \frac{1}{2}$ and when $x = 0$, $u = 0$.

$$\therefore \int_0^{1/4} \frac{dx}{\sqrt{1-4x^2}} = \int_0^{1/2} \frac{du}{2\sqrt{1-u^2}}$$

$$= \frac{1}{2}\int_0^{1/2} \frac{du}{\sqrt{1-u^2}}$$

$$= \frac{1}{2}\Big[\arcsin u\Big]_0^{1/2}$$

$$= \frac{1}{2}(\arcsin \tfrac{1}{2} - \arcsin 0)$$

$$= \frac{1}{2} \times \frac{\pi}{6}$$

$$= \frac{\pi}{12}$$

For $\int_0^{1/4} \frac{x\,dx}{\sqrt{1-4x^2}}$ we substitute $u^2 = 1-4x^2$

Differentiating implicitly

$$2u\frac{du}{dx} = -8x$$

$$\therefore \quad x\,dx \equiv -\frac{u}{4}\,du$$

When $x = \frac{1}{4}$ $\qquad u^2 = 1 - \frac{1}{4} = \frac{3}{4} \qquad \therefore \quad u = \frac{\sqrt{3}}{2}$

When $x = 0$ $\qquad u^2 = 1 \qquad \therefore \quad u = 1$

Hence $$\int_0^{1/4} \frac{x\,dx}{\sqrt{1-4x^2}} = -\frac{1}{4}\int_1^{\sqrt{3}/2} \frac{u\,du}{u}$$

$$= -\frac{1}{4}\int_1^{\sqrt{3}/2} du$$

$$= -\frac{1}{4}\Big[u\Big]_1^{\sqrt{3}/2}$$

$$= \frac{1}{4} - \frac{\sqrt{3}}{8}$$

EXERCISE

9. If $x = \sin\theta$ $\quad dx \equiv \cos\theta\, d\theta$

When $x = \frac{1}{2}$ $\quad \sin\theta = \frac{1}{2}$

$$\therefore \quad \theta = \arcsin\frac{1}{2} \qquad \text{giving} \quad \theta = \frac{\pi}{6}$$

When $x = 0$ $\quad \sin\theta = 0 \qquad$ giving $\theta = 0$

hence
$$\int_0^{1/2} \frac{x^2\,dx}{\sqrt{1-x^2}} = \int_0^{\pi/6} \frac{\sin^2\theta\cos\theta\,d\theta}{\sqrt{1-\sin^2\theta}}$$
$$= \int_0^{\pi/6} \frac{\sin^2\theta\cos\theta\,d\theta}{\cos\theta}$$
$$\therefore \quad I = \int_0^{\pi/6} \sin^2\theta\,d\theta$$

In order to find this integral we must use the double-angle result
$$\cos 2\theta = 1 - 2\sin^2\theta$$

i.e.
$$\sin^2\theta = \frac{1}{2}(1-\cos 2\theta)$$

Substituting
$$I = \frac{1}{2}\int_0^{\pi/6} (1-\cos 2\theta)\,d\theta$$
$$= \frac{1}{2}\left[\theta - \frac{1}{2}\sin 2\theta\right]_0^{\pi/6}$$
$$= \frac{1}{2}\left(\frac{\pi}{6} - \frac{1}{2}\sin\frac{\pi}{3}\right)$$
$$= \frac{1}{2}\left(\frac{\pi}{6} - \frac{\sqrt{3}}{4}\right)$$
$$= \frac{\pi}{12} - \frac{\sqrt{3}}{8}$$

10. If
$$t = \tan\frac{x}{2}$$
$$\frac{dt}{dx} = \frac{1}{2}\sec^2\frac{x}{2}$$
$$= \frac{1}{2}\left(1+\tan^2\frac{x}{2}\right)$$
$$\therefore \quad \frac{dt}{dx} = \frac{1}{2}(1+t^2)$$

i.e.
$$dx = \frac{2dt}{1+t^2}$$

Using the t-substitution, we have
$$\cos x = \frac{1-t^2}{1+t^2}$$

When $x = \pi/2$, $\quad t = \tan\pi/4 \quad \therefore \quad t = 1$

When $x = 0$, $\quad t = \tan 0 \quad \therefore \quad t = 0$

EXERCISE

hence
$$\int_0^{\pi/2} \frac{dx}{2+\cos x} = \int_0^1 \frac{2dt/(1+t^2)}{2+\left(\frac{1-t^2}{1+t^2}\right)}$$
$$= \int_0^1 \frac{2dt}{2(1+t^2)+(1-t^2)}$$
$$= \int_0^1 \frac{2dt}{3+t^2}$$
$$= 2\int_0^1 \frac{dt}{t^2+(\sqrt{3})^2}$$

This is a standard integral. Using the result $\int \frac{dx}{a^2+x^2} = \frac{1}{a}\arctan\frac{x}{a}$ we have

$$\int_0^{\pi/2} \frac{dx}{2+\cos x} = \frac{2}{\sqrt{3}}\left[\arctan\frac{t}{\sqrt{3}}\right]_0^1$$
$$= \frac{2}{\sqrt{3}}\left(\frac{\pi}{6}\right)$$
$$= \frac{\pi}{3\sqrt{3}}$$

INTEGRATION BY PARTS

If u and v are two functions of x and $y = uv$, the product rule for differentiation states that

$$\frac{dy}{dx} = u\frac{dv}{dx}+v\frac{du}{dx}$$

Integrating throughout w.r.t. x gives

$$\int\frac{dy}{dx}dx = \int u\frac{dv}{dx}dx+\int v\frac{du}{dx}dx \tag{9.7}$$

hence
$$y = \int u\frac{dv}{dx}dx+\int v\frac{du}{dx}dx$$

⇒
$$uv = \int u\frac{dv}{dx}dx+\int v\frac{du}{dx}dx$$

Rearranging
$$\int u\frac{dv}{dx}dx = uv-\int v\frac{du}{dx}dx \tag{9.8}$$

This method of integration is called integration by parts. It is particularly useful when one of the functions occurring in the integrand on the LHS is directly integrable. Note that one function is integrated, while the other is differentiated. If the product involves a power of x it is useful to differentiate this in order to simplify the resulting integral on the RHS.

The result (9.8) applies to indefinite integrals. If, however, we had integrated throughout (9.8) w.r.t. x from a to b the resulting integration by parts formula becomes:

$$\int_a^b u\frac{dv}{dx}dx = \Big[uv\Big]_a^b - \int_a^b v\frac{du}{dx}dx \tag{9.9}$$

EXERCISE/INTEGRATION BY PARTS

Example

Find $\int x\,e^x\,dx$

Let $e^x = \frac{dv}{dx}$ and $u = x$

$$\frac{dv}{dx} = e^x \Rightarrow v = e^x$$

$$u = x \Rightarrow du \equiv dx$$

Substituting

$$\int x\,e^x\,dx = x\,e^x - \int e^x\,dx$$

$$= x\,e^x - e^x + c$$

$$\therefore \int x\,e^x\,dx = (x-1)e^x + c$$

EXERCISE

1. Use integration by parts to obtain

$$\int x^3\,e^{-x^2/2}\,dx$$ (NI 1981, part)

2. Use integration by parts to find

$$\int x\log_e x\,dx$$ (WJEC 1982, part)

3. Find $\int 2x\,e^{2x}\,dx$ (WJEC 1980, part)

4. Using integration by parts, or otherwise, find

$$\int x\,e^{-x}\,dx$$ (WJEC 1981, part)

Worked Solutions

1. $$\int x^3 e^{-x^2/2}\,dx = \int x^2(x\,e^{-x^2/2})\,dx$$

We rewrite the integral like this because the expression in brackets is directly integrable. In order to simplify the integral we take $u = x^2$, $dv/dx = x\,e^{-x^2/2}$.

If $\frac{dv}{dx} = x\,e^{-x^2/2}$ $\qquad v = -e^{-x^2/2}$

If $u = x^2$ $\qquad \frac{du}{dx} = 2x$

Substituting in the integration by parts formula gives

$$\int x^3\,e^{-x^2/2}\,dx = -x^2e^{-x^2/2} + \int 2x\,e^{-x^2/2}\,dx$$

$$= -x^2\,e^{-x^2/2} - 2e^{-x^2/2} + c$$

$$= -(x^2+2)e^{-x^2/2} + c$$

2. In this problem we take $\mathrm{d}v/\mathrm{d}x = x$ and $u = \log_e x$, because the integral of $\log_e x$ can itself only be determined by integration by parts.

$$\frac{\mathrm{d}v}{\mathrm{d}x} = x \quad \Rightarrow \quad v = \frac{x^2}{2}$$

$$u = \log_e x \quad \Rightarrow \quad \frac{\mathrm{d}u}{\mathrm{d}x} = \frac{1}{x}$$

Integration by parts gives

$$\int x \log_e x \, \mathrm{d}x = \frac{x^2}{2}\log_e x - \int \frac{x^2}{2}\left(\frac{1}{x}\right)\mathrm{d}x$$

$$= \frac{x^2}{2}\log_e x - \int \frac{x}{2}\,\mathrm{d}x$$

$$= \frac{x^2}{2}\log_e x - \frac{x^2}{4} + c$$

3. We take $\dfrac{\mathrm{d}v}{\mathrm{d}x} = \mathrm{e}^{2x}$ and $u = 2x$

$$\frac{\mathrm{d}v}{\mathrm{d}x} = \mathrm{e}^{2x} \quad \Rightarrow \quad v = \frac{1}{2}\mathrm{e}^{2x}$$

$$u = 2x \quad \Rightarrow \quad \frac{\mathrm{d}u}{\mathrm{d}x} = 2$$

Substituting

$$\int 2x\mathrm{e}^{2x}\,\mathrm{d}x = x\,\mathrm{e}^{2x} - \int \tfrac{1}{2}\mathrm{e}^{2x} \times 2\,\mathrm{d}x$$

$$= x\,\mathrm{e}^{2x} - \int \mathrm{e}^{2x}\,\mathrm{d}x$$

$$= x\,\mathrm{e}^{2x} - \tfrac{1}{2}\mathrm{e}^{2x} + c$$

$$= (x - \tfrac{1}{2})\mathrm{e}^{2x} + c$$

4. In order to simplify this integral we take $\mathrm{d}v/\mathrm{d}x = \mathrm{e}^{-x}$ and $u = x$.

$$\frac{\mathrm{d}v}{\mathrm{d}x} = \mathrm{e}^{-x} \quad \Rightarrow \quad v = -\mathrm{e}^{-x}$$

$$u = x \quad \Rightarrow \quad \frac{\mathrm{d}u}{\mathrm{d}x} = 1$$

Substituting

$$\int x\mathrm{e}^{-x}\,\mathrm{d}x = -x\mathrm{e}^{-x} + \int \mathrm{e}^{-x}\,\mathrm{d}x$$

$$= -x\mathrm{e}^{-x} - \mathrm{e}^{-x} + c$$

$$= -\mathrm{e}^{-x}(x+1) + c$$

REDUCTION FORMULAE

Suppose we are given an integral, I_n, in which the integrand involves the integer n as a parameter. Applying integration by parts it is sometimes possible to express I_n in terms of I_{n-1}. The process can be repeated again to find I_{n-1} in terms of I_{n-2}. In each step the value of the parameter, n, is reduced. The connection between I_n and I_m, where $m < n$, is referred to as a reduction formula. By continually repeating this process we can reduce the value of n to a value which enables us to directly evaluate the integral.

Worked Example

If $I_n = \int_1^e x(\ln x)^n \, dx$ where n is a positive integer, prove that

$$I_n = \tfrac{1}{2}e^2 - \tfrac{1}{2}nI_{n-1}$$

Evaluate I_3. (O 1977)

Solution

Let $\dfrac{dv}{dx} = x$ and $u = (\ln x)^n$

$$\frac{dv}{dx} = x \Rightarrow v = \frac{x^2}{2}$$

$$u = (\ln x)^n \Rightarrow \frac{du}{dx} = n(\ln x)^{n-1} \times \frac{1}{x}$$

Applying integration by parts

$$\int_1^e x(\ln x)^n \, dx = \left[\frac{x^2}{2}(\ln x)^n\right]_1^e - \int_1^e \frac{x^2}{2} \times \frac{n}{x}(\ln x)^{n-1} \, dx$$

$$= \frac{1}{2}e^2 - \frac{n}{2}\int_1^e x(\ln x)^{n-1} \, dx$$

but $\int_1^e x(\ln x)^{n-1} \, dx = I_{n-1}$

$$\therefore \int_1^e x(\ln x)^n \, dx = \frac{1}{2}e^2 - \frac{n}{2}I_{n-1}$$

This is the reduction formula. If $n = 3$, we have

$$I_3 = \frac{1}{2}e^2 - \frac{3}{2}I_2 \qquad (1)$$

Similarly $$I_2 = \frac{1}{2}e^2 - I_1 \qquad (2)$$

and $$I_1 = \frac{1}{2}e^2 - \frac{1}{2}I_0 \qquad (3)$$

but $$I_0 = \int_1^e x \, dx$$

$$= \left[\frac{x^2}{2}\right]_1^e$$

$$\therefore I_0 = \frac{1}{2}(e^2 - 1) \qquad (4)$$

Substituting the results (2), (3) and (4) into (1) gives

$$I_3 = \frac{1}{2}e^2 - \frac{3}{2}\left[\frac{1}{2}e^2 - \left(\frac{1}{2}e^2 - \frac{1}{2}I_0\right)\right]$$

$$= \frac{1}{2}e^2 - \frac{3}{4}I_0$$

$$= \frac{1}{2}e^2 - \frac{3}{4}\left[\frac{1}{2}(e^2 - 1)\right]$$

$$= \frac{1}{2}e^2 - \frac{3}{8}e^2 + \frac{3}{8}$$

$$\therefore \quad I_3 = \frac{1}{8}(e^2+3)$$

Worked Example

If $I_n = \int_0^1 (1-x^2)^n \, dx \ (n > 0)$, prove that

$$(2n+1)I_n = 2nI_{n-1}$$

(i) Find I_n in terms of n where n is an integer.

(ii) Evaluate $I_{5/2}$. (O 1978)

Solution

To find this integral we put $x = \sin\theta$

$$x = \sin\theta \quad \Rightarrow \quad \frac{dx}{d\theta} = \cos\theta$$

If $x = 1, \ \sin\theta = 1$ $\quad \therefore \quad \theta = \frac{\pi}{2}$

If $x = 0, \ \sin\theta = 0$ $\quad \therefore \quad \theta = 0$

Substituting $$I_n = \int_0^{\pi/2} (1-\sin^2\theta)^n \cos\theta \, d\theta$$

$$= \int_0^{\pi/2} \cos^{2n+1}\theta \, d\theta$$

To integrate this by parts we let

$$\frac{dv}{d\theta} = \cos\theta \quad \Rightarrow \quad v = \sin\theta$$

$$u = \cos^{2n}\theta \quad \Rightarrow \quad \frac{du}{d\theta} = 2n\cos^{2n-1}\theta\,(-\sin\theta)$$

Substituting in the integration by parts formula

$$\int_0^{\pi/2} \cos^{2n+1}\theta \, d\theta = \Big[\cos^{2n}\theta \sin\theta\Big]_0^{\pi/2} - \int_0^{\pi/2} 2n\cos^{2n-1}\theta(-\sin^2\theta)\, d\theta$$

$$= 2n\int_0^{\pi/2} \cos^{2n-1}\theta \sin^2\theta \, d\theta$$

(since $\cos\pi/2 = 0$ and $\sin 0 = 0$)

hence $$I_n = 2n\int_0^{\pi/2} \cos^{2n-1}\theta(1-\cos^2\theta)\, d\theta$$

$$= 2n\int_0^{\pi/2} \cos^{2n-1}\theta - 2n\int_0^{\pi/2} \cos^{2n+1}\theta \, d\theta$$

$$\therefore \quad I_n = 2n\int_0^{\pi/2} \cos^{2n-1}\theta - 2nI_n$$

$$\therefore \quad (2n+1)I_n = 2nI_{n-1} \qquad (1)$$

This establishes the reduction formula.

(i)
$$I_0 = \int_0^{\pi/2} \cos\theta \, d\theta$$

$$\therefore \quad I_0 = \Big[\sin\theta\Big]_0^{\pi/2}$$

$$= \sin\frac{\pi}{2} - \sin 0$$

$$\therefore \quad I_0 = 1$$

From (1)
$$I_n = \frac{2n}{2n+1} I_{n-1} \qquad (2)$$

$$\therefore \quad I_{n-1} = \frac{(2n-2)}{(2n-1)} I_{n-2} \qquad (3)$$

$$I_{n-2} = \frac{(2n-4)}{(2n-3)} I_{n-3} \qquad (4)$$

$$\vdots \qquad \vdots$$

$$I_1 = \frac{2}{3} I_0 = \frac{2}{3} \qquad \text{(since } I_0 = 1\text{)} \qquad (5)$$

Combining the results (2), (3), (4) and (5)

$$I_n = \frac{2n}{(2n+1)} \frac{(2n-2)}{(2n-1)} \frac{(2n-4)}{(2n-3)} \cdots \frac{2}{3}$$

(ii) The reduction formula is still valid for non-integer values of n.

When $n = 5/2$
$$I_{5/2} = \frac{5}{6} I_{3/2}$$

When $n = 3/2$
$$I_{3/2} = \frac{3}{4} I_{1/2}$$

$$I_{5/2} = \frac{5}{6} \times \frac{3}{4} I_{1/2} \qquad (6)$$

where
$$I_{1/2} = \int_0^{\pi/2} \cos^2\theta \, d\theta$$

To evaluate this integral we use the double-angle formula

$$\cos 2\theta = 2\cos^2\theta - 1$$

$$\cos^2\theta = \frac{1}{2}(1 + \cos 2\theta)$$

hence
$$\int_0^{\pi/2} \cos^2\theta \, d\theta = \frac{1}{2} \int_0^{\pi/2} (1 + \cos 2\theta) \, d\theta$$

$$= \frac{1}{2} \left[\theta + \frac{1}{2}\sin 2\theta\right]_0^{\pi/2}$$

$$= \frac{\pi}{4}$$

Substituting in (6)

$$I_{5/2} = \frac{5}{6}\times\frac{3}{4}\times\frac{\pi}{4}$$

giving $$I_{5/2} = \frac{5}{32}\pi$$

EXERCISE

1. Prove that if $I_n = \int_0^{\pi/4} \tan^n\theta \, d\theta$ where n is any integer $\geqslant 0$, then

$$I_n = \frac{1}{n-1} - I_{n-2} \qquad (n \geqslant 2)$$

Evaluate I_5 to two decimal places. (WJEC 1981, part)

2. $$I_{m,n} = \int_0^{\infty} \frac{x^m}{(1+x)^n} \, dx$$

where m and n are non-negative integers and $n > m+1$.
Prove that, if $m \geqslant 1$,

$$I_{m,n} = \frac{m}{n-1} I_{m-1,n-1}$$

Find $I_{m,n}$ in terms of $I_{0,n-m}$ and hence find $I_{m,n}$ as a function of m and n, giving your answer in terms of factorials. (O 1979)

3. If $I_n = \int_0^1 x^n(1-x)^{1/2} \, dx$, where n is a non-negative integer, prove that, when $n \geqslant 1$, $(2n+3)I_n = 2nI_{n-1}$.
Hence, or otherwise, evaluate I_n.

Use this result to evaluate $\int_0^{\pi/2} \sin^{2n+1}\theta \, \cos^2\theta \, d\theta$ (O 1981)

4. Given that, for $n \geqslant 0$, $I_n = \int_0^1 x^n e^{-2x} \, dx$

(i) Show that $I_1 = \frac{1}{4}(1-3e^{-2})$

(ii) Prove that, for $n \geqslant 1$, $I_n = -\frac{1}{2}e^{-2} + \frac{n}{2}I_{n-1}$

(iii) Evaluate I_2 in terms of e, and

(iv) Deduce, or otherwise obtain, the value of

$$\int_1^e \left(\frac{2\log_e x}{x}\right)^3 dx$$ (NI 1982)

Worked Solutions

1.
$$I_n = \int_0^{\pi/4} \tan^n\theta \, d\theta$$
$$= \int_0^{\pi/4} \tan^{n-2}\theta(\tan^2\theta)\, d\theta$$
$$= \int_0^{\pi/4} \tan^{n-2}\theta(\sec^2\theta - 1) d\theta \qquad (\text{using } \sec^2\theta = 1 + \tan^2\theta)$$
$$= \int_0^{\pi/4} \tan^{n-2}\theta \sec^2\theta \, d\theta - \int_0^{\pi/4} \tan^{n-2}\theta \, d\theta$$
$$\therefore \; I_n = \int_0^{\pi/4} \tan^{n-2}\theta \sec^2\theta \, d\theta - I_{n-2} \qquad (1)$$

Integrating by parts
$$\int_0^{\pi/4} \tan^{n-2}\theta \sec^2\theta \, d\theta = \Big[\tan^{n-1}\theta\Big]_0^{\pi/4} - \int_0^{\pi/4} \tan\theta \frac{d}{d\theta}(\tan^{n-2}\theta)\, d\theta$$
$$= 1 - \int_0^{\pi/4} (n-2)\tan^{n-2}\theta \sec^2\theta \, d\theta$$
$$= 1 - (n-2)\int_0^{\pi/2} \tan^{n-2}\theta\,(1 + \tan^2\theta)\, d\theta$$
$$= 1 - (n-2)\int_0^{\pi/4} \tan^{n-2}\theta \, d\theta - (n-2)\int_0^{\pi/4} \tan^n\theta \, d\theta$$
$$= 1 - (n-2)I_{n-2} - (n-2)I_n \qquad (2)$$

Substituting (2) in (1) gives
$$I_n = 1 - (n-2)I_{n-2} - (n-2)I_n - I_{n-2}$$
$$\therefore \; I_n = \frac{1}{n-1} - I_{n-2} \qquad (n \geqslant 2) \qquad (3)$$

$n = 5$ in (3) gives
$$I_5 = \frac{1}{4} - I_3$$

$n = 3$ in (3) gives
$$I_3 = \frac{1}{2} - I_1$$

hence
$$I_5 = \frac{1}{4} - \left(\frac{1}{2} - I_1\right)$$
$$\therefore \; I_5 = I_1 - \frac{1}{4} \qquad (4)$$

but
$$I_1 = \int_0^{\pi/4} \tan\theta \, d\theta = \int_0^{\pi/4} \frac{\sin\theta}{\cos\theta} d\theta$$
$$= \int_0^{\pi/4} \frac{-\frac{d}{d\theta}(\cos\theta)}{\cos\theta} d\theta$$

which is now in the standard form for a logarithmic integral.

EXERCISE

Consequently $$I_1 = -\left[\log_e \cos\theta\right]_0^{\pi/4}$$
$$= -\log_e \cos\frac{\pi}{4} + \log_e \cos 0$$
$$= -\log_e \frac{1}{\sqrt{2}}$$
$$\therefore \quad I_1 = \frac{1}{2}\log_e 2$$

Substituting in (4)
$$I_5 = \frac{1}{2}\log_e 2 - \frac{1}{4}$$
$$= \frac{1}{2}(0.693) - 0.25$$
$$= 0.10 \quad \text{(correct to two decimal places)}$$

2. $$I_{m,n} = \int_0^\infty \frac{x^m}{(1+x)^n}\,dx$$
$$= \int_0^\infty x^m(1+x)^{-n}\,dx$$

To integrate this by parts we put $u = x^m$ and $\dfrac{dv}{dx} = (1+x)^{-n}$.

If $u = x^m$ $\qquad \dfrac{du}{dx} = mx^{m-1}$

If $\dfrac{dv}{dx} = (1+x)^{-n}$ $\qquad v = \dfrac{1}{1-n}(1+x)^{1-n}$

Integrating by parts
$$\int_0^\infty x^m(1+x)^{-n}\,dx = \left[\frac{x^m}{(1-n)(1+x)^{n-1}}\right]_0^\infty - \int_0^\infty \frac{mx^{m-1}}{(1-n)(1+x)^{n-1}}\,dx$$

Since $n > m+1$, $\lim\limits_{x\to\infty} \dfrac{x^m}{(1+x)^{n-1}} = 0$ with the result that the value of the expression in the square brackets is zero at both the upper and lower limit of integration.

Hence $$\int_0^\infty \frac{x^m}{(1+x)^n}\,dx = \frac{m}{n-1}\int_0^\infty \frac{x^{m-1}\,dx}{(1+x)^{n-1}}$$
$$\therefore \quad I_{m,n} = \frac{m}{n-1} I_{m-1,n-1} \qquad (1)$$

Replacing m by $(m-1)$ and n by $(n-1)$ in (1) gives
$$I_{m-1,n-1} = \left(\frac{m-1}{n-2}\right) I_{m-2,n-2}$$

Similarly

$$I_{m-2,n-2} = \left(\frac{m-2}{n-3}\right) I_{m-3,n-3}$$

and $$I_{1,n-m+1} = \frac{1}{n-m} I_{0,n-m}$$

$$\therefore \quad I_{m,n} = \frac{m}{(n-1)} \times \frac{(m-1)}{(n-2)} \times \frac{(m-2)}{(n-3)} \times \ldots \frac{1}{(n-m)} \times I_{0,n-m} \qquad (2)$$

$$= \frac{m!(n-m-1)!}{(n-1)!} I_{0,n-m}$$

Now $$I_{0,n-m} = \int_0^\infty \frac{dx}{(1+x)^{n-m}}$$

$$= \left[\frac{(1+x)^{m-n+1}}{m-n+1}\right]_0^\infty$$

$$= \left[\frac{1}{(m-n+1)(1+x)^{n-m-1}}\right]_0^\infty$$

$$\therefore \quad I_{0,n-m} = -\frac{1}{m-n+1}$$

$$\left(\text{since } \lim_{x\to\infty} \frac{1}{(1+x)^{n-m}} = 0 \text{ if } n > m+1\right)$$

or $$I_{0,n-m} = \frac{1}{(n-m-1)} \qquad (3)$$

Substituting (3) in (2) gives

$$I_{m,n} = \frac{m!(n-m-1)!}{(n-1)!(n-m-1)}$$

Simplifying to

$$I_{m,n} = \frac{m!(n-m-2)!}{(n-1)!}$$

3. $$I_n = \int_0^1 x^n(1-x)^{1/2}\,dx$$

If $\dfrac{dv}{dx} = (1-x)^{1/2}$ $\qquad v = -\dfrac{2}{3}(1-x)^{3/2}$

If $u = x^n$ $\qquad \dfrac{du}{dx} = nx^{n-1}$

Integrating by parts

$$\int_0^1 x^n(1-x)^{1/2}\,dx = \left[-\frac{2}{3}x^n(1-x)^{3/2}\right]_0^1 + \frac{2n}{3}\int_0^1 x^{n-1}(1-x)^{3/2}\,dx$$

$$= \frac{2n}{3}\int_0^1 x^{n-1}(1-x)(1-x)^{1/2}\,dx$$

$$= \frac{2n}{3}\int_0^1 x^{n-1}(1-x)^{1/2}\,dx - \frac{2n}{3}\int_0^1 x^n(1-x)^{1/2}\,dx$$

EXERCISE

$$\therefore \quad I_n = \frac{2n}{3} I_{n-1} - \frac{2n}{3} I_n$$

$$\therefore \quad (2n+3)I_n = 2nI_{n-1}$$

or $$I_n = \left(\frac{2n}{2n+3}\right) I_{n-1} \qquad (1)$$

$$\therefore \quad I_{n-1} = \left(\frac{2n-2}{2n+1}\right) I_{n-2}$$

and $$I_{n-2} = \left(\frac{2n-4}{2n-1}\right) I_{n-3}$$

$$\vdots \qquad \vdots$$

$$I_1 = \frac{2}{5} I_0$$

giving $$I_n = \frac{2n}{2n+3} \frac{(2n-2)}{(2n+1)} \frac{(2n-4)}{(2n-1)} \cdots \frac{2}{5} I_0 \qquad (2)$$

where $$I_0 = \int_0^1 (1-x)^{1/2}\,\mathrm{d}x = \left[-\frac{2}{5}(1-x)^{3/2}\right]_0^1$$

$$= \frac{2}{3}$$

Substituting in (2)

$$I_n = \frac{2n}{2n+3} \frac{(2n-2)(2n-4)}{(2n+1)(2n-1)} \cdots \frac{2}{5} \times \frac{2}{3} \qquad (3)$$

In order to use the result (3) to find $\int_0^{\pi/2} \sin^{2n+1}\theta \cos^2\theta\,\mathrm{d}\theta$ we put $x = \sin^2\theta$. Differentiating gives $\mathrm{d}x/\mathrm{d}\theta = 2\sin\theta\cos\theta$. Also, when $x = 1$, $\theta = \pi/2$ and when $x = 0$, $\theta = 0$. Hence

$$\int_0^1 x^n(1-x)^{1/2}\,\mathrm{d}x = \int_0^{\pi/2} \sin^{2n}\theta\,(1-\sin^2\theta)^{1/2} \times 2\sin\theta\cos\theta\,\mathrm{d}\theta$$

$$= 2\int_0^{\pi/2} \sin^{2n+1}\theta \cos^2\theta\,\mathrm{d}\theta$$

$$\therefore \int_0^{\pi/2} \sin^{2n+1}\theta\cos^2\theta\,\mathrm{d}\theta = \frac{1}{2} I_n$$

$$= \frac{2n}{(2n+3)} \frac{(2n-2)}{(2n+1)} \frac{(2n-4)}{(2n-1)} \cdots \frac{2}{5} \times \frac{1}{3}$$

4. (i) If $I_n = \int_0^1 x^n e^{-2x}\,\mathrm{d}x$ then

$$I_1 = \int_0^1 x e^{-2x}\,\mathrm{d}x$$

Integrating by parts

$$I_1 = \left[\frac{-x}{2}\,e^{-2x}\right]_0^1 + \frac{1}{2}\int_0^1 e^{-2x}\,dx$$

$$= -\frac{1}{2}e^{-2} + \frac{1}{2}\left[-\frac{1}{2}e^{-2x}\right]_0^1$$

$$= -\frac{1}{2}e^{-2} - \frac{1}{4}e^{-2} + \frac{1}{4}$$

giving
$$I_1 = \frac{1}{4}(1-3e^{-2})$$

(ii) Integrating by parts

$$\int_0^1 x^n e^{-2x}\,dx = \left[-\frac{x^n}{2}\,e^{-2x}\right]_0^1 + \frac{n}{2}\int_0^1 x^{n-1}e^{-2x}\,dx$$

$$\therefore\ I_n = -\frac{1}{2}e^{-2} + \frac{n}{2}I_{n-1}$$

(iii)
$$I_2 = -\frac{1}{2}e^{-2} + I_1$$

$$= -\frac{1}{2}e^{-2} + \frac{1}{4} - \frac{3}{4}e^{-2}$$

hence
$$I_2 = \frac{1}{4} - \frac{5}{4}e^{-2}$$

(iv) Let
$$I_3 = \int_0^1 u^3 e^{-2u}\,du$$

If $u = \log_e x$

$$\frac{du}{dx} = \frac{1}{x}$$

When $u = 1$, $x = e$ and when $u = 0$, $x = 1$.
Hence

$$I_3 = \int_1^e (\log_e x)^3 e^{-2\log_e x}\,\frac{dx}{x}$$

$$\therefore\ I_3 = \int_1^e \frac{(\log_e x)^3}{x^3}\,dx$$

but
$$I_3 = -\frac{1}{2}e^{-2} + \frac{3}{2}I_2$$

$$= -\frac{1}{2}e^{-2} + \frac{3}{2}\left(\frac{1}{4} - \frac{5}{4}e^{-2}\right)$$

giving

$$I_3 = \frac{3}{8} - \frac{19}{8}e^{-2} \qquad \text{where} \quad I_3 = \int_1^e \frac{(\log_e x)^3}{x^3}\,dx$$

EXERCISE

The given integral

$$\int_1^e \frac{(2\log_e x)^3}{x^3} = 8\int_1^e \frac{(\log_e x)^3}{x^3}\,dx$$

$$= 8I_3$$

$$\therefore \quad \int_1^e \frac{(2\log_e x)^3}{x^3} = 3 - 19e^{-2}$$

EXERCISE

10 APPLICATIONS OF INTEGRATION

INTEGRATION AS A SUMMATION

The area between the curve $y = f(x)$, the x-axis and the ordinates $x = a$ and $x = b$ can be subdivided into a number of vertical rectangles (Fig. 10.1). If we let δx denote the width of each rectangle, where $\delta x = (b - a)/n$, the rectangles will be of equal width.

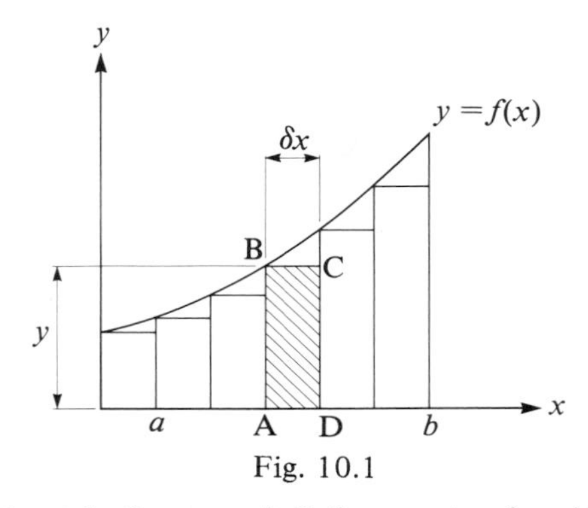

Fig. 10.1

The area is approximately the sum of all these rectangles. ABCD is a typical such rectangle of area $y \times \delta x$. Summing all of these rectangles will give an approximation to the area under the curve between $x = a$ and $x = b$. Moreover, the accuracy of this approximation will improve as n increases. Using the summation symbol we have

$$\text{Area} \approx \sum_{x=a}^{x=b} y\,\delta x$$

If we now let n become infinitely large, we replace δx by $\mathrm{d}x$ and the summation becomes an integral. Consequently, we have

$$\boxed{\text{Area} = \int_a^b y\,\mathrm{d}x} \qquad (10.1)$$

In some problems it is necessary to consider the area as being divided into horizontal rectangles rather than vertical rectangles as above. This may arise if we wish to find the area between the curve and the y-axis. In this case the length of each typical rectangle ABCD (Fig. 10.2) is x and its height δy. The area enclosed by the curve, the y-axis and the straight lines $y = b$ and $y = a$ is therefore

$$\boxed{\text{Area} = \int_a^b x\,\mathrm{d}y} \qquad (10.2)$$

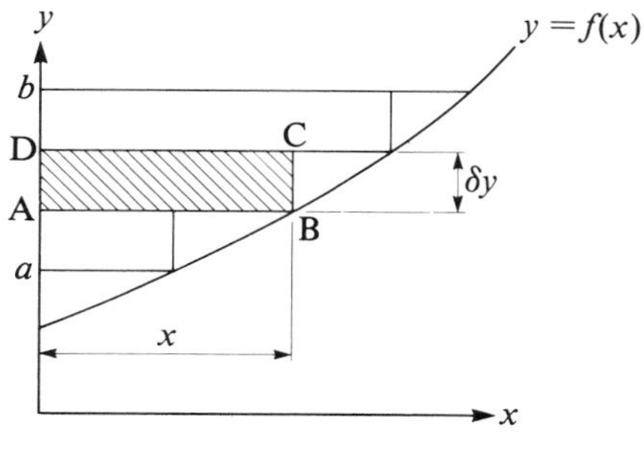

Fig. 10.2

THE AREA ENCLOSED BY TWO CURVES

Suppose we wish to find the area enclosed by the two curves $y = f_1(x)$ and $y = f_2(x)$ (Fig. 10.3). If we divide the area into vertical rectangles such as ABCD, we can find the area by integrating with respect to x as in (10.1). Let y_A denote the ordinate at the point A and y_D the ordinate at D. The area of the typical rectangle ABCD is given by $AD \times \delta x$, where

$$\begin{aligned} AD &= y_A - y_D \\ &= f_1(x) - f_2(x) \end{aligned}$$

Consequently the area of ABCD $= [f_1(x) - f_2(x)]\,\delta x$

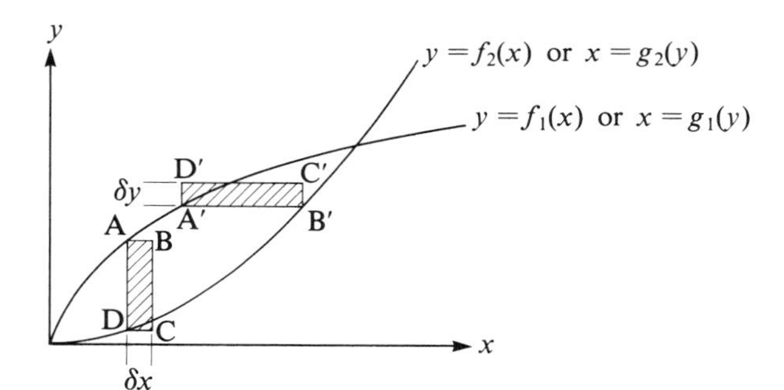

Fig. 10.3

The area enclosed by these two curves is the sum of the areas of all such typical rectangles as ABCD when $\delta x \to 0$. This sum is found by integration and is given by

$$\begin{aligned} \text{Area} &= \int_a^b [f_1(x) - f_2(x)]\,dx \\ &= \int_a^b f_1(x)\,dx - \int_a^b f_2(x)\,dx \end{aligned}$$

It is also possible to divide the area enclosed between the curves $y = f_1(x)$ and $y = f_2(x)$ into horizontal rectangles such as A′B′C′D′ (Fig. 10.3). We will assume that the two curves $y = f_1(x)$ and $y = f_2(x)$ have inverse relationships

$x = g_1(y)$ and $x = g_2(y)$, respectively. The width of the typical rectangle $A'B'C'D'$ is $A'B'$ and is given by

$$\begin{aligned} A'B' &= x_{B'} - x_{A'} \\ &= g_2(y) - g_1(y) \\ \therefore \quad \text{area of } A'B'C'D' &= A'B' \times \delta y \\ &= [g_2(y) - g_1(y)]\,\delta y \end{aligned}$$

The required area is now found by integration and is given by

$$\begin{aligned} \text{Area} &= \int_a^b [g_2(y) - g_1(y)]\,\delta y \\ &= \int_a^b g_2(y)\,dy - \int_a^b g_1(y)\,dy \end{aligned}$$

Worked Example

Sketch the curve $y = -x^2 + 4x$, between the origin O and the point A, where $x = 4$. The line $y = 3$ cuts the curve in points B and C. Find the area of OBCA. (WJEC 1982, part)

Solution

Since the coefficient of x^2 is negative, the curve will be concave downwards. Furthermore, the curve cuts the x-axis when $x = 0$ and $x = 4$. The sketch of the curve is shown in Fig. 10.4.

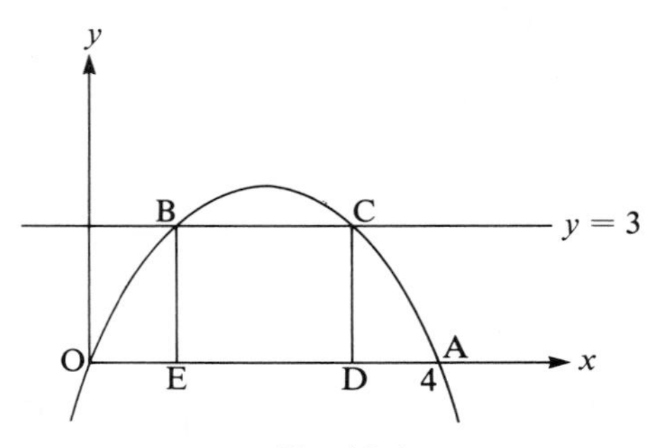

Fig. 10.4

From Fig. 10.4, we have

$$\text{Area OBCA} = \text{area OBE} + \text{rectangle BCDE} + \text{area CDA}$$

In order to find the points B and C we need to solve the quadratic equation

$$\begin{aligned} 3 &= -x^2 + 4x \\ \text{i.e.} \quad x^2 - 4x + 3 &= 0 \\ (x-3)(x-1) &= 0 \\ \therefore \quad x = 3 \quad &\text{or} \quad x = 1 \end{aligned}$$

The point E corresponds to $x = 1$, and the point D to $x = 3$. The areas OBE and CDA can now be found by integration

$$\begin{aligned} \text{Area OBE} &= \int_0^1 (-x^2 + 4x)\,dx \\ &= \left[-\frac{x^3}{3} + 2x^2 \right]_0^1 \end{aligned}$$

THE AREA ENCLOSED BY TWO CURVES

$$= -\tfrac{1}{3} + 2$$
$$= 1\tfrac{2}{3} \text{ units}^2$$

$$\text{Area CDA} = \int_3^4 (-x^2 + 4x)\,dx$$
$$= \left[-\frac{x^3}{3} + 2x^2\right]_3^4$$
$$= \left(\frac{-64}{3} + 32\right) - (-9 + 18)$$
$$= 1\tfrac{2}{3} \text{ units}^2$$
$$\text{area of rectangle BCDE} = \text{BE} \times \text{ED}$$
$$= 6 \text{ units}^2$$

Hence $\quad$ total area $= 9\tfrac{1}{3}$ units^2

EXERCISE

1. Verify that each of the curves $y^2 = 3x$ and $x^2 = 3y$ passes through the point (3, 3) and find the area of the finite region bounded by these curves. (LU 1980)

2. Sketch the curve with equation $y^2 = x(2-x)^2$ and show that the region enclosed by the loop has area $32\sqrt{2}/15$. (WJEC 1980, part)

3. Sketch the graphs of $y^2 = 16x$ and $y = x - 5$.
   Find (i) the coordinates of their points of intersection, (ii) the area of the finite region enclosed between the graphs. (AEB 1980)

Worked Solutions

1. Substituting $x = 3$ in $y^2 = 3x$ gives

$$y^2 = 9$$
$$\therefore \quad y = \pm 3$$

hence the curve $y^2 = 3x$ passes through (3, 3).
Substituting $x = 3$ in $x^2 = 3y$ gives

$$9 = 3y$$
$$\therefore \quad y = 3$$

hence $x^2 = 3y$ also passes through (3, 3).
The curves $y^2 = 3x$ and $x^2 = 3y$ intersect at the origin and at the point (3, 3). The curve $x^2 = 3y$ will increase more rapidly than $y^2 = 3x$ and will therefore, be above it as shown in Fig. 10.5.

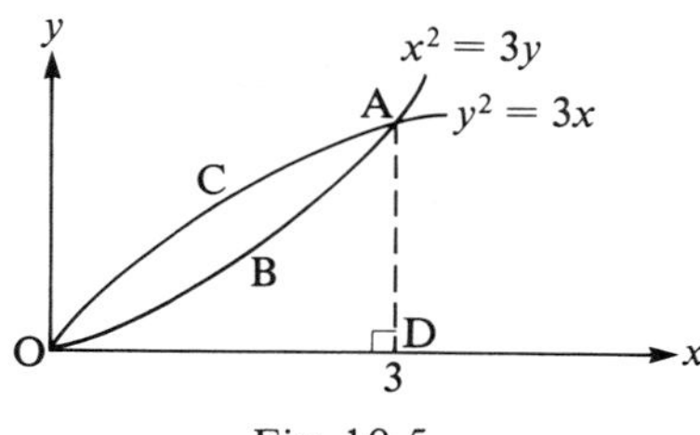

Fig. 10.5

Area of enclosed region OCAB $=$ area of OCAD $-$ area OBAD

$$= \int_0^3 \sqrt{3x}\,dx - \int_0^3 \frac{x^2}{3}\,dx$$

$$= \left[\frac{2}{3}\sqrt{3}\,x^{3/2}\right]_0^3 - \left[\frac{x^3}{9}\right]_0^3$$

$$= \frac{2}{3}\times 9 - \frac{1}{9}\times 27$$

$$= (6-3)\text{ units}^2$$

$$= 3\text{ units}^2$$

2. If $y^2 = x(2-x)^2$ $\qquad y = \pm\sqrt{x}\,(2-x)$

For each value of x there are two values of y of equal magnitude but opposite sign. Consequently, the curve is symmetrical about the x-axis, which it also intersects when $x = 0$ and when $x = 2$. The sketch of the curve is shown in Fig. 10.6.

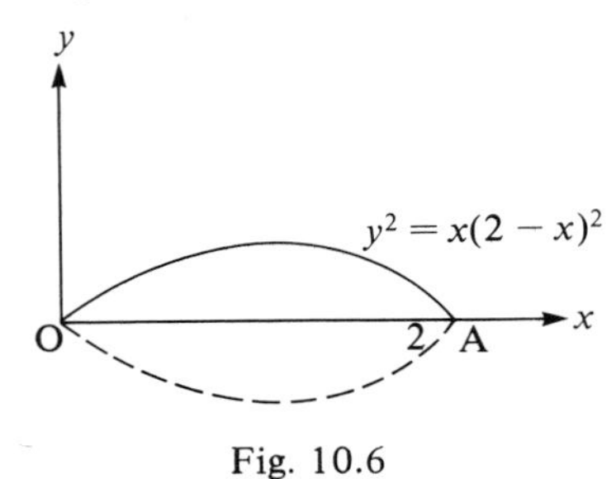

Fig. 10.6

The area enclosed by the curve and the x-axis in the first quadrant is

$$\int_0^2 y\,dx$$

$$= \int_0^2 \sqrt{x}\,(2-x)\,dx$$

Since the equation $y = \sqrt{x}\,(2-x)$ represents the part of the curve in the first quadrant

$$\text{Area} = \int_0^2 (2x^{1/2} - x^{3/2})\,dx$$

$$= \left[\frac{4}{3}x^{3/2} - \frac{2}{5}x^{5/2}\right]_0^2$$

$$= \frac{8}{3}\sqrt{2} - \frac{8}{5}\sqrt{2}$$

$$= \frac{16}{15}\sqrt{2}$$

By symmetry the area under the x-axis will have the same value. Hence

$$\text{Total area} = \frac{32}{15}\times\sqrt{2}$$

EXERCISE

3. If $y^2 = 16x$ $\qquad y = \pm 4\sqrt{x}$

hence each value of x gives rise to two values of y of equal magnitude but of opposite sign. The resulting curve is symmetrical about the x-axis.

The graph of $y = x - 5$ is a straight line passing through the points $(5, 0)$ and $(0, -5)$ (Fig. 10.7).

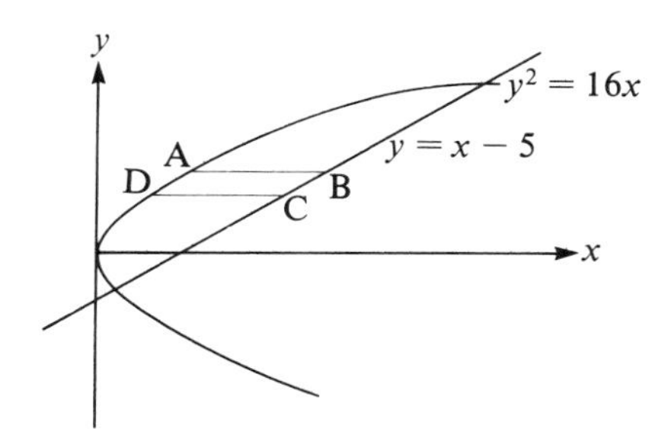

Fig. 10.7

To find the points of intersection we solve the equations simultaneously. This gives

$$(x-5)^2 = 16x$$
$$\therefore \quad x^2 - 10x + 25 = 16x$$
$$x^2 - 26x + 25 = 0$$
$$(x-1)(x-25) = 0$$

hence $\qquad x = 1 \quad \text{or} \quad x = 25$

It is easily calculated from the equation $y = x - 5$ that when $x = 1$, $y = -4$ and when $x = 25$, $y = 20$. In order to determine the area enclosed by these graphs, it is easier to divide the area into horizontal rectangles such as ABCD. All such rectangles are bounded by the curve $y^2 = 16x$ and the straight line $y = x - 5$. If we take AB as the typical length of each horizontal rectangle, we have

$$\text{AB} = x\text{-coordinate at B} - x\text{-coordinate at A}$$
$$\Rightarrow \quad \text{AB} = (y+5) - \frac{y^2}{16}$$
$$\therefore \quad \text{Area} = \int_{-4}^{20} \left(y - \frac{y^2}{16} + 5 \right) dy$$
$$= \left[\frac{y^2}{2} - \frac{y^3}{48} + 5y \right]_{-4}^{20}$$
$$= \left(200 - \frac{500}{3} + 100 \right) - \left(8 + \frac{64}{48} - 20 \right)$$
$$= 144 \text{ units}^2$$

SOLIDS OF REVOLUTION

Suppose the curve $y = f(x)$ is rotated completely about the x-axis through 360°. The solid so formed is called a solid of revolution (Fig. 10.8).

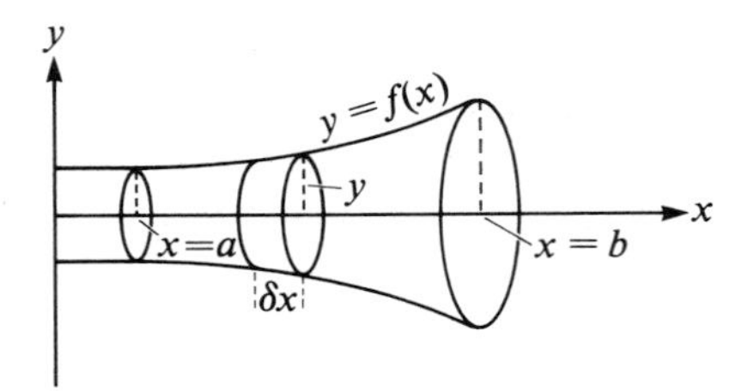

Fig. 10.8

We can regard this solid as made up of an infinite number of small cylinders of radius y and height δx, where the volume of each cylinder is given by $\pi y^2\,\delta x$. The volume of the solid between $x = a$ and $x = b$ is obtained by summing all of these cylindrical discs. If we denote the volume by V, we have

$$V \approx \sum_{x=a}^{x=b} \pi y^2\,\delta x$$

When $\delta x \to 0$, the summation becomes an integral and δx is replaced by $\mathrm{d}x$. We then have

$$\boxed{V = \int_a^b \pi y^2\,\mathrm{d}x} \tag{10.3}$$

for the volume of the solid of revolution formed when $y = f(x)$ is rotated about the x-axis.

A similar result is obtained for the volume of the solid of revolution formed by rotating $x = f(y)$ about the y-axis (Fig. 10.9).

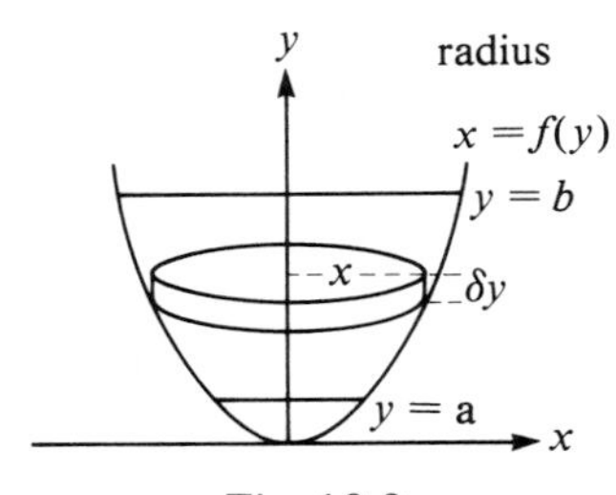

Fig. 10.9

In this case the volume of each typical cylinder of radius x and height δy is $\pi x^2\,\delta y$. By analogy with (10.3) the appropriate integral is

$$\boxed{V = \int_a^b \pi x^2\,\mathrm{d}y} \tag{10.4}$$

for the volume of the solid of revolution formed when the curve $x = f(y)$ between $y = a$ and $y = b$ is rotated completely about the y-axis.

Worked Example

Find the volume of the solid formed by rotating the area of the region bounded by $x = 0$, $y = 0$ and $y = 1 + \cos x$ through four right angles about the x-axis. (O 1979)

<u>SOLIDS OF REVOLUTION</u>

Solution

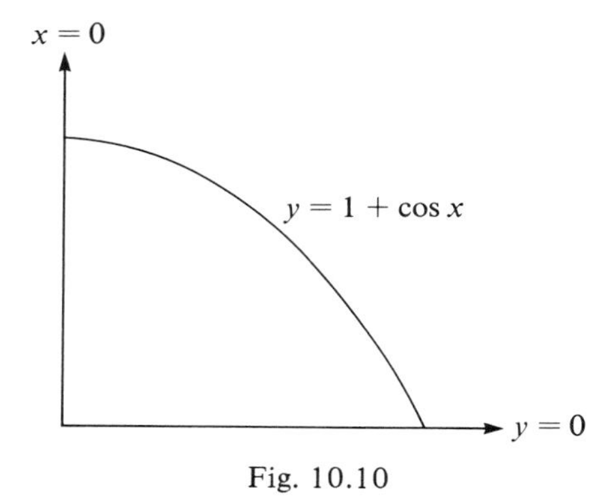

Fig. 10.10

Since the curve is rotated about the x-axis we must use (10.3). $y = 0$ is the equation of the x-axis and $x = 0$ is the equation of the y-axis. The curve $y = 1 + \cos x$ cuts the x-axis when $x = \pi$ so that the integral required for the volume is

$$V = \int_0^\pi \pi(1 + \cos x)^2 \, dx$$

$$= \pi \int_0^\pi (1 + 2\cos x + \cos^2 x)\, dx$$

To evaluate this integral we must use the double-angle result

$$\cos^2 x = \tfrac{1}{2}(1 + \cos 2x)$$

Substituting gives $$V = \pi \int_0^\pi \left(\frac{3}{2} + 2\cos x + \frac{1}{2}\cos 2x\right) dx$$

$$= \pi \left[\frac{3}{2}x + 2\sin x + \frac{1}{4}\sin 2x\right]_0^\pi$$

$$= \frac{3}{2}\pi^2 \qquad (\sin \pi = \sin 2\pi = 0)$$

EXERCISE

1. Show that the area of the region between the curve $y = (1 - x)/x$ and the lines $x = 1$, $y = 1$ is $1 - \log_e 2$. Find the volume of the solid formed when this region is rotated about the line $x = 1$. (WJEC 1981, part)

2. The region enclosed by the x-axis, between the limits $x = 0$ and $x = \pi/3$, and the curve $y = 2\sin x + \tan x$ is rotated completely about the x-axis. Prove that the volume of the solid so formed is

$$\frac{\pi}{6}[2\pi + 24\log_e(2 + \sqrt{3}) - 9\sqrt{3}\,] \qquad \text{(AEB 1982)}$$

3. Determine the volume generated when the region bounded by the lines $y = \frac{1}{4}$, $y = \frac{1}{2}$ and the curve $y = \dfrac{1}{2 + x^2}$ is rotated through π radians about the y-axis. (NI 1981, part)

Worked Solution

1. The curve $y = (1-x)/x$ cuts the line $y = 1$ when

$$1 = \frac{1-x}{x}$$

$$x = 1-x$$

$$2x = 1 \qquad \text{giving} \qquad x = \tfrac{1}{2}$$

We can divide the required area into vertical strips such as ABCD (see Fig. 10.11).

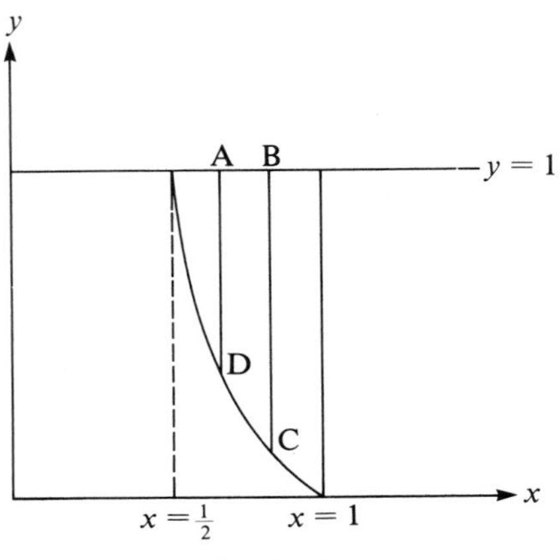

Fig. 10.11

Now

$$\begin{aligned} AD &= y_A - y_D \\ &= 1 - \frac{1-x}{x} \\ &= 2 - \frac{1}{x} \end{aligned}$$

$$\begin{aligned} \text{Area} &= \int_{1/2}^{1} \left(2 - \frac{1}{x}\right) dx \\ &= \Big[2x - \log_e x\Big]_{1/2}^{1} \\ &= (2 - \log_e 1) - (1 - \log_e \tfrac{1}{2}) \\ &= 1 + \log_e \tfrac{1}{2} \\ &= 1 - \log_e 2 \end{aligned}$$

In order to find the volume formed by rotating the given region about the line $x = 1$, we shift the origin to $x = 1$, $y = 0$ by means of the substitution $X = x - 1$. The volume, V, is given by

$$V = \int_0^1 \pi X^2 \, dy \qquad (1)$$

The equation of the curve in the new coordinate system is

$$y = \frac{1-(X+1)}{X+1}$$

EXERCISE

$$= \frac{-X}{X+1}$$

$$yX + y = -X$$

$$\therefore \quad X = \frac{-y}{y+1}$$

Substituting in (1) gives

$$V = \pi \int_0^1 \frac{y^2}{(y+1)^2}\, dy$$

If $u = y + 1$ $\qquad du \equiv dy$

When $y = 0$, $u = 1$ and when $y = 1$, $u = 2$. Hence

$$V = \pi \int_1^2 \frac{(u-1)^2}{u^2}\, du$$

$$= \pi \int_1^2 \left(1 - \frac{2}{u} + \frac{1}{u^2}\right) du$$

$$= \pi \left[u - 2\log_e u - \frac{1}{u}\right]_1^2$$

$$= \pi \left[\left(2 - 2\log_e 2 - \frac{1}{2}\right) - (1 - 2\log_e 1 - 1)\right]$$

$$\therefore \quad V = \pi \left(\frac{3}{2} - 2\log_e 2\right)$$

2. $$V = \pi \int_0^{\pi/3} y^2\, dx \qquad \text{where} \quad y = 2\sin x + \tan x$$

Substituting gives

$$V = \pi \int_0^{\pi/3} (2\sin x + \tan x)^2\, dx$$

$$= \pi \int_0^{\pi/3} (4\sin^2 x + 4\sin x \tan x + \tan^2 x)\, dx$$

$$= \pi \int_0^{\pi/2} \left\{2(1 - \cos 2x) + \frac{4\sin^2 x}{\cos x} + (\sec^2 x - 1)\right\} dx$$

$$= \pi \int_0^{\pi/2} \left\{2 - 2\cos 2x + \frac{4(1 - \cos^2 x)}{\cos x} + (\sec^2 x - 1)\right\} dx$$

$$= \pi \int_0^{\pi/3} \left\{1 - 2\cos 2x + 4\sec x - 4\cos x + \sec^2 x\right\} dx$$

$$= \pi \left[x - \sin 2x + 4\log_e(\sec x + \tan x) - 4\sin x + \tan x\right]_0^{\pi/3}$$

$$= \pi \left[\frac{\pi}{3} - \sin\frac{2\pi}{3} + 4\log_e\left(\sec\frac{\pi}{3} + \tan\frac{\pi}{3}\right) - 4\sin\frac{\pi}{3} + \tan\frac{\pi}{3}\right]$$

$$= \pi \left[\frac{\pi}{3} - \frac{\sqrt{3}}{2} + 4\log_e(2 + \sqrt{3}) - 2\sqrt{3} + \sqrt{3}\right]$$

EXERCISE

$$= \pi\left[\frac{\pi}{3}-\frac{3}{2}\sqrt{3}+4\log_e(2+\sqrt{3})\right]$$

$$\therefore \quad V = \frac{\pi}{6}[2\pi+24\log_e(2+\sqrt{3})-9\sqrt{3}]$$

3. The function $y = 1/(2+x^2)$ is an even function of x and the graph is, therefore, symmetrical about the y-axis. Consequently, it is only necessary to rotate the entire curve through π radians in order to form a solid of revolution with the same volume as that obtained by rotating the part of the curve in the first quadrant only through 2π radians.

Hence the volume will be given by

$$V = \int_{1/4}^{1/2} \pi x^2 \, dy$$

$$= \pi \int_{1/4}^{1/2} x^2 \, dy \qquad (1)$$

The equation of the curve is

$$y = \frac{1}{1+2x^2}$$

$$y(2+x^2) = 1$$

$$2y+x^2y = 1$$

$$x^2y = 1-2y$$

$$\therefore \quad x^2 = \frac{1-2y}{y}$$

Substituting in (1) gives

$$V = \pi\int_{1/4}^{1/2}\left(\frac{1}{y}-2\right)dy$$

$$= \pi\Big[\log_e y - 2y\Big]_{1/4}^{1/2}$$

$$= \pi\{(\log_e\tfrac{1}{2}-1)-(\log_e\tfrac{1}{4}-\tfrac{1}{2})\}$$

$$\therefore \quad V = \pi(\log_e 2-\tfrac{1}{2})$$

EXERCISE

11 DIFFERENTIAL EQUATIONS

INTRODUCTION

A differential equation is a relationship between a function and its derivatives. The order of a differential equation is the order of the highest derivative appearing in the equation. We will only be concerned with first-order equations that are either of the variable-separable type or those that can be solved by the use of an integrating factor.

VARIABLE-SEPARABLE DIFFERENTIAL EQUATIONS

A differential equation of the form

$$\frac{dy}{dx} = P(y)Q(x) \qquad (11.1)$$

where $P(y)$ is a function of y and $Q(x)$ a function of x is a variable-separable type of differential equation.

The equation (11.1) can be rearranged as

$$\frac{1}{P(y)}\frac{dy}{dx} = Q(x)$$

Integrating throughout with respect to x gives

$$\int\frac{dy}{P(y)} = \int Q(x)\,dx$$

In this form the differential equation may be solved provided the integrals on both the LHS and RHS can be found.

Worked Example

Given that $y > \frac{1}{2}$, find the general solution for the differential equation

$$\frac{dy}{dx} + 2xy = x$$

Given that $y = 1$ when $x = 1$, express y in terms of x. (AEB 1982)

Solution

If $\frac{dy}{dx} + 2xy = x$

$$\frac{dy}{dx} = x - 2xy$$

$$= x(1-2y)$$

Separating the variables and integrating

$$\int\frac{dy}{1-2y} = \int x\,dx$$

$$-\frac{1}{2}\int\frac{-2dy}{1-2y} = \int x\,dx$$

$$\Rightarrow \qquad -\frac{1}{2}\ln|1-2y| = \frac{x^2}{2}+c$$

Since $y > \frac{1}{2}$ we take the solution

$$\ln(2y-1) = x^2+d \qquad \text{(where } d = -2c\text{)}$$

Taking the antilog:

$$2y-1 = e^{(-x^2+d)}$$

$$\text{or} \quad 2y-1 = e^d e^{-x^2}$$

$$= Ke^{-x^2} \qquad \text{(where } K = e^d\text{)}$$

hence

$$y = \tfrac{1}{2}(1+Ke^{-x^2})$$

The value of the arbitrary constant K may be found by substituting in the given values of x and y. When $x = 1$ and $y = 1$, we have

$$1 = \tfrac{1}{2}(1+Ke^{-1})$$

giving

$$K = e$$

The required solution is therefore

$$y = \tfrac{1}{2}(1+e^{(1-x^2)})$$

Worked Example

Solve the differential equation

$$\frac{dy}{dx} = \frac{y^2-1}{2\tan x}$$

given that $y = 3$ when $x = \pi/2$.

Hence express y in terms of x. (AEB 1981)

Solution

Rearranging the given equation and integrating we have

$$\int\frac{dy}{y^2-1} = \int\frac{dx}{2\tan x}$$

$$\therefore \quad \int\frac{dy}{(y-1)(y+1)} = \frac{1}{2}\int\frac{\cos x}{\sin x}dx \qquad (1)$$

In order to obtain the integral on the LHS we use partial fractions.

$$\frac{1}{(y-1)(y+1)} = \frac{A}{(y-1)}+\frac{B}{(y+1)}$$

$$1 = A(y+1)+B(y-1)$$

Putting $y = 1$ $\qquad 1 = 2A \qquad \therefore \quad A = \frac{1}{2}$

Putting $y = -1$ $\qquad 1 = -2B \qquad \therefore \quad B = -\frac{1}{2}$

hence

$$\frac{1}{(y-1)(y+1)} = \frac{1}{2}\left(\frac{1}{y-1}-\frac{1}{y+1}\right)$$

Substituting these partial fractions in (1) gives

$$\frac{1}{2}\int\left(\frac{1}{y-1}-\frac{1}{y+1}\right)dy = \frac{1}{2}\int\frac{\cos x}{\sin x}dx$$

All of these integrals are of the standard form (9.3) with the derivative of the denominator equal to the numerator. This gives

$$\ln(y-1)-\ln(y+1) = \ln\sin x+\ln c \qquad (2)$$

where c is an arbitrary constant introduced by the integration. Note that it is sometimes convenient to introduce a logarithmic arbitrary constant. Using the rules of logarithms, (2) can be simplified to

$$\ln\frac{(y-1)}{y+1} = \ln c \sin x$$

$$\therefore \quad \frac{y-1}{y+1} = c\sin x$$

This is the general solution of the differential equation. However, we may find the value of c by substituting in the given values of x and y.

When $x = \pi/2$ and $y = 3$, we have

$$\frac{1}{2} = c\sin\frac{\pi}{2} \qquad \therefore \quad c = \frac{1}{2}$$

hence
$$\frac{y-1}{y+1} = \frac{1}{2}\sin x$$

Making y the subject of the formula gives

$$2(y-1) = (y+1)\sin x$$

Rearranging
$$2y - y\sin x = 2+\sin x$$

Factorising
$$y(2-\sin x) = 2+\sin x$$

$$\therefore \quad y = \frac{2+\sin x}{2-\sin x}$$

EXERCISE

1. Solve the differential equation

$$\frac{1}{x}\frac{dy}{dx} = \sqrt{2y(x+2)}$$

given that $y = 0$ when $x = -2$. (NI 1982)

2. Find the solution of the differential equation

$$\frac{dy}{dx} = \frac{x(1-y^2)}{y(1+x^2)}$$

for which $y = \frac{1}{2}$ when $x = 1$. (O 1977)

3. Find the general solution of the differential equation

$$2x\frac{dy}{dx} + y^2 = 1$$

Sketch the particular solution passing through the point $(\frac{1}{2}, \frac{3}{2})$.
(WJEC 1982, part)

4. If y is a solution of the differential equation

$$\frac{dy}{dx} = \frac{1+y^2}{1+x^2}$$

deduce that $y = x + k(1+xy)$, where k is a constant.

(You may assume that $\tan^{-1}a - \tan^{-1}b = \tan^{-1}\dfrac{a-b}{1+ab} + n\pi$, n is an integer.) (WJEC 1980, part)

5. Find y in terms of x if $dy/dx = (1+y)^2\sin^2 x\cos x$ and $y = 2$ when $x = 0$. (AEB 1980)

6. Given that $(1+\sin^2 x)\,dy/dx = e^{-2y}\sin 2x$ and $y = 1$ when $x = 0$, find the value of y when $x = \pi/2$. (AEB 1980)

7. Solve the differential equation $(1+e^y)\,dy/dx = e^{2y}\cos^2 x$ given that $y = 0$ when $x = 0$. (AEB 1981)

8. The differential equation $$\frac{dy}{dx} = \frac{y^2-2y-3}{x^2-2x+5}$$ is defined in the region $-1 < y < 3$. Show that the particular solution passing through the point $x = 1$, $y = 1$ is
$$y = \frac{3-e^{2\theta}}{1+e^{2\theta}} \quad \text{where} \quad \theta = \tan^{-1}\frac{1}{2}(x-1)$$
(WJEC 1981, part)

Worked Solutions

1.
$$\frac{1}{x}\frac{dy}{dx} = \sqrt{2y}(x+2)$$
$$\therefore \int\frac{dy}{\sqrt{2y}} = \int x\sqrt{x+2}\,dx$$

To find the integral on the RHS we substitute $u^2 = x+2$.

If $u^2 = x+2$ $\qquad dx \equiv 2u\,du$

$$\therefore \frac{1}{\sqrt{2}}\int y^{-1/2}\,dy = 2\int(u^2-2)u^2\,du$$
$$= 2\int(u^4-2u^2)\,du$$

Integrating

$$\frac{1}{\sqrt{2}}2y^{1/2}+c = 2\left(\frac{u^5}{5}-\frac{2u^3}{3}\right)$$
$$= \frac{2}{15}u^3(3u^2-10)$$

Substituting back for x on the RHS gives

$$\sqrt{2y}+c = \frac{2}{15}(x+2)^{3/2}(3x-4)$$

Putting $x = -2$ and $y = 0$ gives $c = 0$

hence
$$\sqrt{2y} = \frac{2}{15}(x+2)^{3/2}(3x-4)$$
$$\therefore y = \frac{2}{225}(x+2)^3(3x-4)^2$$

2.
$$\frac{dy}{dx} = \frac{x(1-y^2)}{y(1+x^2)}$$
$$\therefore -\frac{1}{2}\int\frac{-2y\,dy}{1-y^2} = \frac{1}{2}\int\frac{2x\,dx}{1+x^2}$$
$$-\tfrac{1}{2}\ln(1-y^2) = \tfrac{1}{2}\ln(1+x^2)+\tfrac{1}{2}\ln c$$
$$\ln(1+x^2)+\ln(1-y^2)+\ln c = 0$$
$$\ln c(1+x^2)(1-y^2) = 0$$

EXERCISE

$$\therefore \quad c(1+x^2)(1-y^2) = 1$$

When $x = 1$ and $y = \frac{1}{2}$, we have

$$\frac{3c}{2} = 1 \qquad \therefore \quad c = \frac{2}{3}$$

Substituting gives

$$\frac{2}{3}(1+x^2)(1-y^2) = 1$$

$$y^2 = 1-\frac{3}{2(1+x^2)}$$

$$\therefore \quad y^2 = \frac{2x^2-1}{2(1+x^2)}$$

hence

$$y = \sqrt{\frac{2x^2-1}{2x^2+2}}$$

3.

$$2x\frac{dy}{dx}+y^2 = 1$$

$$2x\frac{dy}{dx} = 1-y^2$$

$$\int\frac{dy}{1-y^2} = \int\frac{dx}{2x} \qquad (1)$$

We now express the LHS in terms of partial fractions:

$$\frac{1}{1-y^2} = \frac{A}{1+y}+\frac{B}{1-y}$$

$$\therefore \quad 1 = A(1-y)+B(1+y)$$

Putting $y = 1$ $\qquad 1 = 2B \qquad \therefore \quad B = \frac{1}{2}$

Putting $y = -1$ $\qquad 1 = 2A \qquad \therefore \quad A = \frac{1}{2}$

hence

$$\frac{1}{1-y^2} = \frac{1}{2(1+y)}+\frac{1}{2(1-y)}$$

Using these partial fractions in (1) gives

$$\frac{1}{2}\int\frac{dy}{1+y}+\frac{1}{2}\int\frac{dy}{1-y} = \frac{1}{2}\int\frac{dx}{x}$$

$$\therefore \quad \frac{1}{2}\ln(1+y)-\frac{1}{2}\ln(1-y) = \frac{1}{2}\ln x+\frac{1}{2}\ln c$$

$$\ln\left(\frac{1+y}{1-y}\right) = \ln cx$$

$$\therefore \quad \frac{1+y}{1-y} = cx$$

which is the general solution of the differential equation. We can find the value of c by putting $x = \frac{1}{2}$ and $y = \frac{3}{2}$. This gives

$$\frac{5/2}{-1/2} = \frac{c}{2} \qquad \therefore \quad c = -10$$

Hence the equation of the curve passing through the point $(\frac{1}{2}, \frac{3}{2})$ is given by

$$\frac{1+y}{1-y} = -10x$$

$$1+y = -10x(1-y)$$

$$= -10x + 10xy$$

$$y(1-10x) = -(10x+1)$$

giving
$$y = \frac{10x+1}{10x-1} \qquad (2)$$

In order to sketch the curve we start by finding the points of intersection on both axes. When $x = 0$ we have $y = -1$ and when $y = 0$ we have $x = -1/10$. The denominator vanishes when $x = 1/10$ which is, therefore, an asymptote of the curve. When $x < 1/10$ the denominator is negative, while for $x < -1/10$ the numerator is negative and for $x > -1/10$ the numerator is positive. Consequently, $y > 0$ when $x < -1/10$ and $y < 0$ when $x > -1/10$. Also, when $x > 1/10$ both numerator and denominator are positive so that $y > 0$.

We now investigate the behaviour of the curve for infinitely large values of x by rewriting the equation of the curve as

$$y = \frac{10x-1+2}{10x-1} = 1 + \frac{2}{10x-1}$$

From this result it is seen that as $x \to \infty$, $y \to 1$ and also when $x \to -\infty$, $y \to 1$ (Fig. 11.1).

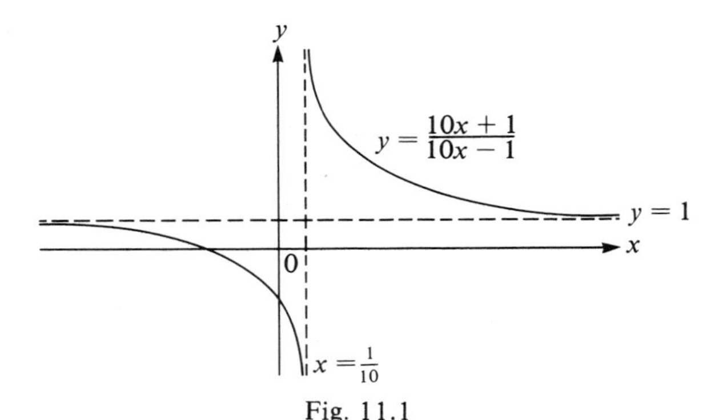

Fig. 11.1

4. If $\dfrac{dy}{dx} = \dfrac{1+y^2}{1+x^2}$
$$\int \frac{dy}{1+y^2} = \int \frac{dx}{1+x^2}$$

$$\therefore \quad \tan^{-1} y = \tan^{-1} x + c$$

$$\tan^{-1} y - \tan^{-1} x = c$$

Using the given result on the LHS we have

$$\tan^{-1} \frac{y-x}{1+xy} = c - n\pi$$

$$\therefore \quad \frac{y-x}{1+xy} = \tan(c - n\pi)$$

EXERCISE

If we let $k = \tan(c - n\pi)$, we have

$$\frac{y-x}{1+xy} = k$$

$$y - x = k(1+xy)$$

$$\therefore \quad y = x + k(1+xy)$$

5. If $\dfrac{dy}{dx} = (1+y^2)\sin^2 x \cos x$

$$\int \frac{dy}{(1+y)^2} = \int \sin^2 x \cos x \, dx$$

Since $d/dx\,(\sin x) = \cos x$ we can use the result (9.6) (p. 99) on the RHS to give

$$\frac{-1}{1+y} = \frac{1}{3}\sin^3 x + c$$

when $x = 0$, $y = 2$ $\quad \therefore \quad \dfrac{-1}{3} = c$

hence $\quad \dfrac{-1}{1+y} = \dfrac{1}{3}\sin^3 x - \dfrac{1}{3}$

Factorising $\quad \dfrac{-1}{1+y} = \dfrac{1}{3}(\sin^3 x - 1)$

Inverting $\quad y + 1 = \dfrac{3}{(1-\sin^3 x)}$

$$y = \frac{3}{1-\sin^3 x} - 1$$

$$= \frac{3-(1-\sin^3 x)}{1-\sin^3 x}$$

$$\therefore \quad y = \frac{2+\sin^3 x}{1-\sin^3 x}$$

6. If $(1+\sin^2 x)\dfrac{dy}{dx} = e^{-2y}\sin 2x$

$$\int e^{2y}\,dy = \int \frac{\sin 2x}{1+\sin^2 x}\,dx$$

$$= \int \frac{2\sin x \cos x}{1+\sin^2 x}\,dx \qquad (\sin 2x = 2\sin x \cos x)$$

$$\therefore \quad \frac{1}{2}e^{2y} = \ln(1+\sin^2 x) + c$$

When $x = 0$, $y = 1$. Substituting gives

$$\frac{1}{2}e^2 = \ln 1 + c$$

$$\therefore \quad c = \frac{e^2}{2}$$

EXERCISE

hence $$\frac{1}{2}e^{2y} = \ln(1+\sin^2 x)+\frac{e^2}{2}$$

When $x = \pi/2$, we have

$$\frac{1}{2}e^{2y} = \ln 2+\frac{e^2}{2}$$

$$e^{2y} = 2\ln 2+e^2$$

$$\therefore\quad 2y = \ln[2\ln 2+e^2]$$

$$y = \tfrac{1}{2}\ln[2\ln 2+e^2]$$

giving $$y = 1.086$$

7. If $(1+e^y)\dfrac{dy}{dx} = e^{2y}\cos^2 x$

$$\int\frac{(1+e^y)}{e^{2y}}\,dy = \int\cos^2 x\,dx$$

$$\int(e^{-2y}+e^{-y})dy = \frac{1}{2}\int(\cos 2x+1)\,dx$$

$$\therefore\quad -\frac{1}{2}e^{-2y}-e^{-y} = \frac{1}{4}\sin 2x+\frac{x}{2}+c$$

When $x = 0$, $y = 0$ and substituting gives

$$-\frac{1}{2}-1 = c \qquad \text{giving} \quad c = -\frac{3}{2}$$

hence $$-\frac{1}{2}e^{-2y}-e^{-y} = \frac{1}{4}\sin 2x+\frac{x}{2}-\frac{3}{2}$$

8. If $\dfrac{dy}{dx} = \dfrac{y^2-2y-3}{x^2-2x+5}$

$$\int\frac{dy}{y^2-2y-3} = \int\frac{dx}{x^2-2x+5} \qquad (1)$$

For the LHS let $$\frac{1}{y^2-2y-3} = \frac{1}{(y-3)(y+1)}$$

$$= \frac{A}{y-3}+\frac{B}{y+1}$$

$$\therefore\quad 1 = A(y+1)+B(y-3)$$

Putting $y = 3$ $\qquad 1 = 4A \qquad \therefore\ A = \frac{1}{4}$

Putting $y = -1$ $\qquad 1 = -4B \qquad \therefore\ B = -\frac{1}{4}$

Using these partial fractions on the LHS of (1) gives

$$\frac{1}{4}\int\frac{dy}{y-3}-\frac{1}{4}\int\frac{dy}{y+1} = \int\frac{dx}{x^2-2x+5}$$

$$= \int\frac{dx}{(x-1)^2+2^2}$$

EXERCISE

We now substitute $u = x - 1$ on the RHS; hence

$$\frac{1}{4}\int\frac{dy}{y-3} - \frac{1}{4}\int\frac{dy}{y+1} = \int\frac{du}{u^2+2^2}$$

Therefore the general solution is

$$\frac{1}{4}\ln\left|\frac{y-3}{y+1}\right| = \frac{1}{2}\tan^{-1}\frac{u}{2} + c$$

$$= \frac{1}{2}\tan^{-1}\left(\frac{x-1}{2}\right) + c$$

If we let $\theta = \tan^{-1}\left(\frac{x-1}{2}\right)$

then $\frac{1}{4}\ln\left|\frac{y-3}{y+1}\right| = \frac{\theta}{2} + c$

Since y takes on values in the range $-1 < y < 3$, we must have

$$\frac{1}{4}\ln\left(\frac{3-y}{y+1}\right) = \frac{\theta}{2} + c$$

When $x = 1$, $y = 1$; substituting gives

$$\frac{1}{4}\ln 1 = \frac{1}{2}\tan^{-1} 0 + c \qquad \therefore \quad c = 0$$

$$\therefore \quad \ln\frac{3-y}{y+1} = 2\theta$$

$$\therefore \quad \frac{3-y}{y+1} = e^{2\theta}$$

Making y the subject $y = \dfrac{3-e^{2\theta}}{1+e^{2\theta}}$

LINEAR DIFFERENTIAL EQUATIONS

Suppose we have a first-order differential equation of the form

$$\frac{dy}{dx} + Py = Q \tag{11.2}$$

where both P and Q are functions of x. This equation is linear in both dy/dx and y. Multiplication of (11.2) throughout by $e^{\int P dx}$ gives

$$\frac{dy}{dx}e^{\int P dx} + Pye^{\int P dx} = Qe^{\int P dx}$$

$$\frac{d}{dx}(ye^{Pdx}) = Qe^{\int P dx}$$

$$ye^{Pdx} = \int Qe^{Pdx} \tag{11.3}$$

This is the general solution of the differential equation. The expression $e^{\int P dx}$ is referred to as an integrating factor (IF) because it renders the LHS directly integrable.

EXERCISE/LINEAR DIFFERENTIAL EQUATIONS

Worked Example

Solve the differential equation

$$\frac{dy}{dx} = y + e^{-x}$$

given that $y = 1$ when $x = 0$. (LU 1981, part)

Solution

If $\dfrac{dy}{dx} = y + e^{-x}$ $\qquad \dfrac{dy}{dx} - y = e^{-x}$

This puts the equation into the form (11.2) with $P = -1$ and $Q = e^{-x}$. The integrating factor is $e^{-\int 1\,dx} = e^{-x}$. Substituting in (11.3) gives

$$ye^{-x} = \int e^{-x} \times e^{-x}\,dx$$

$$= \int e^{-2x}\,dx$$

$$\therefore \quad ye^{-x} = -\frac{1}{2}e^{-2x} + c$$

$$\therefore \quad y = -\frac{1}{2}e^{-x} + ce^{x}$$

When $x = 0$, $y = 1$; substituting gives

$$1 = -\frac{1}{2} + c \qquad \therefore \quad c = \frac{3}{2}$$

hence

$$y = \frac{3}{2}e^{x} - \frac{1}{2}e^{-x}$$

EXERCISE

1. Solve the differential equation

$$2\frac{dy}{dx} + y = 3e^{x}$$

subject to the condition $y(1) = 0$. (NI 1981, part)

2. Show that, for the differential equation

$$\frac{dy}{dx} = 1 + \frac{2xy}{1-x^2}$$

defined in $-1 < x < 1$, the particular solution passing through the point $x = 0$, $y = -\frac{2}{3}$ is

$$y = \frac{(x-1)(x+2)}{3(x+1)}$$

(WJEC 1980, part)

3. Find the general solution of the differential equation

$$\frac{dy}{dx} + \frac{xy}{1-x^2} = x \qquad |x| < 1$$

(WJEC 1981, part)

4. Find the general solution of the differential equation

$$\frac{dy}{dx} + ky = a \sin mx$$

where a, k and m are constants. If $a = 1$, $k = 2$ and $m = 1$, find the particular solution which has value 1 when $x = 0$.

$$\left[\int e^{kx} \sin mx \, dx = \frac{e^{kx}}{k^2 + m^2}(k \sin mx - m \cos mx)\right]$$

(WJEC 1982, part)

Worked Solutions

1. The given equation can be rewritten as

$$\frac{dy}{dx} + \frac{y}{2} = \frac{3}{2} e^x$$

Hence $$\text{IF} = e^{\int 1/2 \, dx} = e^{x/2}$$

The general solution is given by

$$ye^{x/2} = \frac{3}{2}\int e^x e^{x/2} \, dx$$

$$= \frac{3}{2}\int e^{3x/2} \, dx$$

$$\therefore \quad ye^{x/2} = e^{3x/2} + c \qquad (1)$$

The given condition to determine the value of c is $y(1) = 0$. The value of y is 0 when $x = 1$. Substituting gives

$$0 = e^{3/2} + c$$

$$\therefore \quad c = -e^{3/2}$$

Substituting this value of c in (1) gives

$$ye^{x/2} = e^{3x/2} - e^{3/2}$$

hence $$y = e^x - e^{(3-x)/2}$$

2. We can rewrite the given equation as

$$\frac{dy}{dx} - \frac{2xy}{1-x^2} = 1$$

Hence $$\text{IF} = e^{\int -2x/(1-x^2) \, dx}$$

$$= e^{\ln(1-x^2)}$$

$$\therefore \quad \text{IF} = (1-x^2)$$

The general solution is given by

$$y(1-x^2) = \int (1-x^2) \, dx$$

$$y(1-x^2) = x - \frac{x^3}{3} + c$$

When $x = 0$, $y = -\frac{2}{3}$; substituting gives

$$\frac{-2}{3} = c$$

hence
$$y(1-x^2) = x-\frac{x^3}{3}-\frac{2}{3}$$
$$= \frac{3x-x^3-2}{3}$$
$$y = \frac{(1-x)(x^2+x-2)}{3(1-x)(1+x)}$$
$$\therefore \quad y = \frac{(x+2)(x-1)}{3(1+x)} \qquad \text{as required}$$

3. In this differential equation
$$P = \frac{x}{1-x^2} = -\frac{1}{2}\left(\frac{-2x}{1-x^2}\right)$$
Hence
$$\text{IF} = e^{\int P\mathrm{d}x}$$
$$= e^{-1/2\int -2x/(1-x^2)\,\mathrm{d}x}$$
$$= e^{-1/2\ln(1-x^2)}$$
giving
$$\text{IF} = \frac{1}{\sqrt{1-x^2}}$$
The general solution is given by
$$\frac{y}{\sqrt{1-x^2}} = \int\frac{x\,\mathrm{d}x}{\sqrt{1-x^2}}$$
$$= -\sqrt{1-x^2}+c \qquad \text{(using 9.6)}$$
$$y = \sqrt{1-x^2}\,(c-\sqrt{1-x^2})$$

4. If $\dfrac{\mathrm{d}y}{\mathrm{d}x}+ky = a\sin mx$

then
$$\text{IF} = e^{\int k\mathrm{d}x}$$
$$= e^{kx}$$
Therefore the general solution is given by
$$ye^{kx} = a\int e^{kx}\sin mx\,\mathrm{d}x$$
$$= \frac{ae^{kx}}{(k^2+m^2)}(k\sin mx - m\cos mx)+c$$
hence
$$y = \frac{a}{k^2+m^2}(k\sin mx - m\cos mx)+ce^{-kx}$$
Substituting $a = 1$, $k = 2$ and $m = 1$ gives
$$y = \frac{1}{5}(2\sin x-\cos x)+ce^{-2x}$$
We require the particular solution that gives $y = 1$ when $x = 0$. Substituting these values
$$1 = \frac{1}{5}(-1)+c \qquad \therefore \quad c = \frac{6}{5}$$
hence
$$y = \frac{1}{5}(2\sin x-\cos x+6e^{-2x})$$

EXERCISE

12 THE CIRCLE AND THE PARABOLA

THE CIRCLE

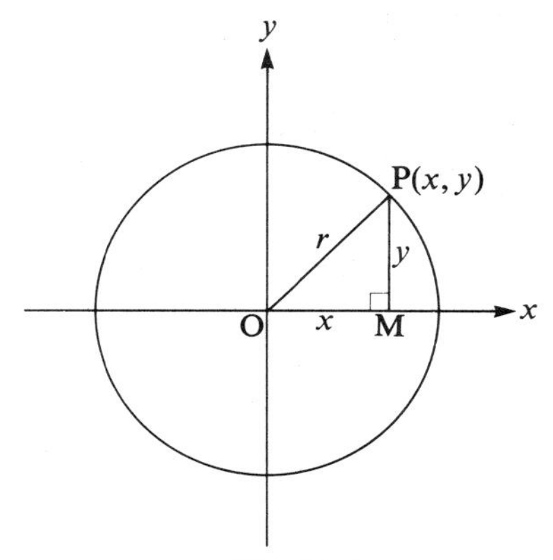

Fig. 12.1

The simplest form for the equation of a circle is when its centre coincides with the origin of the coordinate system. If P represents a typical point on the circumference of the circle, ΔOPM is right-angled at M (Fig. 12.1). We can apply Pythagoras' theorem to this triangle to give

$$x^2+y^2 = r^2 \tag{12.1}$$

as the equation of the circle of radius r with its centre at the origin of the coordinate system.

Suppose now that the centre of the circle of radius r is at the point (a, b) (see Fig. 12.2). At the point (a, b) we can introduce a new system of axes (X, Y), which will be connected to the original system by the equations

$$X = x-a \tag{12.2}$$

$$Y = y-b \tag{12.3}$$

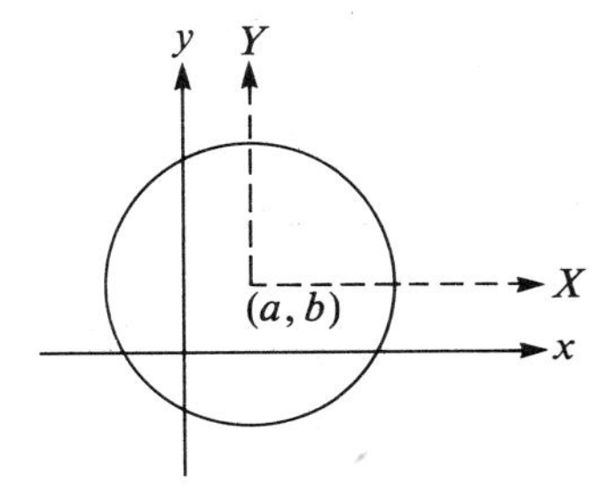

Fig. 12.2

The equation of the circle referred to the (X, Y) system is given by (from (12.1))

$$X^2+Y^2 = r^2 \qquad (12.4)$$

Substituting (12.2) and (12.3) into this equation gives

$$(x-a)^2+(y-b)^2 = r^2 \qquad (12.5)$$

as the equation of the circle, centre (a, b) and radius r.

The standard form for the equation of a circle is found by replacing a and b by $-g$ and $-f$, respectively. Equation (12.5) can then be rearranged and simplified to

$$x^2+y^2+2gx+2fy+c = 0 \qquad (12.6)$$

where

$$r^2 = g^2+f^2-c \qquad (12.7)$$

and the centre is $(-g, -f)$.

THE EQUATION OF THE TANGENT

Suppose we wish to find the equation of the tangent to the circle through the point (x_1, y_1) on its circumference. The gradient of the tangent at (x_1, y_1) is the same as the gradient of the curve at this point. Consequently, we need to find $\mathrm{d}y/\mathrm{d}x$ from the standard equation (12.6). Differentiating (12.6) implicitly gives

$$2x+2y\frac{\mathrm{d}y}{\mathrm{d}x}+2g+2f\frac{\mathrm{d}y}{\mathrm{d}x} = 0$$

$$(y+f)\frac{\mathrm{d}y}{\mathrm{d}x} = -(x+g)$$

$$\frac{\mathrm{d}y}{\mathrm{d}x} = -\frac{(x+g)}{(y+f)}$$

At the particular point (x_1, y_1) we have

$$\frac{\mathrm{d}y}{\mathrm{d}x} = -\frac{(x_1+g)}{(y_1+f)} \qquad (12.8)$$

The equation of the tangent through the point (x_1, y_1) is given by

$$y-y_1 = m(x-x_1)$$

where $m = \mathrm{d}y/\mathrm{d}x$ and is given by (12.8).

Substituting from (12.8) into this equation and using (12.6) we find after some simplification that the equation of the tangent through the point (x_1, y_1) on the circumference of the circle is given by

$$xx_1+yy_1+g(x+x_1)+f(y+y_1)+c = 0 \qquad (12.9)$$

CONDITIONS FOR TANGENCY

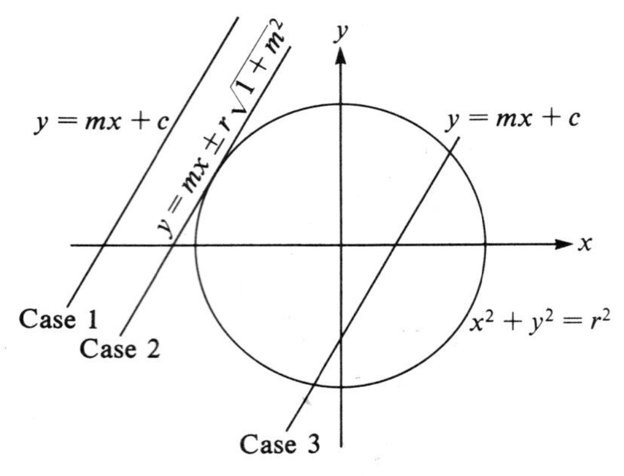

Fig. 12.3

Fig. 12.3 shows three parallel lines. In Case 1 the straight line is external to the circle, whereas in Cases 2 and 3 it touches and intersects the circle, respectively. We now examine the conditions for these three possibilities.

In order to find the points of intersection (if any) of the straight line and the circle we need to solve, simultaneously, the equations

$$y = mx + c \tag{12.10}$$

$$x^2 + y^2 = r^2 \tag{12.11}$$

Substituting (12.10) into (12.11) gives

$$x^2 + (mx + c)^2 = r^2 \tag{12.12}$$

$$x^2(1 + m^2) + 2mcx + (c^2 - r^2) = 0 \tag{12.13}$$

The roots of this quadratic equation can be classified as follows, using the discriminant

$b^2 < 4ac. \Rightarrow$ Imaginary roots $\Rightarrow$ no points of intersection (Case 1)

$b^2 = 4ac \Rightarrow$ Coincident roots $\Rightarrow$ $y = mx + c$ is a tangent (Case 2)

$b^2 > 4ac \Rightarrow$ Real, distinct roots $\Rightarrow$ $y = mx + c$ is a chord (Case 3)

where $b = 2mc$, $a = 1 + m^2$ and $c = c^2 - r^2$.

The condition for tangency is established from the requirement that $b^2 = 4ac$. This gives

$$(2mc)^2 = 4(1 + m^2)(c^2 - r^2)$$

$$m^2c^2 = (1 + m^2)(c^2 - r^2)$$

$$c^2 = r^2(1 + m^2)$$

$$c = \pm r\sqrt{1 + m^2} \tag{12.14}$$

Hence the straight line $y = mx \pm r\sqrt{1 + m^2}$ is a tangent to $x^2 + y^2 = r^2$ for all values of m. There are two tangents depending on whether we take the positive or the negative root of (12.14). These two tangents are at opposite ends of the same diameter.

THE EQUATION OF A CIRCLE THROUGH POINTS ON THE DIAMETER

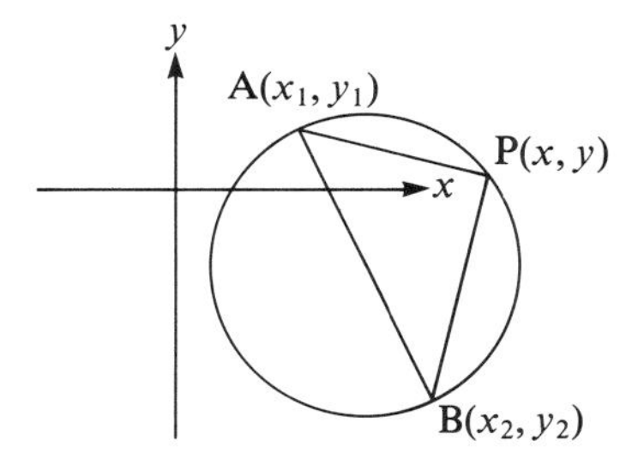

Fig. 12.4

We now investigate the equation of a circle when two points (x_1, y_1) and (x_2, y_2) at opposite ends of a diameter are given (Fig. 12.4). Let $P(x, y)$ represent any point on the circumference of the circle. Since the angle subtended by the diameter of the circle at the circumference is 90°, the straight line AP is perpendicular to BP.

<u>THE EQUATION OF A CIRCLE THROUGH POINTS ON THE DIAMETER</u>

$$\text{The gradient of AP} = \frac{y-y_1}{x-x_1}$$

$$\text{The gradient of BP} = \frac{y-y_2}{x-x_2}$$

AP is perpendicular to BP

$$\therefore \quad \frac{(y-y_1)}{(x-x_1)}\frac{(y-y_2)}{(x-x_2)} = -1$$

which gives $$(x-x_1)(x-x_2)+(y-y_1)(y-y_2) = 0 \qquad (12.15)$$
as the equation of the circle through the diametrically opposite points (x_1, y_1) and (x_2, y_2).

THE CONDITION FOR CIRCLES TO TOUCH EXTERNALLY

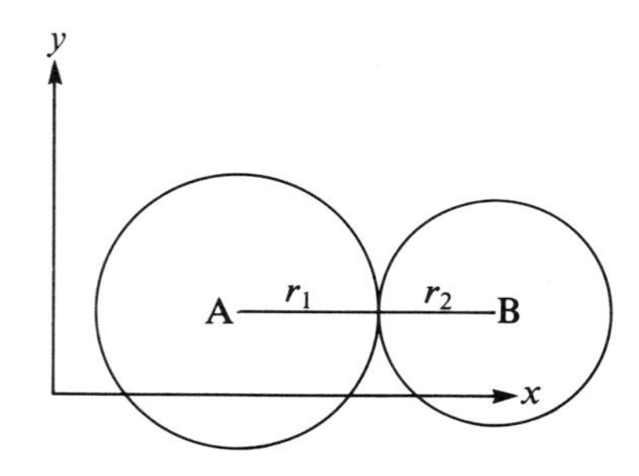

Fig. 12.5

Two circles, centres A and B (Fig. 12.5) touch externally if they intersect at only one point, and the sum of the radii of the circles is equal to the distance between their centres.

$$AB = r_1+r_2$$

THE CONDITION FOR CIRCLES TO TOUCH INTERNALLY

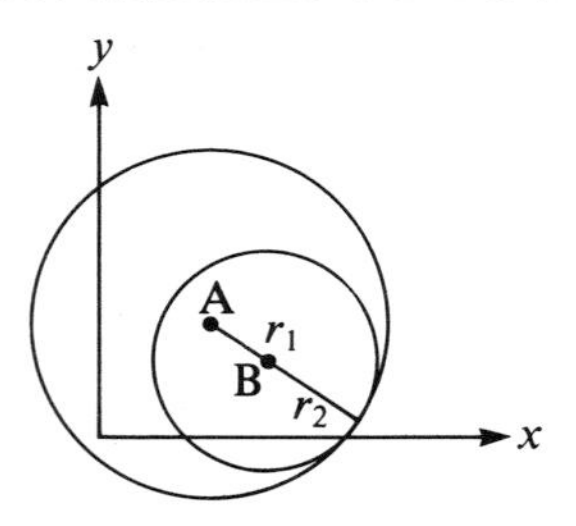

Fig. 12.6

The two circles, centres at A and B (Fig. 12.6), touch internally if they intersect at only one point and the difference of the radii of the circles is equal to the distance between their centres.

$$AB = r_1-r_2$$

ORTHOGONAL CIRCLES

Two circles that intersect at right-angles are called orthogonal circles. The condition for this is that the angle between the radii of the two circles at the point of intersection is 90° as shown in Fig. 12.7.

THE CONDITION FOR CIRCLES TO TOUCH

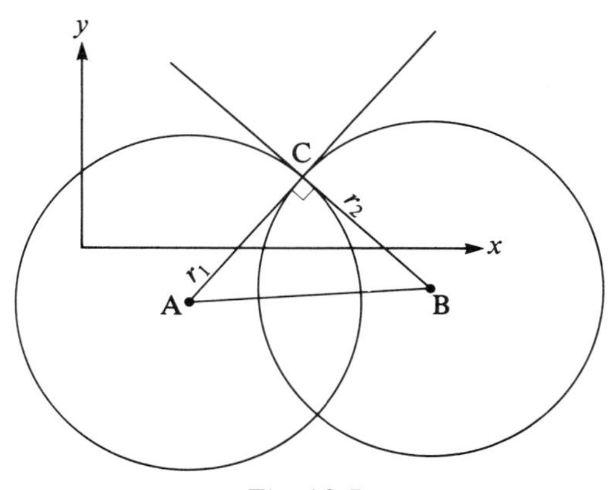

Fig. 12.7

Applying Pythagoras' theorem to the right-angled $\triangle$ABC we have

$$AB^2 = r_1^2 + r_2^2$$

Sum of squares of radii = square of distance between their centres

Worked Example

Find the centre and radius of the circle

$$x^2 + y^2 - 4x - 8y + 17 = 0$$

and show the circle on a diagram.

Show that the angle θ between the two tangents from the origin is such that

$$\tan\theta = \sqrt{51/7} \qquad \text{(NI 1980)}$$

Solution

The given circle is

$$x^2 + y^2 - 4x - 8y + 17 = 0 \qquad (1)$$

We compare this circle with the standard form for the equation of the circle

$$x^2 + y^2 + 2gx + 2fy + c = 0 \qquad (2)$$

$$\therefore \quad 2g = -4 \qquad \text{giving} \quad g = -2$$

and

$$2f = -8 \qquad \text{giving} \quad f = -4$$

Therefore the centre of the circle is $(2, 4)$. The radius of the circle is given by

$$r^2 = g^2 + f^2 - c$$

$$\therefore \quad r^2 = 4 + 16 - 17$$

$$r = \sqrt{3}$$

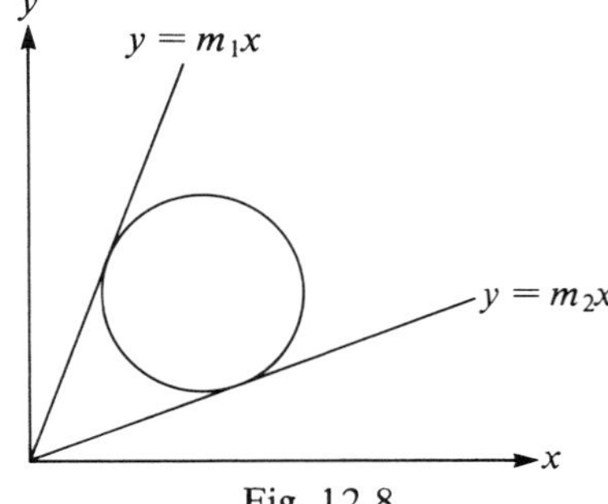

Fig. 12.8

The given circle (Fig. 12.8) has no points of intersection on either the x-axis or the y-axis, since $\sqrt{3} < 2$ and $\sqrt{3} < 4$. In order to find the values of m we substitute $y = mx$ in (1). This gives

$$x^2 + m^2x^2 - 4x - 8mx + 17 = 0$$
$$x^2(1 + m^2) - 4(1 + 2m)x + 17 = 0$$

For tangents $b^2 = 4ac$

$$\therefore \quad 16(1 + 2m)^2 = 4(1 + m^2) \times 17$$
$$4(1 + 4m + 4m^2) = 17(1 + m^2)$$
$$\therefore \quad m^2 - 16m + 13 = 0$$

Solving the quadratic $\quad m = \dfrac{16 \pm \sqrt{204}}{2}$

$$\therefore \quad m_1 = 8 + \sqrt{51}$$

and $\quad m_2 = 8 - \sqrt{51}$

To find the tangent of the angle between these two lines we use the result

$$\tan\theta = \frac{m_1 - m_2}{1 + m_1m_2}$$
$$\therefore \quad \tan\theta = \frac{2\sqrt{51}}{1 + (8 + \sqrt{51})(8 - \sqrt{51})}$$
$$= \frac{2\sqrt{51}}{1 + 64 - 51}$$
$$\therefore \quad \tan\theta = \frac{\sqrt{51}}{7} \quad \text{as required}$$

EXERCISE

1. The points A and B have coordinates $(18/5, 21/5)$ and $(2/5, 9/5)$ respectively. Show that the circle having AB as diameter has equation
$$x^2 + y^2 - 4x - 6y + 9 = 0$$
Sketch the circle.
Show also that the distance of the centre C of the circle from the line $3x + 2y - 4 = 0$ is greater than the radius of the circle. (WJEC 1981, part)

2. Find the centre and radius of the circle $x^2 + y^2 - 4x - 6y - 12 = 0$. Find the points of intersection of the line $y = 2x + 4$ and the given circle and prove that the length of the chord cut off is $4\sqrt{5}$.
Show that the circle which has the same centre as the given circle and which touches the given line passes through the point $(0, 2)$.
What is the equation of the tangent to this second circle at $(0, 2)$?
(SUJB 1981)

3. Find the centre and radius of each of the circles C_1 and C_2 whose equations are $x^2 + y^2 - 16y + 32 = 0$ and $x^2 + y^2 - 18x + 2y + 32 = 0$, respectively, and show that the circles touch externally. Find the coordinates of their point of contact and show that the common tangent at that point passes through the origin. The other tangents from the origin, one to each circle, are drawn. Find, correct to the nearest degree, the angle between these tangents. (SUJB 1980)

4. Prove that the circles with equations
$$x^2 + y^2 + 2g_1x + 2f_1y + c_1 = 0$$
$$x^2 + y^2 + 2g_2x + 2f_2y + c_2 = 0$$

cut orthogonally if

$$2g_1g_2 + 2f_1f_2 = c_1 + c_2$$

Prove that the circles with equations

$$x^2 + y^2 + 2x - 6y + 7 = 0$$
$$x^2 + y^2 - 4x - 8y + 13 = 0$$

cut orthogonally. Show that there are two circles of radius $\sqrt{6}$ that are orthogonal to both these circles; show that one of the required circles has equation

$$5(x^2 + y^2) - 8x - 6y - 25 = 0$$

and give the equation of the other. (WJEC 1982)

Worked Solutions

1. As the points A and B are at opposite ends of a diameter, we use result (12.15) with $(x_1, y_1) = (18/5, 21/5)$ and $(x_2, y_2) = (2/5, 9/5)$. Substituting gives

$$\left(x - \frac{18}{5}\right)\left(x - \frac{2}{5}\right) + \left(y - \frac{21}{5}\right)\left(y - \frac{9}{5}\right) = 0$$

Multiplying each bracket by 5 to remove the fractions gives

$$(5x - 18)(5x - 2) + (5y - 21)(5y - 9) = 0$$
$$25x^2 + 25y^2 - 100x - 150y + 225 = 0$$
$$\therefore \quad x^2 + y^2 - 4x - 6y + 9 = 0 \quad \text{as required}$$

where $g = -2$, $f = -3$ and $c = 9$.

Therefore centre of circle $(-g, -f)$ is $(2, 3)$. The radius is given by

$$r^2 = g^2 + f^2 - c$$
$$\therefore \quad r^2 = 4 + 9 - 9$$
$$= 4$$
$$\therefore \quad r = 2$$

The sketch of the circle is shown in Fig. 12.9.

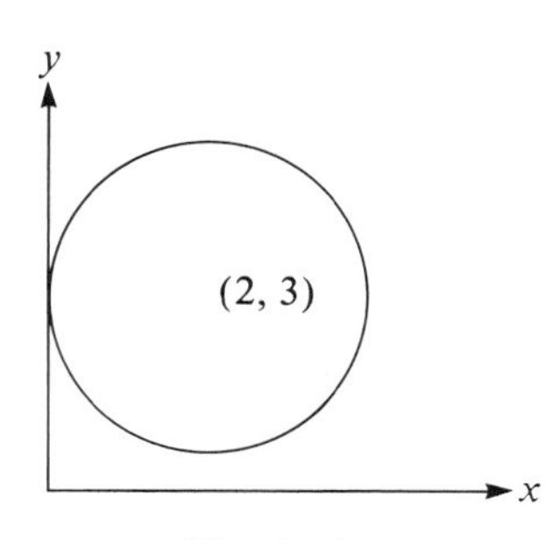

Fig. 12.9

The distance, d, of the centre of the circle, $(2, 3)$, from the straight line $3x + 2y - 4 = 0$ is given by

$$d = \frac{3 \times 2 + 2 \times 3 - 4}{\sqrt{3^2 + 2^2}}$$

$$d = \frac{8}{\sqrt{13}} \approx 2.22$$

hence $\quad d > r$

EXERCISE

2. The given circle is

$$x^2+y^2-4x-6y-12 = 0 \qquad (1)$$

We compare this with the standard form of the equation of the circle

$$x^2+y^2+2gx+2fy+c = 0 \qquad (2)$$

hence $2g=-4$, $2f=-6$ and $c=-12$

$$\therefore \quad g = -2, \quad f = -3 \qquad (3)$$

Therefore centre $(-g,-f)$ is $(2,3)$. The radius is given by

$$r^2 = g^2+f^2-c$$
$$\therefore \quad r^2 = 4+9+12$$
$$= 25$$
$$\therefore \quad r = 5$$

To find the points of intersection of $y=2x+4$ with the circle, we substitute the equation of the straight line into (1). This gives

$$x^2+(2x+4)^2-4x-6(2x+4)-12 = 0$$

which simplifies to

$$5x^2-20 = 0$$
$$x^2 = 4$$
$$\therefore \quad x = 2 \quad \text{or} \quad x = -2$$

When $x=2$, $y=8$ and when $x=-2$, $y=0$. The two points of intersection are $(2,8)$ and $(-2,0)$. The distance, d, between these two points is given by

$$d = \sqrt{(2+2)^2+(8-0)^2}$$
$$= \sqrt{80}$$
$$\therefore \quad d = 4\sqrt{5}$$

The distance from the centre of the circle to the tangent is equal to the radius of the circle. The equation of the tangent can be written in the form $2x-y+4=0$. The distance, d, of the point $(2,3)$ from this straight line is given by

$$d = \frac{2\times 2-3+4}{\sqrt{2^2+1^2}}$$

$$\therefore \quad d = \frac{5}{\sqrt{5}} = \sqrt{5} \qquad \text{(the distance } d \text{ is the radius of the circle)}$$

The radius of the circle is given by $r^2=g^2+f^2-c$

$$(\sqrt{5})^2 = g^2+f^2-c$$

The values of g and f are given by (3) because the centre of the second circle is the same as for the first circle.

$$\therefore \quad 5 = 2^2+(3)^2-c$$
$$c = 4+9-5$$

giving

$$c = 8$$

The equation of the required circle is

$$x^2+y^2-4x-6y+8 = 0 \qquad (4)$$

When $x=0$ in (4), we have

$$y^2-6y+8 = 0$$
$$(y-2)(y-4) = 0$$
$$\therefore \quad y = 2$$

Hence the circle given by (4) passes through $(0,2)$.

EXERCISE

The equation of the tangent at $x=0$, $y=2$ is found from (12.10). This gives

$$2y-2x-3(y+2)+8 = 0$$
$$\therefore \quad y = 2(1-x)$$

3. For circle C_1 $\qquad x^2+y^2-16y+32 = 0 \qquad (1)$

where $g=0$, $f=-8$, $c=32$.

Therefore centre $(-g,-f)$ is $(0,8)$. The radius is given by

$$r^2 = g^2+f^2-c$$
$$= 64-32$$
$$\therefore \quad r = 4\sqrt{2}$$

For circle C_2 $\qquad x^2+y^2-18x+2y+32 = 0 \qquad (2)$

where $g=-9$, $f=1$, $c=32$

Therefore centre $(-g,-f)$ is $(9,-1)$. The radius is given by

$$r^2 = 9^2+1^2-32$$
$$= 50$$
$$\therefore \quad r = 5\sqrt{2}$$

For the circles to touch externally we must have

Sum of radii = distance between centres

Since the sum of radii $= 4\sqrt{2}+5\sqrt{2} = 9\sqrt{2}$, which is the distance between the centres, the circles touch externally.

In order to find the point of contact of the two circles we solve equations (1) and (2) simultaneously.

(1)$-$(2) gives $\qquad 18x-18y = 0$

$$\therefore \quad x = y \qquad (3)$$

Substituting (3) in (1) gives

$$2x^2-16x+32 = 0$$
$$x^2-8x+16 = 0$$
$$(x-4)^2 = 0$$
$$\therefore \quad x = 4 \quad \text{and} \quad y = 4$$

The equation of the tangent through $x=4$, $y=4$ is given by (12.9). If we substitute the values of g, f and c for C_1 and put $x=4$, $y=4$ we have

$$4x+4y-8(y+4)+32 = 0$$
$$\therefore \quad y = x$$

which is a straight line through the origin as required.

The other tangents through the origin will have an equation of the form

$$y = mx \qquad (4)$$

Substituting in (1) gives

$$x^2(1+m^2)-16mx+32 = 0$$

For equal roots $b^2 = 4ac$

$$\therefore \quad 256m^2 = 4(1+m^2)\times 32$$
$$2m^2 = 1+m^2$$
$$m^2 = 1$$
$$\therefore \quad m = 1 \quad \text{or} \quad m = -1$$

Hence $y = -x$ is the equation of the other tangent to C_1 through the origin.

Substituting (4) in (2) gives

$$x^2(1+m^2)+x(2m-18)+32 = 0$$

For equal roots $b^2 = 4ac$

$$\therefore \quad (2m-18)^2 = 4(1+m^2)\times 32$$
$$31m^2+18m-49 = 0$$
$$(31m+49)(m-1) = 0$$
$$\therefore \quad m = \frac{-49}{31} \quad \text{or} \quad m = 1$$

Let θ denote the angle between the straight lines $y = -x$ and $y = -49x/31$.

We have
$$\tan\theta = \frac{-1+49/31}{1+49/31} = \frac{18}{80}$$
$$\therefore \quad \theta = 13^\circ$$

4.

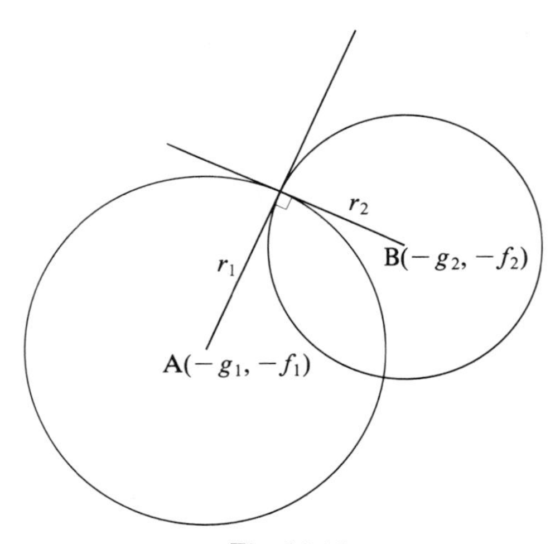

Fig. 12.10

For the circles to be orthogonal (Fig. 12.10) we require

$$r_1^2+r_2^2 = AB^2 \qquad (1)$$

But
$$r_1^2 = g_1^2+f_1^2-c_1$$
and
$$r_2^2 = g_2^2+f_2^2-c_2$$
Also
$$AB^2 = (-g_2+g_1)^2+(-f_2+f_1)^2$$

Substituting in (1) gives

$$g_1^2+f_1^2-c_1+g_2^2+f_2^2-c_2 = g_1^2-2g_1g_2+g_2^2+f_1^2-2f_1f_2+f_2^2$$

Simplifying
$$2g_1g_2+2f_1f_2 = c_1+c_2$$

For $x^2+y^2+2x-6y+7=0$

$$g_1 = 1, \quad f_1 = -3, \quad c_1 = 7 \qquad \text{Centre}\,(-1, 3) \qquad (2)$$

and for $x^2+y^2-4x-8y+13=0$

$$g_2 = -2, \quad f_2 = -4, \quad c_2 = 13 \qquad \text{Centre}\,(2, 4) \qquad (3)$$

EXERCISE

Substituting

$$2g_1g_2+2f_1f_2 = -4+24$$
$$= 20$$

Also $\qquad c_1+c_2 = 20$

hence

$$2g_1g_2+2f_1f_2 = c_1+c_2 \qquad \text{and the circles are orthogonal}$$

Let the required circles which are orthogonal to both (2) and (3) have centre $(-g, -f)$. For these circles $r=\sqrt{6}$, i.e.

$$r^2 = 6$$

$$\therefore \quad g^2+f^2-c = 6 \qquad (4)$$

The radius of the circle given by (2) is given by

$$r_1^2 = 1+9-7 = 3 \qquad (5)$$

The radius of the circle given by (3) is given by

$$r_2^2 = 4+16-13 = 7$$

For orthogonality to (2) we require

$$6+3 = (-g+1)^2+(-f-3)^2$$

i.e. $\qquad 9 = g^2-2g+1+f^2+6f+9$

$$\therefore \quad 0 = g^2+f^2-2g+6f+1 \qquad (6)$$

For orthogonality to (3) we require

$$6+7 = (-g-2)^2+(-f-4)^2$$

i.e. $\qquad 13 = g^2+4g+4+f^2+8f+16$

$$\therefore \quad 0 = g^2+4g+f^2+8f+7 \qquad (7)$$

(6)−(7) gives $\qquad 0 = -6g-2f-6$

$$\therefore \quad f = -(3+3g) \qquad (8)$$

Substituting (8) in (6) gives

$$0 = g^2+(3+3g)^2-2g+6(-3-3g)+1$$
$$5g^2-g-4 = 0$$
$$(5g+4)(g-1) = 0$$

$$\therefore \quad g = 1 \quad \text{or} \quad g = \frac{-4}{5} \qquad \text{(giving two circles)}$$

When $g = 1$, substituting in (8) gives

$$f = -6 \qquad (9)$$

When $g = \frac{-4}{5}$, substituting in (8) gives

$$f = \frac{-2}{3} \qquad (10)$$

Substituting the values of g and f given by (9) in (4) gives

$$1^2+(-6)^2-c = 6$$
$$\therefore \quad c = 31$$

Substituting the values of g and f given by (10) in (4) gives

$$\frac{16}{25}+\frac{9}{25}-c = 6$$
$$\therefore \quad c = -5$$

When $g = 1$, $f = -6$ and $c = 31$ the required circle has the equation

$$x^2 + y^2 + 2x - 12y + 31 = 0$$

Finally, when $g = -4/5$, $f = -3/5$ and $c = -5$ the required circle has the equation

$$5(x^2 + y^2) - 8x - 6y - 25 = 0$$

THE PARABOLA

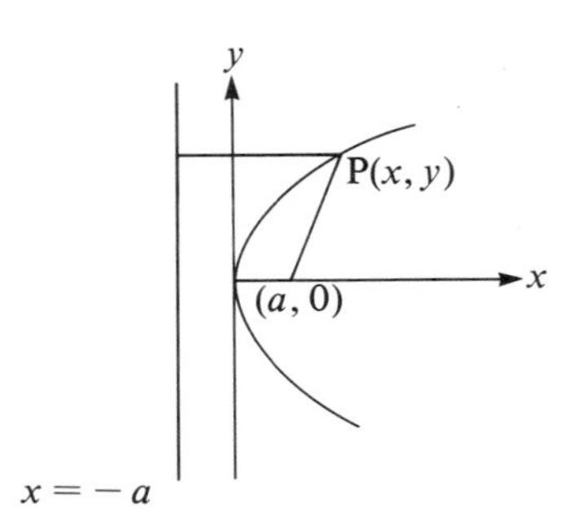

Fig. 12.11

The parabola (Fig. 12.11) may be defined as the locus of a point which moves such that its distance from a fixed point is equal to its distance from a fixed straight line. The fixed point is called the focus of the parabola and the fixed straight line is called the directrix of the parabola. In order to get the simplest possible form for the equation of the parabola we let the focus have coordinates $x = a$, $y = 0$ and we let the directrix have the equation $x = -a$. The resulting equation for the parabola is

$$\boxed{y^2 = 4ax} \qquad (12.16)$$

THE EQUATION OF THE TANGENT

The equation of the tangent through the point (x_1, y_1) on the curve is given by

$$y - y_1 = m(x - x_1) \qquad (12.17)$$

where $m = \mathrm{d}y/\mathrm{d}x$ at $x = x_1$, $y = y_1$.

Differentiating (12.16) implicitly gives

$$2y\frac{\mathrm{d}y}{\mathrm{d}x} = 4a$$

$$\therefore \quad \frac{\mathrm{d}y}{\mathrm{d}x} = \frac{2a}{y}$$

At $x = x_1$ and $y = y_1$, we have

$$\frac{\mathrm{d}y}{\mathrm{d}x} = \frac{2a}{y_1}$$

Substituting in (12.17) gives

$$y - y_1 = \frac{2a}{y_1}(x - x_1)$$

$$yy_1 - y_1^2 = 2ax - 2ax_1$$

EXERCISE/THE PARABOLA/THE EQUATION OF THE TANGENT

but $y_1^2 = 4ax_1$ since the point (x_1, y_1) is on the curve. Hence

$$yy_1 - 4ax_1 = 2ax - 2ax_1$$

$$\therefore \quad \boxed{yy_1 = 2a(x + x_1)} \tag{12.18}$$

PARAMETRIC COORDINATES

Parametric coordinates enable us to specify any point on the parabola by a single parameter which is usually denoted by t. The equation $y^2 = 4ax$ is satisfied when $x = at^2$ and $y = 2at$. Consequently, the equations

$$x = at^2 \tag{12.19}$$

$$y = 2at \tag{12.20}$$

provide a parametric representation of the parabola. Each point on the parabola is specified by a single value of t.

THE EQUATION OF THE TANGENT AND NORMAL IN PARAMETRIC COORDINATES

In order to establish the equations of the tangent and the normal to the parabola when the coordinates are defined parametrically, we need to find dy/dx from the parametric equations (12.19) and (12.20) using the result that

$$\frac{dy}{dx} = \frac{dy/dt}{dx/dt} \tag{12.21}$$

If $x = at^2$ $\qquad \dfrac{dx}{dt} = 2at$

If $y = 2at$ $\qquad \dfrac{dy}{dt} = 2a$

Substituting these results into (12.21) gives

$$\frac{dy}{dx} = \frac{1}{t}$$

The equation of the tangent is found from

$$y - y_1 = m(x - x_1) \tag{12.22}$$

by putting $x_1 = at^2$, $y_1 = 2at$ and $m = 1/t$

$$y - 2at = \frac{1}{t}(x - at^2)$$

$$\therefore \quad \boxed{y = \frac{x}{t} + at} \tag{12.23}$$

The normal is perpendicular to the tangent. If m_1 denotes the gradient of the tangent and m_2 the gradient of the normal, we require $m_1 m_2 = -1$ for perpendicularity.

Since $m_1 = 1/t$, this gives $m_2 = -t$. We can now find the equation of the normal by substituting into (12.22) with $m = m_2$, $x_1 = at^2$ and $y_1 = 2at$.

This gives
$$y - 2at = -t(x - at^2)$$
$$= -xt + at^3$$
$$\therefore \quad \boxed{y + xt = 2at + at^3} \qquad (12.24)$$

Worked Example

P is the point $(ap^2, 2ap)$ on the parabola $y^2 = 4ax$. QSR is the chord that passes through the focus S of the parabola and is parallel to the tangent at P.

If Q has coordinates $(aq^2, 2aq)$, show, by considering the gradient of the line QS, or otherwise, that $q^2 - 2pq - 1 = 0$ and hence that $q = p \pm \sqrt{p^2 + 1}$.

If W is the midpoint of QR, prove that PW is parallel to the axis of the parabola and that the length of PW is $a(1 + p^2)$. (SUJB 1981)

Solution

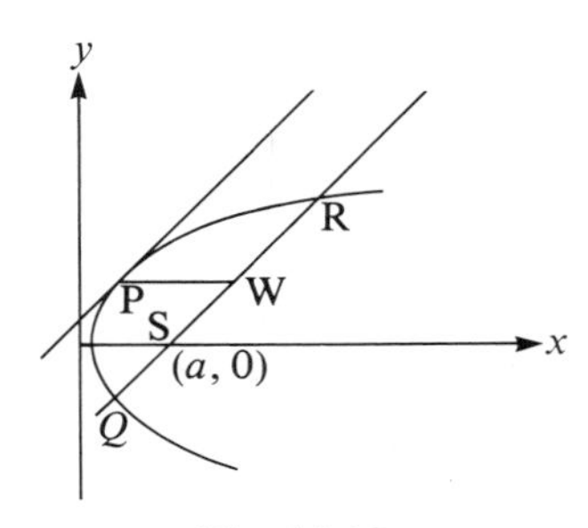

Fig. 12.12

The chord QR (Fig. 12.12) will have an equation of the form
$$y = mx + c \qquad (1)$$
This particular chord passes through the focus of the parabola. Putting $x = a,\ y = 0$ gives
$$0 = ma + c$$
hence
$$y = m(x - a) \qquad (2)$$
The gradient of the tangent through the point $P(ap^2, 2ap)$ is $1/p$. For the chord given by (2) to be parallel to the tangent at P we must have $m = 1/p$. Substituting in (2) gives
$$y = \frac{1}{p}(x - a) \qquad (3)$$
The straight line (3) must also pass through the point $Q(aq^2, 2aq)$. Putting $x = aq^2,\ y = 2aq$ in (3) gives
$$2aq = \frac{1}{p}(aq^2 - a)$$
Simplifying gives
$$q^2 - 2pq - 1 = 0$$
Solving the quadratic gives
$$q = p \pm \sqrt{p^2 + 1}$$
The point Q will have parameter $q_1 = p - \sqrt{p^2 + 1}$ and the point R will have parameter $q_2 = p + \sqrt{p^2 + 1}$.

TANGENT AND NORMAL IN PARAMETRIC COORDINATES

The y-coordinate of W is $\frac{1}{2}(2aq_1 + 2aq_2)$

$$= a(q_1 + q_2)$$
$$= 2ap$$
$$= \text{the } y\text{-coordinate of P}$$

hence PW is parallel to the x-axis.

The length of PW $= \frac{1}{2}a(q_1^2 + q_2^2) - ap^2$

$$= \tfrac{1}{2}a[(p^2 - 2p\sqrt{p^2+1} + p^2 + 1) + (p^2 + 2p\sqrt{p^2+1} + p^2 + 1)] - ap^2$$
$$= \tfrac{1}{2}a(4p^2 + 2) - ap^2$$
$$= 2ap^2 + a - ap^2$$
$$\text{PW} = a(1 + p^2)$$

EXERCISE

1. Show that, if $t + u = -p$ and $tu = 2$, then the normals at the two distinct points $T(at^2, 2at)$, $U(au^2, 2au)$ on the parabola $y^2 = 4ax$ intersect at a third point $P(ap^2, 2ap)$ on the curve. Deduce that the chord TU meets the axis of the parabola at a fixed point. (NI 1981)

2. Show that the equation of the chord of the parabola $y^2 = 4x$ joining the points $P(p^2, 2p)$ and $Q(q^2, 2q)$ is $(p+q)y - 2x = 2pq$ and find the condition that this chord should pass through the point $A(3, 0)$. If, in addition, the line PO meets the line $x = -3$ at the point L, show that LQ is parallel to OA, O being the origin. If PQ is also normal to the parabola at P show that $p^2 + pq + 2 = 0$ and hence find the possible values of p and the length PQ. (SUJB 1980)

3. Show that the gradient of the line joining the points $P(ap^2, 2ap)$ and $Q(aq^2, 2aq)$ on the parabola $y^2 = 4ax$ is $2/(p+q)$ and write down the equation of the chord PQ. Find the relation between p and q if PQ passes through the point $(2a, 0)$. With this restriction find the equation of the locus of R, the intersection of the tangents at P and Q. Show that the tangent of the angle PRQ can be expressed as $(2 + p^2)/p$. (SUJB 1978)

4. The normal to the parabola $y^2 = 4ax$ at the point $P(at^2, 2at)$ cuts the x-axis at the point G. The midpoint of PG is M, and O is the origin.
   (i) Prove that the equation of the normal is $y + tx = 2at + at^3$.
   (ii) Prove that M is the point $(at^2 + a, at)$.
   (iii) Find the cartesian equation of the locus of the point M as t varies. (AEB 1982)

Worked Solutions

1. The equation of the normal at $T(at^2, 2at)$ is

$$y + tx = 2at + at^3 \quad (1)$$

The equation of the normal at $U(au^2, 2au)$ is

$$y + ux = 2au + au^3 \quad (2)$$

$(1) - (2)$ gives

$$(t-u)x = 2a(t-u) + a(t^3 - u^3)$$
$$= 2a(t-u) + a(t-u)(t^2 + ut + u^2)$$
$$\therefore \quad x = 2a + a(t^2 + ut + u^2)$$
$$= 4a + a(t^2 + u^2) \qquad (\text{since } tu = 2) \quad (3)$$

If $t+u = -p$

$$t^2+2ut+u^2 = p^2$$
$$t^2+u^2 = p^2-2ut$$
$$= p^2-4 \qquad \text{(since } ut = 2) \qquad (4)$$

Substituting (4) in (3) gives

$$x = ap^2$$

Dividing (1) by t gives

$$\frac{y}{t}+x = 2a+at^2 \qquad (5)$$

Dividing (2) by u gives

$$\frac{y}{u}+x = 2a+au^2 \qquad (6)$$

(5)−(6) gives

$$y\left(\frac{1}{t}-\frac{1}{u}\right) = a(t^2-u^2)$$
$$y\frac{(u-t)}{ut} = a(t-u)(t+u)$$
$$y = -aut(t+u)$$
$$\therefore \quad y = 2ap \qquad \text{(since } t+u = -p,\ tu = 2)$$

hence the normals intersect at a point on the parabola.

The equation of the chord TU is given by

$$\frac{y-2at}{2a(u-t)} = \frac{x-at^2}{a(u^2-t^2)}$$
$$y-2at = \frac{2(x-at^2)}{u+t}$$

Putting $y = 0$ gives

$$-2at = \frac{2(x-at^2)}{u+t}$$
$$2x-2at^2 = -2atu-2at^2$$
$$x = -atu$$
$$\therefore \quad x = -2a \qquad \text{(since } tu = 2)$$

hence the chord TU meets the axis of the parabola at a fixed point.

2. The equation of the chord PQ is given by

$$\frac{y-2p}{2(q-p)} = \frac{x-p^2}{q^2-p^2}$$
$$y-2p = \frac{2(x-p^2)}{(q+p)}$$
$$(q+p)(y-2p) = 2(x-p^2)$$
$$(q+p)y-2p^2-2pq = 2x-2p^2$$
$$\therefore \quad (q+p)y-2x = 2pq$$

Putting $x = 3,\ y = 0$

$$-6 = 2pq$$
$$\therefore \quad pq = -3 \qquad (1)$$

EXERCISE

which is the condition for the chord PQ to pass through A.

The gradient of the line PO is $\frac{2p}{p^2} = \frac{2}{p}$

The equation of PO is given by $\quad y = \frac{2}{p}x$

Therefore when $x = -3 \quad y = \frac{-6}{p} \quad (2)$

The line LQ will be parallel to the x-axis and hence to OA if the y-coordinates at L and Q are the same.

The y-coordinate at Q is $2q$

$$= \frac{-6}{p} \quad [\text{since } q = -3/p \text{ from } (1)] \quad (3)$$

(2) and (3) are the same, hence LQ is parallel to OA.

The equation of the normal at P is

$$y + px = 2ap + ap^3 \quad (4)$$

The equation of the chord PQ may be written as

$$y - \frac{2x}{p+q} = \frac{2pq}{p+q} \quad (5)$$

Comparing coefficients of x in (4) and (5) gives

$$p = \frac{-2}{p+q}$$

$$\therefore \quad p^2 + pq + 2 = 0 \quad (6)$$

From (1) we have $\quad q = \frac{-3}{p}$

Substituting in (6) gives

$$p^2 - 3 + 2 = 0$$

$$p^2 = 1$$

$$\therefore \quad p = 1 \quad \text{or} \quad p = -1$$

From (1) when $p = 1, \quad q = -3 \quad (7)$

when $p = -1, \quad q = 3 \quad (8)$

Now $\quad PQ^2 = (p^2 - q^2)^2 + 4(p-q)^2$

It is seen from this expression for the length PQ that it will have the same value for either the solution (7) or (8). Hence

$$PQ^2 = 128$$

$$\therefore \quad PQ = 8\sqrt{2}$$

3. The gradient of PQ is $\frac{2a(p-q)}{a(p^2-q^2)}$

$$= \frac{2}{p+q} \quad (1)$$

The equation of the chord PQ is given by

$$y - 2ap = \frac{2}{p+q}(x - ap^2)$$

EXERCISE

When $x = 2a$ and $y = 0$, we have

$$-2ap = \frac{2}{p+q}(2a-ap^2)$$

$$\therefore \quad pq = -2 \tag{2}$$

The equation of the tangent at P is

$$y = \frac{x}{p}+ap \tag{3}$$

The equation of the tangent at Q is

$$y = \frac{x}{q}+aq \tag{4}$$

Solving (3) and (4) simultaneously for the points of intersection

$$x\left(\frac{1}{p}-\frac{1}{q}\right) = a(q-p)$$

$$x\frac{(q-p)}{pq} = a(q-p)$$

$$\therefore \quad x = apq \tag{5}$$

Substituting (2) in (5) gives

$$x = -2a \tag{6}$$

Substituting (5) in (3) gives

$$y = a(p+q)$$

$$\therefore \quad y = a\left(p-\frac{2}{p}\right) \tag{7}$$

Since the y-coordinate varies while the x-coordinate remains fixed, the locus is the straight line $x = 2a$.

Let m_1 denote the gradient of PR, which is given by

$$m_1 = \frac{-ap-2a/p}{-2a-ap^2}$$

$$\therefore \quad m_1 = \frac{p^2+2}{p^3+2p}$$

giving $$m_1 = \frac{1}{p}$$

If m_2 denotes the gradient of RQ it is given by

$$m_2 = \frac{ap-(2a/p)-2aq}{-2a-aq^2}$$

$$\therefore \quad m_2 = \frac{(2/p)+p}{-2-(4/p^2)} \qquad \left(\text{since } q = \frac{-2}{p}\right)$$

giving $$m_2 = \frac{-p}{2}$$

The angle θ, where θ = angle PRQ, is given by

$$\tan\theta = \frac{m_1-m_2}{1+m_1m_2}$$

EXERCISE

$$\therefore \quad \tan\theta = \frac{(1/p)+(p/2)}{1+(1/p)(-p/2)}$$

which gives

$$\tan\theta = \frac{p^2+2}{p}$$

4. (i) If $x = at^2$ $\qquad \dfrac{dx}{dt} = 2at$

If $y = 2at$ $\qquad \dfrac{dy}{dt} = 2a$

$$\therefore \quad \frac{dy}{dx} = \frac{2a}{2at} = \frac{1}{t}$$

The gradient of the normal, m, is therefore given by

$$m = -t$$

The equation of the normal is

$$y-2at = -t(x-at^2)$$

which can be rearranged as

$$y+tx = 2at+at^3$$

(ii) When $y = 0$, we have $tx = 2at+at^3$

$$\therefore \quad x = 2a+at^2$$

M, the midpoint of PG is given by

$$[\tfrac{1}{2}(at^2+2a+at^2), \tfrac{1}{2}(2at)]$$

$$\therefore \quad \text{M is } (a+at^2, at)$$

$$\therefore \quad x = a(1+t^2) \qquad (1)$$

and

$$y = at \qquad (2)$$

(iii) To find the locus of M we need to eliminate t between equations (1) and (2). From equation (2) we have

$$t = \frac{y}{a} \qquad (3)$$

Substituting (3) in (1) gives

$$x = a\left(1+\frac{y^2}{a^2}\right)$$

$$\therefore \quad y^2 = a(x-a)$$

which is the equation of the locus of M. This represents a parabola with its vertex at the point $x = a$, $y = 0$.

EXERCISE

13 THREE-DIMENSIONAL GEOMETRY

RIGHT-HANDED SYSTEMS OF AXES

In two-dimensional coordinate geometry, a point is specified by two coordinates that are measured relative to the x- and y-axes which, for convenience, are taken to be perpendicular. The extra dimension of space requires an additional coordinate. A point is specified by reference to three mutually perpendicular axes which are usually labelled the x-, y- and z-axes.

The x-, y- and z-axes are assigned in an order that defines a right-handed system. Such a set of axes requires that a screw that is pointing in the direction of the positive z-axis, when rotated from x towards y, will advance in the positive direction along the z-axis. Similarly, a screw that is pointing in the direction of the positive x-axis, when rotated from y towards z, will advance in the positive direction along the x-axis.

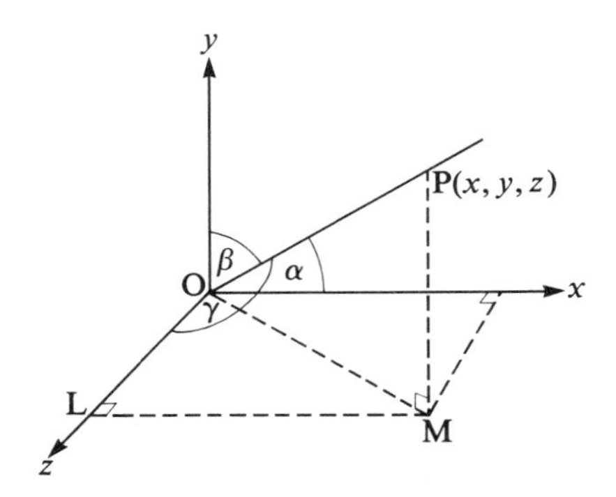

Fig. 13.1

THE DISTANCE OF A POINT FROM THE ORIGIN

In the right-angled triangle OMP (see Fig. 13.1), we have

$$OP^2 = OM^2 + MP^2 \qquad (13.1)$$

In the right-angled triangle OML we have

$$OM^2 = OL^2 + LM^2 \qquad (13.2)$$

Substituting (13.2) into (13.1) gives

$$OP^2 = OL^2 + LM^2 + MP^2$$

However, since $OL = z$, $MP = y$, $LM = x$ and $OP = d$, this gives

$$d^2 = x^2 + y^2 + z^2$$

$$\therefore \quad \boxed{d = \sqrt{x^2 + y^2 + z^2}} \qquad (13.3)$$

DIRECTION RATIOS AND COSINES

The straight line OP makes angles α, β and γ with the three coordinate axes. From the definition of the cosine ratio we have

$$\cos\alpha = \frac{x}{d} \tag{13.4}$$

$$\cos\beta = \frac{y}{d} \tag{13.5}$$

$$\cos\gamma = \frac{z}{d} \tag{13.6}$$

$$\therefore \quad \cos^2\alpha + \cos^2\beta + \cos^2\gamma = \frac{x^2+y^2+z^2}{d^2}$$

$$\therefore \quad \boxed{\cos^2\alpha + \cos^2\beta + \cos^2\gamma = 1} \qquad (\text{since } d^2 = x^2+y^2+z^2) \tag{13.7}$$

The quantities (13.4), (13.5) and (13.6) are called direction cosines (DCs). From the DCs we note that

$$\cos\alpha : \cos\beta : \cos\gamma = x : y : z \tag{13.8}$$

The quantities on the RHS of (13.8) are called direction ratios (DRs). The connection between the DRs and the DCs may be summarised as follows

$$\text{DRs} = (a, b, c)$$

$$\text{DCs} = \left(\frac{a}{d}, \frac{b}{d}, \frac{c}{d}\right) \tag{13.9}$$

where

$$d = \sqrt{a^2+b^2+c^2}$$

THE EQUATION OF A STRAIGHT LINE

(1) Through a point in a given direction

The direction of any straight line in space is determined by its direction ratios. Suppose the DRs of a line are (a, b, c) and it passes through the point (x_1, y_1, z_1). The equation of this straight line is given by

$$\boxed{\frac{x-x_1}{a} = \frac{y-y_1}{b} = \frac{z-z_1}{c} = \lambda} \tag{13.10}$$

where λ enables us to define the straight line parametrically.

(2) Joining two given points

The equation of a straight line joining the points (x_1, y_1, z_1) and (x_2, y_2, z_2) is given by

$$\boxed{\frac{x-x_1}{x_2-x_1} = \frac{y-y_1}{y_2-y_1} = \frac{z-z_1}{z_2-z_1} = \lambda} \tag{13.11}$$

where λ enables us to define the straight line parametrically.

The DRs of this straight line are given by $(x_2-x_1, y_2-y_1, z_2-z_1)$.

THE ZERO DIRECTION RATIO

A straight line parallel to the x-axis and hence perpendicular to both the y- and z-axes will have $\alpha = 0$, $\beta = 90°$ and $\gamma = 90°$. The direction cosines of such a line are $\cos\alpha = 1$, $\cos\beta = 0$ and $\cos\gamma = 0$, hence the direction ratios are $(1, 0, 0)$. Similarly, a straight line parallel to the y-axis will have $\alpha = 90^\circ$, $\beta = 0^\circ$ and $\gamma = 90^\circ$ with direction ratios $(0, 1, 0)$. These examples show that a zero direction ratio indicates that the straight line is perpendicular to the axis of the component to which it refers.

Example

Consider the point $(2, 4, 3)$. The equation of the straight line through this point with DRs $(1, 1, 1)$ is given by

$$\frac{x-2}{1} = \frac{y-4}{1} = \frac{z-3}{1} = \lambda$$

However, the equation of the straight line through this point with DRs $(1, 0, 0)$ is

$$\frac{x-2}{1} = \frac{y-4}{0} = \frac{z-3}{0} = \lambda$$

Since this straight line is parallel to the x-axis, both the y and z values remain unchanged while x varies. Because division by zero is undefined, the equation of such a straight line is usually written as

$$y = 4, \quad z = 3 \quad \text{and} \quad \frac{x-2}{1} = \lambda$$

PARALLEL, NON-PARALLEL AND SKEW LINES

Parallel straight lines have identical direction ratios. Non-parallel straight lines have different direction ratios and may or may not intersect. Non-parallel straight lines that do not intersect are called skew lines.

THE ANGLE BETWEEN STRAIGHT LINES

The angle, θ, between two straight lines is defined as the angle between their directions. This definition enables us to calculate the angle between skew lines. Let L_1 denote the first straight line with DCs (l_1, m_1, n_1) and L_2 the second straight line with DCs (l_2, m_2, n_2). The angle θ between them is given by

$$\boxed{\cos\theta = l_1 l_2 + m_1 m_2 + n_1 n_2} \qquad (13.12)$$

From this result we can easily deduce the condition for perpendicularity. This requires $\cos\theta = 0$. Hence the condition is

$$\boxed{l_1 l_2 + m_1 m_2 + n_1 n_2 = 0 \quad \text{for perpendicularity}} \qquad (13.13)$$

THE DISTANCE BETWEEN TWO POINTS

The distance between the two points $P_1(x_1, y_1, z_1)$ and $P_2(x_2, y_2, z_2)$ is the extension to three coordinates of the corresponding two-dimensional result. If d denotes the distance between P_1 and P_2 we have

$$d = \sqrt{(x_2 - x_1)^2 + (y_2 - y_1)^2 + (z_2 - z_1)^2} \qquad (13.14)$$

THE DISTANCE OF A POINT FROM A STRAIGHT LINE

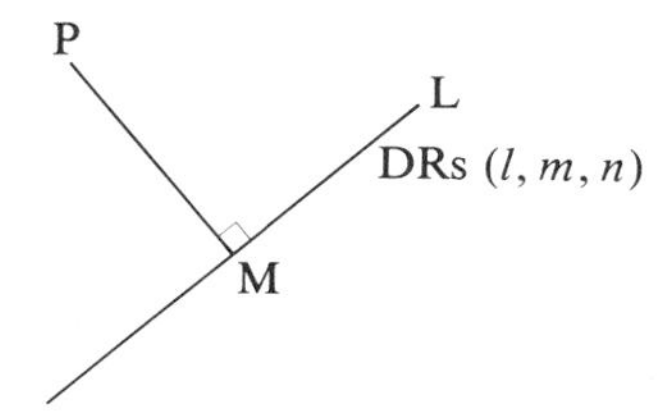

Fig. 13.2

Since M is any point on the line L we can express the coordinates of M parametrically. From the parametric coordinates of M we can find the direction ratios of PM. However, since PM is perpendicular to L, we can use the condition for perpendicularity (13.13) which enables us to obtain the value of the parameter at M. The value of the parameter at M establishes the coordinates of M. The distance PM can then be found from (13.14).

Example

Find the distance from the point P(3, 1, 4) to the straight line L:

$$\frac{x-1}{3} = \frac{y}{-1} = \frac{z+2}{1} = \lambda$$

Any point on this straight line is given by the parametric equations

$$x = 3\lambda + 1 \quad (1)$$
$$y = -\lambda \quad (2)$$
$$z = \lambda - 2 \quad (3)$$

In particular, the point that is at the foot of the perpendicular from P to the straight line L, will be given by equations (1), (2) and (3). If we denote this point by M, the DRs of the straight line PM are $(3\lambda-2, -\lambda-1, \lambda-6)$.

Since PM is perpendicular to L, the condition (13.13) requires

$$3(3\lambda-2)-(-\lambda-1)+(\lambda-6) = 0$$
$$11\lambda-11 = 0$$
$$\therefore \quad \lambda = 1$$

Substituting this value of λ into equations (1), (2) and (3) gives the coordinates of M as $(4, -1, -1)$. The distance, d, between P and M is calculated from (13.14). This gives

$$d^2 = (-1)^2 + 2^2 + 5^2$$
$$\therefore \quad d = \sqrt{30}$$

THE EQUATION OF A PLANE

The general equation of a plane is

$$ax + by + cz = d$$
where the DRs of the normal to the plane are (a, b, c) (13.15)

If the direction ratios are replaced by the direction cosines by dividing throughout by $\sqrt{(a^2+b^2+c^2)}$ the RHS of the resulting equation represents the perpendicular distance, p, from the origin to the plane.

$$lx + my + nz = p$$

where the DCs of the normal to the plane are (l, m, n) and p is the perpendicular distance of the plane from the origin (13.16)

THE DISTANCE OF A POINT FROM A PLANE

Suppose the equation of the plane, π, can be written in the form

$$ax + by + cz + d = 0$$

The distance of the point $P(x_1, y_1, z_1)$ from this plane is found by putting $x = y_1$, $y = y_1$ and $z = z_1$ in the expression $ax + by + cz + d$. If this is divided by $\sqrt{(a^2 + b^2 + c^2)}$, the result is the distance, D, of the point from the plane.

$$D = \frac{ax_1 + by_1 + cz_1 + d}{\sqrt{a^2 + b^2 + c^2}}$$

P has coordinates (x_1, y_1, z_1)

π is $ax + by + cz + d = 0$

D = distance of P from π (13.17)

THE ANGLE BETWEEN TWO PLANES

The angle between any two planes is equal to the angle between the normals to the planes

Let the plane π_1 be given by

$$a_1x + b_1y + c_1z = d_1 \qquad (13.18)$$

and the plane π_2 by

$$a_2x + b_2y + c_2z = d_2 \qquad (13.19)$$

If $r_1 = \sqrt{(a_1^2 + b_1^2 + c_1^2)}$ and $r_2 = \sqrt{(a_2^2 + b_2^2 + c_2^2)}$

we have DCs of π_1, which are (l_1, m_1, n_1) where $l_1 = \frac{a_1}{r_1}$, $m_1 = \frac{b_1}{r_1}$ and $n_1 = \frac{c_1}{r_1}$.

DCs of π_2 are (l_2, m_2, n_2) where $l_2 = \frac{a_2}{r_2}$, $m_2 = \frac{b_2}{r_2}$ and $n_2 = \frac{c_2}{r_2}$.

The angle θ between the planes π_1 and π_2 is given by

$$\cos\theta = l_1l_2 + m_1m_2 + n_1n_2 \qquad (13.20)$$

Worked Example

The line p is given by $\frac{x-6}{5} = \frac{y-4}{2} = \frac{z-4}{1}$

The line q is given by $\frac{x-4}{3} = \frac{y-3}{1} = \frac{z-5}{2}$

(i) Show that these lines intersect and find the coordinates of the point of intersection.

(ii) Find the cosine of the acute angle between the lines p and q.

(iii) Find the cartesian equation of the plane π which contains the lines p and q and show that the distance of π from the origin is $14/\sqrt{59}$.

THE EQUATION OF A PLANE/THE DISTANCE OF A POINT FROM A PLANE/THE ANGLE BETWEEN TWO PLANES

(iv) Find cartesian equations for the line which is perpendicular to the plane π and passes through the point T(0, 10, 3). Find also the point V where this line meets the plane π. (AEB 1982)

Solution

Introducing the parameter λ for the line p we have

$$\frac{x-6}{5} = \frac{y-4}{2} = \frac{z-4}{1} = \lambda$$

$$x = 5\lambda+6 \quad (1)$$

$$y = 2\lambda+4 \quad (2)$$

$$z = \lambda+4 \quad (3)$$

Using the parameter μ for the line q gives

$$\frac{x-4}{3} = \frac{y-3}{1} = \frac{z-5}{2} = \mu$$

$$x = 3\mu+4 \quad (4)$$

$$y = \mu+3 \quad (5)$$

$$z = 2\mu+5 \quad (6)$$

At the point of intersection the x-coordinates will be identical. Equating (1) and (4) gives

$$5\lambda+6 = 3\mu+4$$

$$\therefore \quad 5\lambda-3\mu = -2 \quad (7)$$

Equating (2) and (5) because the y-coordinates must be identical at the point of intersection, gives

$$2\lambda+4 = \mu+3$$

$$\therefore \quad 2\lambda-\mu = -1 \quad (8)$$

Solving (7) and (8) simultaneously

(8) × 3 $\quad 6\lambda-3\mu = -3 \quad (9)$

(7) − (9) $\quad -\lambda = 1$

$$\therefore \quad \lambda = -1 \quad (10)$$

Substituting (10) in (8) gives

$$-2-\mu = -1$$

$$-\mu = 1$$

$$\therefore \quad \mu = -1 \quad (11)$$

We must now check that the z-coordinates given by (3) and (6) are equal.

Substituting (10) in (3) gives $z = 3$.

Substituting (11) in (6) gives $z = 3$.

This establishes that p and q intersect. The x-coordinate at the point of intersection is given by (1) with $\lambda = -1$, which gives $x = 1$. The y-coordinate is found from (2) on putting $\lambda = -1$, which gives $y = 2$.

Consequently, the point of intersection is (1, 2, 3).

(ii) DCs of p are

$$\left(\frac{5}{\sqrt{5^2+2^2+1^2}}, \frac{2}{\sqrt{5^2+2^2+1^2}}, \frac{1}{\sqrt{5^2+2^2+1^2}}\right)$$

$$= \left(\frac{5}{\sqrt{30}}, \frac{2}{\sqrt{30}}, \frac{1}{\sqrt{30}}\right)$$

DCs of q are

$$\left(\frac{3}{\sqrt{3^2+1^2+2^2}}, \frac{1}{\sqrt{3^2+1^2+2^2}}, \frac{2}{\sqrt{3^2+1^2+2^2}}\right)$$

$$= \left(\frac{3}{\sqrt{14}}, \frac{1}{\sqrt{14}}, \frac{2}{\sqrt{14}}\right)$$

The angle, θ, between the lines p and q is given by (13.12) as

$$\cos\theta = \frac{1}{\sqrt{14}\sqrt{30}}(15+2+2) = \frac{19}{\sqrt{420}}$$

(iii) Let (a, b, c) denote the DRs of the normal to the plane π. The normal to π will be perpendicular to p. Using the condition for perpendicularity (13.13) gives

$$5a+2b+c = 0 \tag{12}$$

The normal to π will also be perpendicular to q, which gives

$$3a+b+2c = 0 \tag{13}$$

Solving (12) and (13) simultaneously

(13) × 2 $\quad 6a+2b+4c = 0 \quad$ (14)

(14) − (12) $\quad a+3c = 0$

$$\therefore \quad a = -3c \tag{15}$$

Substituting (15) in (12)

$$-15c+2b+c = 0$$

$$\therefore \quad b = 7c$$

Hence the DRs of the normal to the plane π are $-3c:7c:c = -3:7:1$

The equation of the plane must be of the form

$$-3x+7x+z = D \tag{16}$$

This plane must contain the point (1, 2, 3). Putting $x = 1$, $y = 2$ and $z = 3$ in (16) gives

$$-3+14+3 = D$$

$$\therefore \quad D = 14$$

Hence the equation of π is

$$-3x+7y+z = 14 \tag{17}$$

The DRs may be replaced by the DCs by dividing throughout by $\sqrt{(-3)^2+7^2+1^2}$ to give

$$\frac{-3x}{\sqrt{59}}+\frac{7y}{\sqrt{59}}+\frac{z}{\sqrt{59}} = \frac{14}{\sqrt{59}}$$

which gives the distance from the origin as $14/\sqrt{59}$.

(iv) A line perpendicular to the plane is a normal to the plane. The DRs of the normal to π are $(-3, 7, 1)$. The line with these DRs passing through T(0, 10, 3) is

$$\frac{x}{-3} = \frac{y-10}{7} = \frac{z-3}{1} = \lambda$$

$$\Rightarrow \quad x = -3\lambda \tag{18}$$

$$y = 7\lambda+10 \tag{19}$$

$$z = \lambda+3 \tag{20}$$

THE ANGLE BETWEEN TWO PLANES

To find V we substitute equations (18), (19) and (20) into (17). This gives

$$9\lambda + 7(7\lambda + 10) + (\lambda + 3) = 14$$
$$59\lambda = -59$$
$$\therefore \quad \lambda = -1 \qquad (21)$$

Substituting (21) in (18), (19) and (20) gives the coordinates of V as (3, 3, 2).

EXERCISE

1. Calculate the coordinates of the foot of the perpendicular from the point P(1, 2, 2) to the plane π with equation $2x - 2y + z = 9$. Find also the coordinates of the point P$'$ which is the mirror image of P in π. Calculate the distance of the point Q(1, 2, 5) from the line PP$'$. (O 1981)

2. The coordinates of the vertices of a tetrahedron are O(0, 0, 0), A(5, 0, 0), B(0, 10, 0) and C(0, 0, 2). Find

(i) the equation of the plane ABC and show that the point D(10, 10, −4) lies in this plane;

(ii) equations of the line through O that is perpendicular to the plane ABC;

(iii) the coordinates of the point M, the foot of the perpendicular from O to the plane ABC.

Show that the point $R(5 - 5t, 10t, 0)$ lies on AB for all values of t and hence find the coordinates of the point L which is on AB and is such that CL is perpendicular to AB. Show that the angle between the planes OAB and ABC is $\cos^{-1}\sqrt{5/6}$. (AEB 1980)

3. The lines L_1 and L_2 have the following equations

$$L_1: \quad \frac{x+1}{2} = \frac{y-2}{-1} = \frac{z-2}{1}$$

$$L_2: \quad \frac{x+5}{1} = \frac{y+1}{-3} = \frac{z-7}{4}$$

Show that the lines intersect and find the coordinates of the point of intersection. Find also

(i) the angle between the lines L_1 and L_2.

(ii) the equation of the plane containing the line L_1 and the origin.

(iii) the perpendicular distance from the point (1, 2, 3) to the line L_1. (AEB 1980)

4. The coordinates of the points A, B and C are as follows:

A(3, 0, 0), B(0, 4, 0), C(0, 0, 5)

(i) Find equations for (a) the line BC, (b) the plane ABC.

(ii) Show that the angle ABC is approximately 60°.

(iii) Find the volume of the tetrahedron ABCD, where D is the point (7, 8, 9). (AEB 1981)

5. The equations of the lines m and n are

$$\frac{x-2}{3} = \frac{y-3}{4} = \frac{z-4}{2}$$

and $$\frac{x-1}{2} = \frac{y-1}{3} = \frac{z+2}{4} \quad \text{respectively.}$$

(i) Prove that m and n intersect and find the coordinate of P, their point of intersection.

(ii) Determine the cosine of the acute angle at which m and n intersect.

(iii) Find in cartesian form the equation of the plane passing through the origin O which contains the line m.

(iv) Find the cosines of the acute angles between OP and m, and between OP and n. Deduce that O is equidistant from m and n. (AEB 1982)

Worked Solutions

1. π

$$2x-2y+z = 9 \quad (1)$$

DRs of the normal to π are $(2,-2,1)$.

The equation of the perpendicular to the plane through P(1, 2, 2) is

$$\frac{x-1}{2} = \frac{y-2}{-2} = \frac{z-2}{1} = t \quad (2)$$

$$x = 2t+1 \quad (3)$$

$$y = 2-2t \quad (4)$$

$$z = t+2 \quad (5)$$

To find the point of intersection of (2) and (1), we substitute (3), (4) and (5) in (1), which gives

$$2(2t+1)-2(2-2t)+(t+2) = 9$$

$$9t = 9$$

$$\therefore \quad t = 1$$

Substituting $t=1$ in (3), (4) and (5) gives the point of intersection as $(3,0,3)$. This point is the midpoint of $P(1,2,2)$ and $P'(x_1,y_1,z_1)$. Hence

$$\tfrac{1}{2}(1+x_1) = 3 \qquad \therefore \quad x_1 = 5$$

$$\tfrac{1}{2}(2+y_1) = 0 \qquad \therefore \quad y_1 = -2$$

$$\tfrac{1}{2}(2+z_1) = 3 \qquad \therefore \quad z_1 = 4$$

giving the coordinates of P' as $(5,-2,4)$.

Let M denote the foot of the perpendicular from Q to PP'. M will have coordinates $(2t+1, 2-2t, t+2)$ from (3), (4) and (5). The DRs of QM are $(2t,-2t,t-3)$.

For QM to be perpendicular to (2) we require

$$4t+(-2)(-2t)+(t-3) = 0$$

$$9t = 3$$

$$\therefore \quad t = \tfrac{1}{3}$$

Hence the coordinates of M are $\left(\frac{5}{3}, \frac{4}{3}, \frac{7}{3}\right)$.

As the coordinates of the point Q are (1, 2, 5)

$$QM^2 = \left(\frac{5}{3}-1\right)^2+\left(\frac{4}{3}-2\right)^2+\left(\frac{7}{3}-5\right)^2$$

$$\therefore \quad QM = 2\sqrt{2}$$

2. (i) The equation of the plane ABC must be of the form

$$ax+by+cz = d \quad (1)$$

EXERCISE

The unknown coefficients in this equation may be determined by substituting the coordinates of the points A, B and C.

$x = 5,\ y = 0,\ z = 0$ in (1) gives

$$5a = d \qquad \therefore\ a = \frac{d}{5} \tag{2}$$

$x = 0,\ y = 10,\ z = 0$ in (1) gives

$$10b = d \qquad \therefore\ b = \frac{d}{10} \tag{3}$$

$x = 0,\ y = 0,\ z = 2$ in (1) gives

$$2c = d \qquad \therefore\ c = \frac{d}{2} \tag{4}$$

Substituting the results (2), (3) and (4) in (1) gives

$$\frac{dx}{5}+\frac{dy}{10}+\frac{dz}{2} = d$$

$$\frac{x}{5}+\frac{y}{10}+\frac{z}{2} = 1$$

$$\therefore\ 2x+y+5z = 10 \tag{5}$$

In order to verify that the point D lies in this plane we put $x = 10$, $y = 10$ and $z = -4$ in the LHS of (5), which gives

$$20+10-20 = 10 = \text{RHS}$$

hence D lies in the plane ABC.

(ii) The DRs of a line perpendicular to the plane ABC are (2, 1, 5). Because the required straight line passes through the origin its equation is

$$\frac{x}{2} = \frac{y}{1} = \frac{z}{5} = k \tag{6}$$

(iii) M is the point of intersection of (6) with (5). From (6) we have

$$x = 2k \tag{7}$$

$$y = k \tag{8}$$

$$z = 5k \tag{9}$$

Substituting these parametric equations in (5) gives

$$4k+k+25k = 10$$

$$30k = 10$$

$$\therefore\ k = \frac{1}{3}$$

hence the coordinates of M are $\left(\frac{2}{3}, \frac{1}{3}, \frac{5}{3}\right)$

The equation of AB is found from

$$\frac{x-x_1}{x_2-x_1} = \frac{y-y_1}{y_2-y_1} = \frac{z-z_1}{z_2-z_1}$$

where $(x_1, y_1, z_1) = (5, 0, 0)$ and $(x_2, y_2, z_2) = (0, 10, 0)$.

Substituting gives

$$\frac{x-5}{-5} = \frac{y}{10} = t, \quad z = 0$$

EXERCISE

The parametric equations are

$$x = 5-5t \quad (7)$$
$$y = 10t \quad (8)$$
$$z = 0 \quad (9)$$

hence $R(5-5t, 10t, 0)$ lies on AB for all values of t (Fig. 13.3). Since L is a point on AB it will be given by a value of t satisfying (7), (8) and (9).

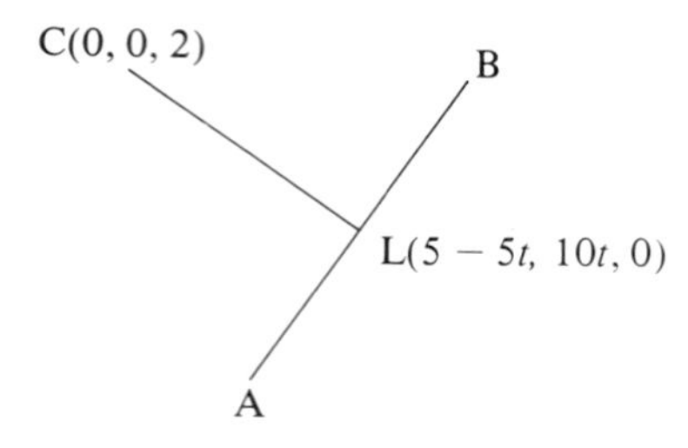

Fig. 13.3

The DRs of CL are $(5-5t, 10t, -2)$.

The DRs of AB are $(-5, 10, 0)$.

CL is perpendicular to AB

$$-5(5-5t)+100t = 0$$
$$-25+25t+100t = 0$$
$$125t = 25$$
$$\therefore \quad t = \frac{1}{5}$$

Substituting $t = \frac{1}{5}$ in (7), (8) and (9) gives the coordinates of L as (4, 2, 0).

The equation of the plane OAB is $z = 0$.

The DCs of the normal to OAB are (0, 0, 1).

From (5) the DRs of the normal to the plane ABC are (2, 1, 5).

Therefore the DCs of the normal to the plane ABC are

$$\left(\frac{2}{\sqrt{30}}, \frac{1}{\sqrt{30}}, \frac{5}{\sqrt{30}}\right)$$

If θ denotes the angle between these planes we have from (13.20)

$$\cos\theta = \frac{5}{\sqrt{30}} = \sqrt{\frac{5}{6}} \qquad \text{as required}$$

3.

$$L_1 \qquad \frac{x+1}{2} = \frac{y-2}{-1} = \frac{z-2}{1} = t$$
$$L_2 \qquad \frac{x+5}{1} = \frac{y+1}{-3} = \frac{z-7}{4} = u$$

The parametric equations for L_1 are

$$x = 2t-1 \quad (1)$$
$$y = 2-t \quad (2)$$
$$z = t+2 \quad (3)$$

The parametric equations for L_2 are

$$x = u-5 \tag{4}$$
$$y = -3u-1 \tag{5}$$
$$z = 4u+7 \tag{6}$$

Equating (1) and (4) $\quad u-5 = 2t-1$

$$u-2t = 4 \tag{7}$$

Equating (2) and (5) $\quad 2-t = -3u-1$

$$3u-t = -3 \tag{8}$$

We need to solve (7) and (8) simultaneously.

(8) × 2 $\quad 6u-2t = -6 \quad (9)$

(9) − (7) $\quad 5u = -10$

$$\therefore \quad u = -2 \tag{10}$$

Substituting in (7) gives

$$-2-2t = 4$$
$$-2t = 6$$
$$\therefore \quad t = -3 \tag{11}$$

Substituting (11) in (1) and (2) gives

$$x = -7, \quad y = 5$$

We need now to check that the z-coordinates given by (3) and (6) are equal. Substituting (11) in (3) gives $z = -1$ and substituting (10) in (6) also gives $z = -1$. Hence

$$L_1 \text{ and } L_2 \text{ intersect at } (-7, 5, -1) \tag{12}$$

(i) If the DRs of L_1 are $(2, -1, 1)$ then the DCs are

$$\left(\frac{2}{\sqrt{6}}, \frac{-1}{\sqrt{6}}, \frac{1}{\sqrt{6}}\right)$$

If the DRs of L_2 are $(1, -3, 4)$ then the DCs are

$$\left(\frac{1}{\sqrt{26}}, \frac{-3}{\sqrt{26}}, \frac{4}{\sqrt{26}}\right)$$

If θ denotes the angle between L_1 and L_2 we have from (13.12)

$$\cos\theta = \frac{1}{\sqrt{6}\sqrt{26}}(2+3+4) = \frac{9}{\sqrt{6}\sqrt{26}} = \frac{3\sqrt{3}}{2\sqrt{13}}$$

hence $\quad \theta = \arccos\dfrac{3\sqrt{3}}{2\sqrt{13}} = 43.9^\circ$

(ii) Since the required plane passes through the origin it must have an equation of the form

$$ax+by+cz = 0 \tag{13}$$

The equation of the plane may be determined by specifying a further two points in the plane in addition to the origin itself. It is convenient to take the point (12) as one of these points. Another point may be found by putting a particular value of t in (1), (2) and (3).

Taking $t = 0$ gives $x = -1$, $y = 2$ and $z = 2$. Substituting these values of x, y and z in (13) gives

$$-a+2b+2c = 0 \tag{14}$$

Putting the coordinates of the point (12) into (13) gives

$$-7a+5b-c = 0 \tag{15}$$

Solving these simultaneously

(15) × 2 $\quad -14a + 10b - 2c = 0 \quad (16)$

(14) + (16) $\quad -15a + 12b = 0$

$$\therefore \quad a = \frac{4b}{5} \quad (17)$$

Substituting in (14) gives

$$\frac{-4b}{5} + 2b + 2c = 0$$

$$\therefore \quad c = \frac{-3b}{5} \quad (18)$$

Substituting (17) and (18) in (13) gives

$$\frac{4bx}{5} + by - \frac{3bz}{5} = 0$$

$$\therefore \quad 4x + 5y - 3z = 0$$

(iii) Let M represent the point that is the foot of the perpendicular from (1, 2, 3) to the line L_1. Let N be the point (1, 2, 3).

The equation of MN is given by

$$\frac{x-1}{2t-2} = \frac{y-2}{-t} = \frac{z-3}{t-1}$$

DRs of MN are $(2t-2, -t, t-1)$.

DRs of L_1 are $(2, -1, 1)$.

For perpendicularity we require

$$2(2t-2) + t + t - 1 = 0$$

$$6t = 5$$

$$\therefore \quad t = \frac{5}{6}$$

Substituting this value of t in (1), (2) and (3) gives

$$x = \frac{5}{3} - 1 = \frac{2}{3}$$

$$y = 2 - \frac{5}{6} = \frac{7}{6}$$

$$z = 2 + \frac{5}{6} = \frac{17}{6}$$

hence M is the point $\left(\frac{2}{3}, \frac{7}{6}, \frac{17}{6}\right)$.

$$\therefore \quad MN^2 = \left(\frac{1}{3}\right)^2 + \left(\frac{5}{6}\right)^2 + \left(\frac{1}{6}\right)^2$$

$$= \frac{1}{9} + \frac{25}{36} + \frac{1}{36}$$

$$\therefore \quad MN = \sqrt{\frac{5}{6}}$$

EXERCISE

4. (i) To find the equation of the line BC we use

$$\frac{x-x_1}{x_2-x_1} = \frac{y-y_1}{y_2-y_1} = \frac{z-z_1}{z_2-z_1}$$

where $(x_1, y_1, z_1) = (0, 4, 0)$ and $(x_2, y_2, z_2) = (0, 0, 5)$. This gives

$$\frac{x-0}{0} = \frac{y-4}{0-4} = \frac{z-0}{5-0}$$

hence the equation is $\quad x = 0, \quad \dfrac{y-4}{-4} = \dfrac{z}{5} \qquad (1)$

The equation of the plane ABC must be of the form

$$ax + by + cz = d \qquad (2)$$

Substituting $x = 3,\ y = 0,\ z = 0$

$$3a = d \qquad \therefore \quad a = \frac{d}{3} \qquad (3)$$

Substituting $x = 0,\ y = 4,\ z = 0$

$$4b = d \qquad \therefore \quad b = \frac{d}{4} \qquad (4)$$

Substituting $x = 0,\ y = 0,\ z = 5$

$$5c = d \qquad \therefore \quad c = \frac{d}{5} \qquad (5)$$

Putting these values into (2) gives

$$\frac{dx}{3} + \frac{dy}{4} + \frac{dz}{5} = d$$

$$\therefore \quad 20x + 15y + 12z = 60 \qquad (6)$$

(ii) The equation of the line AB is

$$\frac{x-3}{-3} = \frac{y}{4} = \frac{z-0}{0}$$

which is usually written

$$\frac{x-3}{-3} = \frac{y}{4}, \quad z = 0$$

DRs of AB are $(-3, 4, 0)$

$$\therefore \quad \text{DCs of AB are } \left(\frac{-3}{5}, \frac{4}{5}, 0\right)$$

DRs of BC are $(0, -4, 5)$

$$\therefore \quad \text{DCs of BC are } \left(0, \frac{-4}{\sqrt{41}}, \frac{5}{\sqrt{41}}\right)$$

If θ denotes the angle between AB and BC, we have

$$\cos\theta = \frac{-16}{5\sqrt{41}} \qquad \therefore \quad \theta = 120^\circ \quad \text{(to the nearest degree)}$$

hence the acute angle between these lines $\approx 60^\circ$.

(iii) Volume of the tetrahedron ABCD $= \frac{1}{3}$(area of base) $\times$ height

To find the height of the tetrahedron we calculate the perpendicular distance of D from the plane $20x + 15y + 12z - 60 = 0$.

This is given by

$$\text{Height} = \frac{20\times 7+15\times 8+12\times 9-60}{\sqrt{400+225+144}}$$

$$= \frac{308}{\sqrt{769}}$$

$$\therefore \quad \text{Height} = 11.11$$

$$\text{Area of } \Delta ABC = \tfrac{1}{2}(AB)(BC)\sin 60^\circ$$

$$AB^2 = 3^2+4^2 \qquad \therefore \quad AB = 5$$

$$BC^2 = 4^2+5^2 \qquad \therefore \quad BC = \sqrt{41}$$

$$\therefore \quad \text{Area of } \Delta ABC = \frac{1}{2}\times 5\times\sqrt{41}\times\frac{\sqrt{3}}{2}$$

$$= 13.86 \text{ units}^2$$

hence

$$\text{Volume of ABCD} = \tfrac{1}{3}\times 13.86\times 11.11$$

$$= 51.32 \text{ units}^3$$

5. (i) If the equation of m is

$$\frac{x-2}{3} = \frac{y-3}{4} = \frac{z-4}{2} = t$$

then

$$x = 3t+2 \qquad (1)$$

$$y = 4t+3 \qquad (2)$$

$$z = 2t+4 \qquad (3)$$

If the equation of n is

$$\frac{x-1}{2} = \frac{y-1}{3} = \frac{z+2}{4} = u$$

then

$$x = 2u+1 \qquad (4)$$

$$y = 3u+1 \qquad (5)$$

$$z = 4u-2 \qquad (6)$$

Equating (1) and (4)

$$3t+2 = 2u+1$$

$$\therefore \quad 3t-2u = -1 \qquad (7)$$

Equating (2) and (5)

$$4t+3 = 3u+1$$

$$\therefore \quad 4t-3u = -2 \qquad (8)$$

We now solve (7) and (8) simultaneously

(7) × 3 $\quad 9t-6u = -3 \qquad (9)$

(8) × 2 $\quad 8t-6u = -4 \qquad (10)$

(9) − (10) $\quad t = 1$

Substituting for t in (7) gives

$$3-2u = -1$$

$$\therefore \quad u = 2 \qquad (11)$$

Substituting for t in (1) gives $x = 5$.

Substituting for t in (2) gives $y = 7$.

EXERCISE

We now need to check that the z-coordinate given by equations (3) and (6) are equal. Putting $t = 1$ in (3) gives $z = 6$. Putting $u = 2$ in (6) gives $z = 6$.

Hence P is the point (5, 7, 6).

(ii) If the DRs of m are (3, 4, 2) the DCs of m are

$$\left(\frac{3}{\sqrt{29}}, \frac{4}{\sqrt{29}}, \frac{2}{\sqrt{29}}\right)$$

If the DRs of n are (2, 3, 4) the DCs of n are

$$\left(\frac{2}{\sqrt{29}}, \frac{3}{\sqrt{29}}, \frac{4}{\sqrt{29}}\right)$$

If θ denotes the acute angle at which m and n intersect, we have

$$\cos\theta = \frac{1}{\sqrt{29}\sqrt{29}}(2\times 3+4\times 3+2\times 4)$$

$$\cos\theta = \frac{26}{29}$$

(iii) The equation of a plane passing through the origin is of the form

$$ax+by+cz = 0 \qquad (12)$$

We need a further two points in addition to the origin itself in order to determine the unknown coefficients in this equation. For convenience we may take one of these points as P(5, 7, 6), which is the point of intersection of the lines m and n. To find another point on m we put $t = 0$ in (1), (2) and (3), which gives (2, 3, 4).

Putting $x = 2$, $y = 3$, $z = 4$ in (12)

$$2a+3b+4c = 0 \qquad (13)$$

Putting $x = 5$, $y = 7$, $z = 6$ in (12)

$$5a+7b+6c = 0 \qquad (14)$$

Solving these simultaneously

(13) × 3 $\quad 6a+9b+12c = 0 \qquad (15)$

(14) × 2 $\quad 10a+14b+12c = 0 \qquad (16)$

(16) − (15) $\quad 4a+5b = 0$

$$\therefore \quad a = \frac{-5b}{4} \qquad (17)$$

Substituting for a in (13):

$$\frac{-5b}{2}+3b+4c = 0$$

$$\therefore \quad c = \frac{-b}{8} \qquad (18)$$

Substituting (17) and (18) in (12) gives

$$\frac{-5bx}{4}+by-\frac{bz}{8} = 0$$

$$\therefore \quad 10x-8y+z = 0$$

(iv) If DRs of m are (3, 4, 2) the DCs of m are

$$\left(\frac{3}{\sqrt{29}}, \frac{4}{\sqrt{29}}, \frac{2}{\sqrt{29}}\right)$$

If DRs of OP are (5, 7, 6) the DCs of OP are

$$\left(\frac{5}{\sqrt{110}}, \frac{7}{\sqrt{110}}, \frac{6}{\sqrt{110}}\right)$$

The angle θ between OP and m is given by

$$\cos\theta = \frac{1}{\sqrt{29}\sqrt{110}}(15+28+12) = \frac{55}{\sqrt{29}\sqrt{110}}$$

If DRs of n are (2, 3, 4) the DCs of n are

$$\left(\frac{2}{\sqrt{29}}, \frac{3}{\sqrt{29}}, \frac{4}{\sqrt{29}}\right)$$

The angle ϕ between OP and n is given by

$$\cos\phi = \frac{1}{\sqrt{29}\sqrt{110}}(10+21+24) = \frac{55}{\sqrt{29}\sqrt{110}}$$

$$\therefore \quad \theta = \phi$$

Therefore OP is the bisector of the angle between m and n. Hence O is equidistant from m and n.

EXERCISE

14 VECTOR ALGEBRA

UNIT VECTORS

In three-dimensional vector algebra we take a right-handed system of axes as a reference frame. Unit vectors $\mathbf{i}, \mathbf{j}$ and $\mathbf{k}$ are taken to act along the x-, y- and z-axes, respectively (Fig. 14.1). The position vector of any point, P, in three-dimensional space can be expressed in terms of these unit vectors as

$$\mathbf{r} = x\mathbf{i}+y\mathbf{j}+z\mathbf{k} \tag{14.1}$$

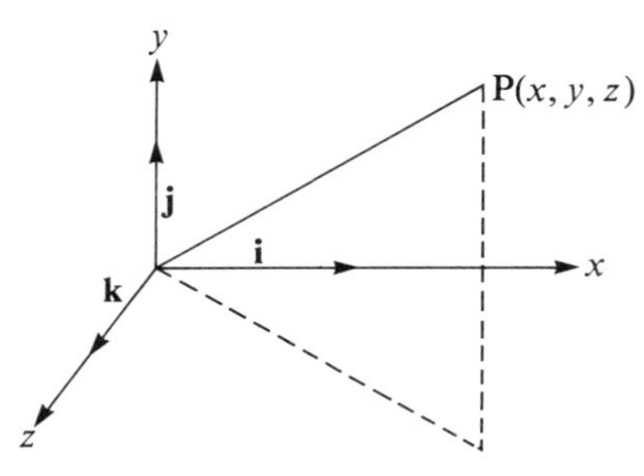

Fig. 14.1

THE COMPONENTS OF A VECTOR

The quantities x, y and z that appear before the unit vectors $\mathbf{i}, \mathbf{j}$ and $\mathbf{k}$ in (14.1) are called the components of the vector $\mathbf{r}$.

This definition may be extended to apply to any vector $\mathbf{a}$ given by

$$\mathbf{a} = a_1\mathbf{i}+a_2\mathbf{j}+a_3\mathbf{k} \tag{14.2}$$

The components of this vector are a_1, a_2 and a_3.

ALTERNATIVE NOTATION FOR VECTORS

An alternative notation for vectors is to list the components either as a row vector

$$\mathbf{a} = (a_1, a_2, a_3)$$

or as a column vector

$$\mathbf{a} = \begin{pmatrix} a_1 \\ a_2 \\ a_3 \end{pmatrix}$$

THE MODULUS OF A VECTOR

The modulus of any vector is its magnitude. The position vector $\mathbf{r}$ of the point P has a modulus, $|\mathbf{r}|$, given by $|\mathbf{r}| = \mathrm{OP}$. However, from the earlier work in Chapter 13, we have

$$OP^2 = x^2+y^2+z^2$$

$$\therefore \quad OP = \sqrt{x^2+y^2+z^2}$$

hence

$$r = \sqrt{x^2+y^2+z^2}$$

This result may be extended to any vector. For example, if the vector **a** is given by $\mathbf{a} = a_1\mathbf{i}+a_2\mathbf{j}+a_3\mathbf{k}$, we have

$$|\mathbf{a}| = \sqrt{a_1^2+a_2^2+a_3^2} \qquad (14.3)$$

THE DRs AND DCs OF A VECTOR

In Chapter 13 we saw that the direction ratios of the point P are $x:y:z$. Consequently, the DRs are determined by the ratios of the components of the position vector **r**.

This result may be generalised to apply to any vector. Once the DRs have been established from the ratios of the components of the vector, the DCs may be calculated by the method given in Chapter 13.

Example

Find the DRs and DCs of the vector $2\mathbf{i}+3\mathbf{j}+6\mathbf{k}$.

DRs are $2:3:6$

DCs are $\left(\frac{2}{7}, \frac{3}{7}, \frac{6}{7}\right)$ (since $7 = \sqrt{2^2+3^2+6^2}$)

THE SCALAR PRODUCT OF TWO VECTORS

The scalar product of two vectors **a** and **b** is defined to be

$$\mathbf{a}\cdot\mathbf{b} = |\mathbf{a}|\,|\mathbf{b}|\cos\theta \qquad (14.4)$$

where the dot separating the two vectors on the LHS denotes the operation of taking their scalar product and θ is the angle contained between them.

If we apply the definition of the scalar product to the mutually perpendicular unit vectors **i** and **j**, we have

$$\mathbf{i}\cdot\mathbf{i} = |\mathbf{i}|\,|\mathbf{j}|\cos 90^\circ$$

hence $\mathbf{i}\cdot\mathbf{j} = 0$ (since $\cos 90^\circ = 0$) (14.5)

Similarly $\mathbf{i}\cdot\mathbf{k} = 0$ (14.6)

and $\mathbf{j}\cdot\mathbf{k} = 0$ (14.7)

since these unit vectors are also mutually perpendicular.

From (14.4) we can obtain the following results

$$\mathbf{i}\cdot\mathbf{j} = |\mathbf{i}|\,|\mathbf{i}|\cos 0$$

since the angle between a vector and itself is zero. Moreover, it follows by the definition of a unit vector that its modulus must be unity, i.e. $|\mathbf{i}| = 1$.

$$\mathbf{i}\cdot\mathbf{i} = \cos\theta$$

$$\therefore \quad \mathbf{i}\cdot\mathbf{i} = 1 \quad \text{(since } \cos 0 = 1\text{)} \qquad (14.8)$$

Similar results may be obtained for the other unit vectors, so that

$$\mathbf{j}\cdot\mathbf{j} = 1 \qquad (14.9)$$

and $\mathbf{k}\cdot\mathbf{k} = 1$ (14.10)

THE SCALAR PRODUCT IN TERMS OF COMPONENTS

For calculation purposes a more convenient result is to express the scalar product of two vectors in terms of its components.

Let $\mathbf{a} = a_1\mathbf{i}+a_2\mathbf{j}+a_3\mathbf{k}$

and $\mathbf{b} = b_1\mathbf{i}+b_2\mathbf{j}+b_3\mathbf{k}$

Hence

$$\begin{aligned}\mathbf{a}\cdot\mathbf{b} &= (a_1\mathbf{i}+a_2\mathbf{j}+a_3\mathbf{k})\cdot(b_1\mathbf{i}+b_2\mathbf{j}+b_3\mathbf{k})\\ &= a_1b_1\mathbf{i}\cdot\mathbf{i}+a_1b_2\mathbf{i}\cdot\mathbf{j}+a_1b_3\mathbf{i}\cdot\mathbf{k}\\ &\quad +a_2b_1\mathbf{i}\cdot\mathbf{j}+a_2b_2\mathbf{j}\cdot\mathbf{j}+a_2b_3\mathbf{j}\cdot\mathbf{k}\\ &\quad +a_3b_1\mathbf{k}\cdot\mathbf{i}+a_3b_2\mathbf{k}\cdot\mathbf{j}+a_3b_3\mathbf{k}\cdot\mathbf{k}\end{aligned}$$

The properties of the scalar product of unit vectors enable us to simplify this considerably with the result that

$$\mathbf{a}\cdot\mathbf{b} = a_1b_1+a_2b_2+a_3b_3 \qquad (14.11)$$

THE UNIT VECTOR IN ANY DIRECTION

Suppose we wish to find the unit vector in the direction of the vector $\mathbf{a}$. We will denote this unit vector by $\hat{\mathbf{a}}$ and it must have the property that

$$\hat{\mathbf{a}}\cdot\hat{\mathbf{a}} = 1 \qquad (14.12)$$

It is easily verified that the unit vector $\hat{\mathbf{a}}$ defined by

$$\hat{\mathbf{a}} = \frac{\mathbf{a}}{|\mathbf{a}|} \qquad (14.13)$$

satisfies the relationship (14.12).

Note $$\hat{\mathbf{a}}\cdot\hat{\mathbf{a}} = \frac{\mathbf{a}}{|\mathbf{a}|}\cdot\frac{\mathbf{a}}{|\mathbf{a}|} = \frac{\mathbf{a}\cdot\mathbf{a}}{|\mathbf{a}|^2} = \frac{|\mathbf{a}|^2}{|\mathbf{a}|^2} = 1$$

THE VECTOR PRODUCT OF TWO VECTORS

We define the vector product of two vectors $\mathbf{a}$ and $\mathbf{b}$ to be

$$\mathbf{a}\times\mathbf{b} = |\mathbf{a}|\,|\mathbf{b}|\sin\theta\,\hat{\mathbf{n}} \qquad (14.14)$$

where the vector $\hat{\mathbf{n}}$ is a unit vector perpendicular to the plane containing $\mathbf{a}$ and $\mathbf{b}$ and θ is the angle between the two vectors. The multiplication sign separating the two vectors on the LHS of (14.14) denotes the operation of taking their vector product.

THE VECTOR PRODUCT IN TERMS OF COMPONENTS

If $\mathbf{a} = (a_1, a_2, a_3)$ and $\mathbf{b} = (b_1, b_2, b_3)$ the vector product of $\mathbf{a}$ and $\mathbf{b}$ in terms of components is given by

$$\mathbf{a}\times\mathbf{b} = \mathbf{i}(a_2b_3-a_3b_2)+\mathbf{j}(a_3b_1-a_1b_3)+\mathbf{k}(a_1b_2-a_2b_1) \qquad (14.15)$$

Students familiar with the properties of determinants may write this as

$$\mathbf{a}\times\mathbf{b} = \begin{vmatrix}\mathbf{i} & \mathbf{j} & \mathbf{k}\\ a_1 & a_2 & a_3\\ b_1 & b_2 & b_3\end{vmatrix} \qquad (14.16)$$

THE VECTOR EQUATION OF A STRAIGHT LINE

(1) Through a point in a given direction

Let P represent a typical point on the straight line AB and $\mathbf{b}$ a vector that is parallel to AB (Fig. 14.2).

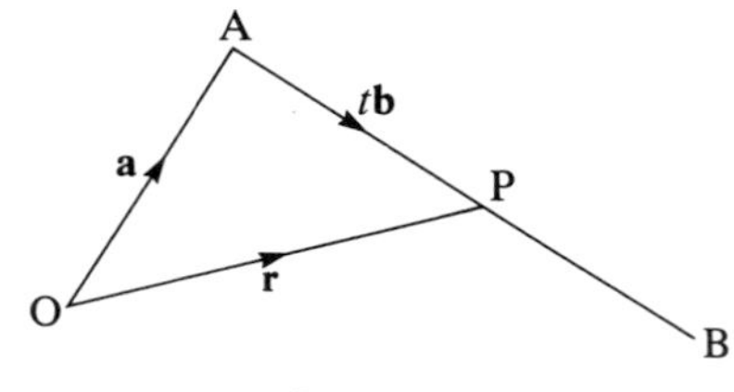

Fig. 14.2

If t is a scalar parameter that can range over all values between plus or minus infinity, the vector $t\mathbf{b}$ is a vector that is also parallel to AB. From the vector addition rule we have

$$\overrightarrow{OP} = \overrightarrow{OA} + \overrightarrow{AP}$$

but $$\overrightarrow{AP} = t\mathbf{b}$$

$$\therefore \quad \overrightarrow{OP} = \overrightarrow{OA} + t\mathbf{b}$$

i.e. $$\mathbf{r} = \mathbf{a} + t\mathbf{b} \qquad (\text{since } \overrightarrow{OP} = \mathbf{r} \text{ and } \overrightarrow{OA} = \mathbf{a}) \qquad (14.17)$$

which is the vector equation of a straight line through the given point A parallel to the vector **b**.

(2) Through two given points

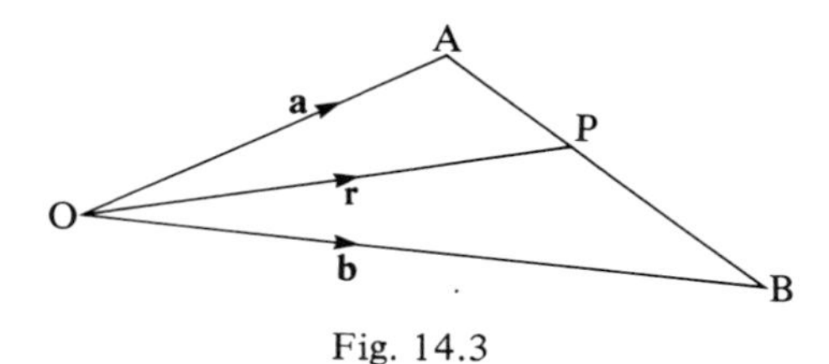

Fig. 14.3

From the vector addition rule we have (for Fig. 14.3)

$$\overrightarrow{OB} = \overrightarrow{OA} + \overrightarrow{AB}$$

$$\therefore \quad \mathbf{b} = \mathbf{a} + \overrightarrow{AB}$$

hence $$\overrightarrow{AB} = \mathbf{b} - \mathbf{a}$$

If P represents any typical point on the straight line AB, we have

$$\overrightarrow{AP} = t\,\overrightarrow{AB} \qquad \text{where } t \text{ is a scalar}$$

$$= t(\mathbf{b} - \mathbf{a})$$

However $$\overrightarrow{OP} = \overrightarrow{OA} + \overrightarrow{AP}$$

$$= \mathbf{a} + t(\mathbf{b} - \mathbf{a}) \qquad (\text{since } \overrightarrow{OA} = \mathbf{a})$$

$$\therefore \quad \mathbf{r} = \mathbf{a} + t\mathbf{b} - t\mathbf{a}$$

giving finally $$\mathbf{r} = (1-t)\mathbf{a} + t\mathbf{b} \qquad (14.18)$$

THE POSITION VECTOR OF A POINT DIVIDING A LINE IN A GIVEN RATIO

Suppose the point P divides AB in the ratio $m:n$ so that $n\overrightarrow{AP} = m\overrightarrow{PB}$.

$$n\overrightarrow{AP} = m\overrightarrow{PB} \quad \Rightarrow \quad n(\mathbf{r} - \mathbf{a}) = m(\mathbf{b} - \mathbf{r})$$

$$n\mathbf{r} - n\mathbf{a} = m\mathbf{b} - m\mathbf{r}$$

$$n\mathbf{r} + m\mathbf{r} = m\mathbf{b} + n\mathbf{a}$$
$$(m+n)\mathbf{r} = m\mathbf{b} + n\mathbf{a}$$
$$\therefore \quad \mathbf{r} = \frac{m\mathbf{b} + n\mathbf{a}}{(m+n)} \qquad (14.19)$$

SPECIAL CASE

If P is the midpoint of AB, $m = n$. The position vector of the midpoint is then given by

$$\mathbf{r} = \tfrac{1}{2}(\mathbf{a} + \mathbf{b}) \qquad (14.20)$$

THE ANGLE BETWEEN TWO VECTORS

The scalar product of two vectors **a** and **b** may be used to calculate the angle θ between them. From (14.4) we have

$$\mathbf{a} \cdot \mathbf{b} = |\mathbf{a}|\,|\mathbf{b}| \cos\theta$$
$$\cos\theta = \frac{\mathbf{a} \cdot \mathbf{b}}{|\mathbf{a}|\,|\mathbf{b}|} \qquad (14.21)$$

Example

Calculate the angle between the two vectors

$$\mathbf{a} = 2\mathbf{i} + 6\mathbf{j} - 3\mathbf{k} \quad \text{and} \quad \mathbf{b} = 4\mathbf{i} - 4\mathbf{j} + 2\mathbf{k}$$

$$|\mathbf{a}|^2 = 2^2 + 6^2 + (-3)^2$$
$$= 49$$
$$\therefore \quad |\mathbf{a}| = 7 \qquad (1)$$
$$|\mathbf{b}|^2 = 4^2 + (-4)^2 + 2^2$$
$$= 36$$
$$\therefore \quad |\mathbf{b}| = 6 \qquad (2)$$

Now
$$\mathbf{a} \cdot \mathbf{b} = (2\mathbf{i} + 6\mathbf{j} - 3\mathbf{k}) \cdot (4\mathbf{i} - 4\mathbf{j} + 2\mathbf{k})$$
$$= 8 - 24 - 6 \qquad \text{[from (14.11)]}$$
$$\therefore \quad \mathbf{a} \cdot \mathbf{b} = -22 \qquad (3)$$

Substituting the results (1), (2) and (3) in (14.21) gives

$$\cos\theta = \frac{-22}{7.6}$$
$$= \frac{-11}{21}$$
$$\therefore \quad \theta = \arccos\left(\frac{-11}{21}\right)$$

i.e.
$$\theta = 121.59^\circ$$

THE VECTOR EQUATION OF A PLANE (NORMAL FORM)

Let $\mathbf{r} = x\mathbf{i} + y\mathbf{j} + z\mathbf{k}$ denote the position vector of any general point contained in the plane π. If the DRs of the normal to the plane π are (a, b, c) we have

$$n = a\mathbf{i} + b\mathbf{j} + c\mathbf{k} \qquad (14.22)$$

representing a vector that is normal to the plane.

Using the definition (14.11) of the scalar product of two vectors, we have

$$\mathbf{r}\cdot\mathbf{n} = (x\mathbf{i}+y\mathbf{j}+z\mathbf{k})\cdot(a\mathbf{i}+b\mathbf{j}+c\mathbf{k})$$

$$\therefore \quad \mathbf{r}\cdot\mathbf{n} = ax+by+cz \qquad (14.23)$$

The general equation of a plane in Cartesian coordinates is, from (13.15)

$$ax+by+cz = d \qquad (14.24)$$

The LHS of (14.24) may be replaced by the LHS of (14.23) to give

$$\mathbf{r}\cdot\mathbf{n} = d \qquad (14.25)$$

which is the vector equation of a plane perpendicular to the vector **n**.

The vector **n** may be expressed in terms of the unit vector $\hat{\mathbf{n}}$ as

$$\mathbf{n} = |\mathbf{n}|\hat{\mathbf{n}} \qquad (14.26)$$

Substituting in (14.25) gives

$$\mathbf{r}\cdot|\mathbf{n}|\hat{\mathbf{n}} = d$$

$$\therefore \quad \mathbf{r}\cdot\hat{\mathbf{n}} = \frac{d}{|\mathbf{n}|} \qquad (14.27)$$

From (14.22) we have

$$|\mathbf{n}| = \sqrt{a^2+b^2+c^2}$$

hence

$$\mathbf{r}\cdot\hat{\mathbf{n}} = \frac{d}{\sqrt{a^2+b^2+c^2}}$$

$$\therefore \quad \mathbf{r}\cdot\hat{\mathbf{n}} = p \qquad \text{by comparison with (13.16)}$$

where p is the perpendicular distance of the plane from the origin.

EXERCISE

1. Given two vectors $\mathbf{a} = 2\mathbf{i}+\mathbf{j}+q\mathbf{k}$, $\mathbf{b} = q\mathbf{i}-2\mathbf{j}+2q\mathbf{k}$ where **i, j, k** are mutually perpendicular unit vectors:
   (i) determine values of q such that **a** and **b** have equal magnitudes.
   (ii) assuming $q = 4$, find the angles between the vectors **b** and $\frac{1}{2}(\mathbf{a}-\frac{1}{2}\mathbf{b})$. (NI 1980)

2. Given that A and B are the points whose position vectors referred to the origin O are $(\mathbf{i}+2\mathbf{j}+\mathbf{k})$ and $(3\mathbf{i}+4\mathbf{j}+2\mathbf{k})$, respectively, determine $\overrightarrow{AB}$ and direction cosines for the line AB. (LU 1980)

3. Find a unit vector which is perpendicular to the vector $(4\mathbf{i}+4\mathbf{j}-7\mathbf{k})$ and to the vector $(2\mathbf{i}+2\mathbf{j}+\mathbf{k})$. (LU 1980)

4. The angles between the non-zero vectors **b** and **c**, **c** and **a**, **a** and **b** are α, β, γ respectively. The vectors **u** and **v** are defined as

$$\mathbf{u} = (\mathbf{a}\cdot\mathbf{c})\mathbf{b}-(\mathbf{a}\cdot\mathbf{b})\mathbf{c}$$

$$\mathbf{v} = (\mathbf{a}\cdot\mathbf{c})\mathbf{b}-(\mathbf{b}\cdot\mathbf{c})\mathbf{a}$$

   Given that **u** and **v** are at right-angles, show that either $\cos\beta = \cos\alpha\cos\gamma$, or **a** is perpendicular to **c**. (LU 1980)

5. Given that $\mathbf{r} = a\mathbf{i}+b\mathbf{j}+c\mathbf{k}$, $\mathbf{k}\times\mathbf{r} = \mathbf{p}$, $\mathbf{r}\times\mathbf{p} = \mathbf{k}$, where **i, j** and **k** are a triad of mutually orthogonal unit vectors and a, b, c are constants, show that

$$a^2+b^2 = 1, \quad c = 0 \qquad \text{(LU 1980)}$$

6. A line is defined by the vector equation $\mathbf{r} = \mathbf{a}+t\mathbf{b}$ and a plane is defined by the equation $\mathbf{r}\cdot\mathbf{c} = p$. Show that, in general, the line meets the plane in one point, and find the parameter t of this point. What happens if **b** and **c** are perpendicular?

If $\mathbf{a} = (1, 2, -3)$, $\mathbf{b} = (2, 1, 2)$, $\mathbf{c} = (2, -1, -1)$ and $p = 4$, find the position vector of the point of intersection and the sine of the angle between the line and the plane. (O 1979)

7. Given that

$$\overrightarrow{OA} = \alpha = (-\mathbf{i}+\mathbf{j}+\mathbf{k})$$
$$\overrightarrow{OB} = \beta = (\mathbf{i}-\mathbf{j}+\mathbf{k})$$
$$\overrightarrow{OC} = \gamma = (\mathbf{i}+\mathbf{j}-\mathbf{k})$$

find

(i) the angle between the straight lines BC and CA,

(ii) a unit vector normal to the plane ABC,

(iii) the perpendicular distance from the origin O to the plane ABC.

Further, show that the points P and Q with position vectors $\alpha+\beta+\gamma$ and $\beta\times\gamma+\gamma\times\alpha+\alpha\times\beta$ are collinear with the origin. (LU 1980)

Worked Solutions

1. (i)

$$|\mathbf{a}|^2 = 2^2+1^2+q^2$$
$$\therefore\ |\mathbf{a}|^2 = 5+q^2$$
$$|\mathbf{b}|^2 = q^2+(-2)^2+(2q)^2$$
$$\therefore\ |\mathbf{b}|^2 = 5q^2+4$$

For $|\mathbf{a}|^2 = |\mathbf{b}|^2$

$$5q^2+4 = 5+q^2$$
$$4q^2 = 1$$
$$q^2 = \tfrac{1}{4}$$
$$\therefore\ q = \tfrac{1}{2} \quad \text{or} \quad q = -\tfrac{1}{2}$$

(ii) If $q = 4$

$$\mathbf{a} = 2\mathbf{i}+\mathbf{j}+4\mathbf{k}$$

and

$$\mathbf{b} = 4\mathbf{i}-2\mathbf{j}+8\mathbf{k}$$
$$\mathbf{a}-\tfrac{1}{2}\mathbf{b} = (2\mathbf{i}+\mathbf{j}+4\mathbf{k})-(2\mathbf{i}-\mathbf{j}+4\mathbf{k})$$
$$= 2\mathbf{j}$$

Let $\mathbf{c} = \mathbf{a}-\tfrac{1}{2}\mathbf{b}$ where $|\mathbf{c}| = 2$

$$|\mathbf{b}|^2 = 4^2+(-2)^2+8^2$$
$$\therefore\ |\mathbf{b}|^2 = 84$$
$$\mathbf{b}\cdot\mathbf{c} = (4\mathbf{i}-2\mathbf{j}+8\mathbf{k})\cdot 2\mathbf{j}$$
$$\therefore\ \mathbf{b}\cdot\mathbf{c} = -4$$

but

$$\cos\theta = \frac{\mathbf{b}\cdot\mathbf{c}}{|\mathbf{b}||\mathbf{c}|} = \frac{-4}{2\sqrt{84}} = \frac{-2}{\sqrt{84}}$$
$$= \frac{-1}{\sqrt{21}}$$
$$\therefore\ \theta = 102.6^\circ$$

2.

$$\overrightarrow{AB} = (3\mathbf{i}+4\mathbf{j}+2\mathbf{k})-(\mathbf{i}+2\mathbf{j}+\mathbf{k})$$
$$\therefore\ \overrightarrow{AB} = 2\mathbf{i}+2\mathbf{j}+\mathbf{k} \qquad (1)$$

$$\therefore \quad |\overrightarrow{AB}| = \sqrt{2^2+2^2+1^2}$$
$$|\overrightarrow{AB}| = 3$$

From (1) the DRs of $\overrightarrow{AB}$ are (2, 2, 1)

and therefore the DCs of $\overrightarrow{AB}$ are $\left(\frac{2}{3}, \frac{2}{3}, \frac{1}{3}\right)$

3. Let $\mathbf{p} = p_1\mathbf{i} + p_2\mathbf{j} + p_3\mathbf{k}$ be a vector that is perpendicular to both the given vectors. Then

$$(p_1\mathbf{i}+p_2\mathbf{j}+p_3\mathbf{k})\cdot(4\mathbf{i}+4\mathbf{j}-7\mathbf{k}) = 4p_1+4p_2-7p_3 = 0 \qquad (1)$$

Also $$(p_1\mathbf{i}+p_2\mathbf{j}+p_3\mathbf{k})\cdot(2\mathbf{i}+2\mathbf{j}+\mathbf{k}) = 2p_1+2p_2+p_3 = 0 \qquad (2)$$

Solving simultaneously

(2) × 2 $$4p_1+4p_2+2p_3 = 0 \qquad (3)$$

(1) − (3) $$-9p_3 = 0$$
$$\therefore \quad p_3 = 0 \qquad (4)$$

Substituting (4) in (2) gives $$2p_1+2p_2 = 0$$
$$\therefore \quad p_1 = -p_2$$

Hence $$p = p_1(\mathbf{i}-\mathbf{j})$$
$$\therefore \quad |\mathbf{p}|^2 = p_1^2+p_1^2$$
$$\therefore \quad |\mathbf{p}| = p_1\sqrt{2}$$

The unit vector $\hat{\mathbf{p}}$ is given by $\mathbf{p}/|\mathbf{p}|$

$$\therefore \quad \hat{\mathbf{p}} = \frac{1}{\sqrt{2}}\mathbf{i} - \frac{1}{\sqrt{2}}\mathbf{j}$$

4. If $\mathbf{u}$ and $\mathbf{v}$ are at right-angles

$$\mathbf{u}\cdot\mathbf{v} = 0$$
$$\therefore \quad [(\mathbf{a}\cdot\mathbf{c})\mathbf{b}-(\mathbf{a}\cdot\mathbf{b})\mathbf{c}]\cdot[(\mathbf{a}\cdot\mathbf{c})\mathbf{b}-(\mathbf{b}\cdot\mathbf{c})\mathbf{a}] = 0$$
$$(\mathbf{a}\cdot\mathbf{c})^2\mathbf{b}\cdot\mathbf{b}-(\mathbf{a}\cdot\mathbf{c})(\mathbf{b}\cdot\mathbf{c})\mathbf{b}\cdot\mathbf{a}-(\mathbf{a}\cdot\mathbf{b})(\mathbf{a}\cdot\mathbf{c})\mathbf{c}\cdot\mathbf{b}+(\mathbf{a}\cdot\mathbf{b})(\mathbf{b}\cdot\mathbf{c})\mathbf{c}\cdot\mathbf{a} = 0$$
$$(\mathbf{a}\cdot\mathbf{c})[(\mathbf{a}\cdot\mathbf{c})\mathbf{b}\cdot\mathbf{b}-(\mathbf{b}\cdot\mathbf{c})\mathbf{b}\cdot\mathbf{a}-(\mathbf{a}\cdot\mathbf{b})\mathbf{c}\cdot\mathbf{b}+(\mathbf{a}\cdot\mathbf{b})(\mathbf{b}\cdot\mathbf{c})] = 0$$
$$(\mathbf{a}\cdot\mathbf{c})[(\mathbf{a}\cdot\mathbf{c})\mathbf{b}\cdot\mathbf{b}-(\mathbf{a}\cdot\mathbf{b})\mathbf{c}\cdot\mathbf{b}] = 0 \qquad (1)$$

First solution:

$$\mathbf{a}\cdot\mathbf{c} = 0$$
$$\therefore \quad \mathbf{a} \text{ is perpendicular to } \mathbf{c}$$

Second solution:

$$(\mathbf{a}\cdot\mathbf{c})\mathbf{b}\cdot\mathbf{b}-(\mathbf{b}\cdot\mathbf{c})\mathbf{b}\cdot\mathbf{a} = 0 \qquad (2)$$

but $$\mathbf{a}\cdot\mathbf{c} = ac\cos\beta$$
$$\mathbf{b}\cdot\mathbf{c} = bc\cos\alpha$$
$$\mathbf{a}\cdot\mathbf{b} = ab\cos\gamma$$

and $$\mathbf{b}\cdot\mathbf{b} = b^2$$

Substituting these results in (2) gives

$$acb^2\cos\beta - ab^2c\cos\alpha\cos\gamma - ab^2c\cos\alpha\cos\gamma + ab^2c\cos\alpha\cos\gamma = 0$$

which simplifies to $$ab^2c(\cos\beta - \cos\alpha\cos\gamma) = 0$$
$$\therefore \quad \cos\beta = \cos\alpha\cos\gamma$$

EXERCISE

5.

$$\mathbf{r} = a\mathbf{i}+b\mathbf{j}+c\mathbf{k} \quad (1)$$
$$\mathbf{k}\times\mathbf{r} = \mathbf{p} \quad (2)$$
$$\mathbf{r}\times\mathbf{p} = \mathbf{k} \quad (3)$$

Substituting (2) in (3) gives

$$\mathbf{r}\times(\mathbf{k}\times\mathbf{r}) = \mathbf{k} \quad (4)$$

but
$$\mathbf{k}\times\mathbf{r} = \begin{vmatrix} \mathbf{i} & \mathbf{j} & \mathbf{k} \\ 0 & 0 & 1 \\ a & b & c \end{vmatrix}$$

$$\therefore \quad \mathbf{k}\times\mathbf{r} = -b\mathbf{i}+a\mathbf{j}$$

Substituting in (4) gives

$$\mathbf{r}\times(-b\mathbf{i}+a\mathbf{j}) = \mathbf{k}$$

but
$$\mathbf{r}\times(-b\mathbf{i}+a\mathbf{j}) = \begin{vmatrix} \mathbf{i} & \mathbf{j} & \mathbf{k} \\ a & b & c \\ -b & a & 0 \end{vmatrix}$$
$$= -ac\mathbf{i}-bc\mathbf{j}+\mathbf{k}(a^2+b^2)$$
$$= \mathbf{k} \qquad \text{(given)}$$
$$\Rightarrow \quad ac = 0, \quad bc = 0 \quad \text{and} \quad a^2+b^2 = 1$$
$$\therefore \quad c = 0 \quad \text{and} \quad a^2+b^2 = 1$$

6.

$$\mathbf{r} = \mathbf{a}+t\mathbf{b} \quad (1)$$
$$\mathbf{r}\cdot\mathbf{c} = p \quad (2)$$

In order to find the points of intersection of (1) and (2) we solve these equations simultaneously. Substituting (1) in (2) gives

$$\mathbf{c}\cdot(\mathbf{a}+t\mathbf{b}) = p$$
$$\mathbf{c}\cdot\mathbf{a}+t\mathbf{b}\cdot\mathbf{c} = p \quad (3)$$
$$t\mathbf{b}\cdot\mathbf{c} = p-\mathbf{c}\cdot\mathbf{a} \quad (4)$$
$$t = \frac{p-\mathbf{c}\cdot\mathbf{a}}{\mathbf{b}\cdot\mathbf{c}} \quad (5)$$

This is the value of the parameter t at the point of intersection of (1) and (2).

If **b** is perpendicular to **c** $\quad \mathbf{b}\cdot\mathbf{c} = 0 \quad (6)$

which, from (4), gives $\quad \mathbf{c}\cdot\mathbf{a} = p \quad (7)$

Since $\mathbf{r} = \mathbf{a}$ satisfies (2), **a** must be the position vector of a point in the plane. The normal to the plane (2) is **c**. It follows from (6) that **b** is either in the plane or is parallel to it. Hence the straight line (1) is contained in the plane.

If $\mathbf{c} = (2,-1,-1)$, $\mathbf{a} = (1,2,-3)$

$$\mathbf{c}\cdot\mathbf{a} = 2-2+3 = 3$$

If $\mathbf{c} = (2,-1,-1)$, $\mathbf{b} = (2,1,2)$

$$\mathbf{b}\cdot\mathbf{c} = 4-1-2 = 1$$

Substituting in (5) gives

$$t = \frac{4-3}{1} = 1 \qquad (\text{since } p = 4)$$

EXERCISE

The position vector of the point of intersection is found by putting $t = 1$ in (1). This gives

$$\mathbf{r} = (1, 2, -3) + (2, 1, 2)$$
$$\therefore \quad \mathbf{r} = (3, 3, -1)$$

The direction ratios of the straight line (1) are proportional to the components of the vector **b**

DRs of the straight line (1) are (2, 1, 2).

Therefore DCs of the straight line (1) are $\left(\frac{2}{3}, \frac{1}{3}, \frac{2}{3}\right)$

c is the normal to the plane (2).

Therefore DRs of **c** are $(2, -1, -1)$

and DCs of **c** are $\left(\frac{2}{\sqrt{6}}, \frac{-1}{\sqrt{6}}, \frac{-1}{\sqrt{6}}\right)$

If θ denotes the angle between the normal to the plane and the straight line given by (1), we have

$$\cos\theta = \frac{1}{3\sqrt{6}}(4 - 1 - 2)$$
$$= \frac{1}{3\sqrt{6}}$$

The angle between the straight line and the plane is $(90^\circ - \theta)$ and, since $\sin(90^\circ - \theta) = \cos\theta$, we have

$$\sin(90^\circ - \theta) = \frac{1}{3\sqrt{6}}$$

7. (i)

$$\overrightarrow{BC} = \overrightarrow{OC} - \overrightarrow{OB}$$
$$= (\mathbf{i} + \mathbf{j} - \mathbf{k}) - (\mathbf{i} - \mathbf{j} + \mathbf{k})$$
$$\therefore \quad \overrightarrow{BC} = 2\mathbf{j} - 2\mathbf{k} \qquad (1)$$

hence

$$|\overrightarrow{BC}| = \sqrt{2^2 + 2^2} = \sqrt{8}$$
$$\overrightarrow{CA} = \overrightarrow{OA} - \overrightarrow{OC}$$
$$= (-\mathbf{i} + \mathbf{j} + \mathbf{k}) - (\mathbf{i} + \mathbf{j} - \mathbf{k})$$
$$\therefore \quad \overrightarrow{CA} = -2\mathbf{i} + 2\mathbf{k} \qquad (2)$$

hence

$$|CA| = \sqrt{(-2)^2 + 2^2} = \sqrt{8}$$
$$\overrightarrow{BC} \cdot \overrightarrow{CA} = (2\mathbf{j} - 2\mathbf{k}) \cdot (-2\mathbf{i} + 2\mathbf{k})$$
$$\therefore \quad \overrightarrow{BC} \cdot \overrightarrow{CA} = -4$$

The angle, θ, between the straight lines $\overrightarrow{BC}$ and $\overrightarrow{CA}$ is found from (14.21). This gives

$$\cos\theta = \frac{\overrightarrow{BC} \cdot \overrightarrow{CA}}{|\overrightarrow{BC}||\overrightarrow{CA}|}$$
$$\therefore \quad \cos\theta = \frac{-4}{\sqrt{8}\sqrt{8}}$$
$$= -\frac{1}{2}$$

EXERCISE

$$\therefore \quad \theta = 120^\circ \quad \text{or} \quad \frac{2\pi}{3}\text{rad}$$

(ii) Let $n = n_1\mathbf{i} + n_2\mathbf{j} + n_3\mathbf{k}$.

The vector $\mathbf{n}$ will be perpendicular to both $\overrightarrow{BC}$ and $\overrightarrow{CA}$. Hence $\mathbf{n}\cdot\overrightarrow{BC} = 0$ and $\mathbf{n}\cdot\overrightarrow{CA} = 0$.

If $\mathbf{n}\cdot\overrightarrow{BC} = 0 \qquad 2n_2 - 2n_3 = 0 \qquad \therefore \quad n_2 = n_3$

If $\mathbf{n}\cdot\overrightarrow{CA} = 0 \qquad -2n_1 + 2n_3 = 0 \qquad \therefore \quad n_1 = n_3$

hence $\qquad n_1 = n_2 = n_3$

The unit normal vector, $\hat{\mathbf{n}}$, is given by

$$\hat{\mathbf{n}} = \frac{1}{\sqrt{3}}(\mathbf{i}+\mathbf{j}+\mathbf{k})$$

(iii) Hence the equation of the plane must be

$$\frac{1}{\sqrt{3}}(x+y+z) = d \tag{3}$$

This plane must pass through the point $(-1, 1, 1)$. Putting $x = -1$, $y = 1$ and $z = 1$ in (3) gives

$$\frac{1}{\sqrt{3}}(-1+1+1) = d \qquad \therefore \quad d = \frac{1}{\sqrt{3}}$$

This value of d represents the distance from the origin to the plane.

$$\overrightarrow{OP} = \alpha+\beta+\gamma$$

$$\therefore \quad \overrightarrow{OP} = \mathbf{i}+\mathbf{j}+\mathbf{k}$$

$$\beta\times\gamma = \begin{vmatrix} \mathbf{i} & \mathbf{j} & \mathbf{k} \\ 1 & -1 & 1 \\ 1 & 1 & -1 \end{vmatrix} = \mathbf{i}(1-1)-\mathbf{j}(-1-1)+\mathbf{k}(1+1)$$

$$= 2\mathbf{j}+2\mathbf{k}$$

$$\gamma\times\alpha = \begin{vmatrix} \mathbf{i} & \mathbf{j} & \mathbf{k} \\ 1 & 1 & -1 \\ -1 & 1 & 1 \end{vmatrix} = \mathbf{i}(1+1)-\mathbf{j}(1-1)+\mathbf{k}(1+1)$$

$$= 2\mathbf{i}+2\mathbf{k}$$

$$\alpha\times\beta = \begin{vmatrix} \mathbf{i} & \mathbf{j} & \mathbf{k} \\ -1 & 1 & 1 \\ 1 & -1 & 1 \end{vmatrix}$$

$$\therefore \quad \alpha\times\beta = \mathbf{i}(1+1)-\mathbf{j}(-1-1)+\mathbf{k}(1-1)$$

$$= 2\mathbf{i}+2\mathbf{j}$$

$$\therefore \quad (\beta\times\gamma)+(\gamma\times\alpha)+(\alpha\times\beta) = 4\mathbf{i}+4\mathbf{j}+4\mathbf{k}$$

$$= 4(\mathbf{i}+\mathbf{j}+\mathbf{k})$$

$$\therefore \quad \overrightarrow{OQ} = 4\overrightarrow{OP}$$

hence both Q and P are collinear with the origin.

15 EQUATIONS AND THE FACTOR AND REMAINDER THEOREMS

INTRODUCTION

In Chapter 2, we established relationships between the roots and the coefficients of quadratic equations. In this chapter we find similar results for the roots and coefficients of cubic and quartic equations.

CUBIC EQUATIONS

The general cubic equation is

$$a_0x^3 + a_1x^2 + a_2x + a_3 = 0$$

Provided $a_0 \neq 0$ this equation may be rewritten as

$$x^3 + \frac{a_1}{a_0}x^2 + \frac{a_2}{a_0}x + \frac{a_3}{a_0} = 0 \qquad (15.1)$$

Denoting the roots of this equation by α, β and γ we have

$$(x-\alpha)(x-\beta)(x-\gamma) = 0$$

Removing brackets and collecting together like terms gives

$$x^3 - (\alpha+\beta+\gamma)x^2 + (\alpha\beta+\alpha\gamma+\beta\gamma)x - \alpha\beta\gamma = 0 \qquad (15.2)$$

Equating coefficients of like powers of x in (15.1) and (15.2)

$$\alpha+\beta+\gamma = \frac{-a_1}{a_0} \qquad (15.3)$$

$$\alpha\beta+\alpha\gamma+\beta\gamma = \frac{a_2}{a_0} \qquad (15.4)$$

$$-\alpha\beta\gamma = \frac{a_3}{a_0} \qquad (15.5)$$

These three key results are fundamental to the solution of problems involving cubic equations.

QUARTIC EQUATIONS

The general quartic equation is

$$a_0x^4 + a_1x^3 + a_2x^2 + a_3x + a_4 = 0 \qquad (15.6)$$

Provided $a_0 \neq 0$ this equation may be rewritten as

$$x^4 + \frac{a_1}{a_0}x^3 + \frac{a_2}{a_0}x^2 + \frac{a_3}{a_0} + \frac{a_4}{a_0} = 0 \qquad (15.7)$$

If the roots of this equation are α, β, γ and δ we have

$$(x-\alpha)(x-\beta)(x-\gamma)(x-\delta) = 0 \qquad (15.8)$$

Removing brackets and simplifying gives

$$x^4-(\alpha+\beta+\gamma+\delta)x^3+(\alpha\beta+\alpha\gamma+\alpha\delta+\beta\gamma+\beta\delta+\delta\gamma)x^2$$
$$-(\alpha\beta\gamma+\alpha\beta\delta+\alpha\delta\gamma+\beta\delta\gamma)x+\alpha\beta\delta\gamma = 0 \qquad (15.9)$$

Comparing (15.7) and (15.9) gives

$$\alpha+\beta+\gamma+\delta = \frac{-a_1}{a_0} \qquad (15.10)$$

$$\alpha\beta+\alpha\gamma+\alpha\delta+\beta\gamma+\beta\delta+\delta\gamma = \frac{a_2}{a_0} \qquad (15.11)$$

$$\alpha\beta\gamma+\alpha\beta\delta+\alpha\delta\gamma+\beta\delta\gamma = \frac{-a_3}{a_0} \qquad (15.12)$$

$$\alpha\beta\delta\gamma = \frac{a_4}{a_0} \qquad (15.13)$$

Worked Example

The equation $px^3+qx^2+rx+s=0$ has roots α, $1/\alpha$ and β. Prove that

$$p^2-s^2 = pr-qs$$

Solve the equation

$$6x^3+11x^2-24x-9 = 0 \qquad \text{(LU 1980)}$$

Solution

Dividing the given cubic equation by p gives

$$x^3+\frac{qx^2}{p}+\frac{r}{p}x+\frac{s}{p} = 0$$

From the standard relationships between the roots and coefficients of a cubic equation, we have

$$\alpha+\frac{1}{\alpha}+\beta = \frac{-q}{p} \qquad \text{(sum of roots)} \qquad (1)$$

$$1+\frac{\beta}{\alpha}+\beta\alpha = \frac{r}{p} \qquad \text{(product of roots in pairs)} \qquad (2)$$

$$-\beta = \frac{s}{p} \qquad \text{(product of all roots)} \qquad (3)$$

Factorising (2) we have

$$\frac{r}{p} = 1+\beta\left(\frac{1}{\alpha}+\alpha\right) \qquad (4)$$

From (1) $$\alpha+\frac{1}{\alpha} = \frac{-q}{p}-\beta \qquad (5)$$

Substituting (5) in (4) gives

$$\frac{r}{p} = 1+\beta\left(\frac{-q}{p}-\beta\right) \qquad (6)$$

$$\therefore \quad pr = p^2-\beta qp-\beta^2p^2$$

Substituting for β from (3) gives

$$pr = p^2+qs-s^2$$

$$\therefore \quad p^2-s^2 = pr-qs \qquad (7)$$

The equation $$6x^3+11x^2-24x-9 = 0 \qquad (8)$$

has $p=6$, $q=11$, $r=-24$ and $s=-9$. These values satisfy (7) and so the cubic has roots of the form α, $1/\alpha$ and β. Dividing (8) by 6 gives

$$x^3+\frac{11}{6}x^2-4x-\frac{3}{2} = 0$$

$$-\beta = \frac{-3}{2}$$

$$\therefore \quad \beta = \frac{3}{2}$$

Using the sum of the roots results (1) with $\beta = 3/2$ gives

$$\alpha+\frac{1}{\alpha}+\frac{3}{2} = \frac{-11}{6}$$

$$3\alpha^2+10\alpha+3 = 0$$

$$(3\alpha+1)(\alpha+3) = 0$$

$$\therefore \quad \alpha = -3 \quad \text{or} \quad \alpha = -\tfrac{1}{3}$$

$$\therefore \quad \text{the roots are } -3, -\tfrac{1}{3}, \tfrac{3}{2}.$$

THE REMAINDER THEOREM

The remainder theorem is a statement about the result of dividing a polynomial by another polynomial which is usually a linear or occasionally a quadratic expression. Let $f(x)$ denote the polynomial. The result of dividing $f(x)$ by $(x-a)$ will be a quotient, $Q(x)$, and a remainder R. The connection between these quantities is such that

$$\frac{f(x)}{x-a} = Q(x)+\frac{R}{x-a}$$

Multiplication throughout by $(x-a)$ gives

$$f(x) = (x-a)\,Q(x)+R$$

If we now put $x=a$, we find $R=f(a)$.

THE FACTOR THEOREM

The factor theorem is a special result that can be obtained directly from the remainder theorem. If $(x-a)$ is a factor of $f(x)$, division of $f(x)$ by $(x-a)$ will give a remainder of zero. This useful deduction from the remainder theorem can be summarised as

$$\boxed{f(a) = 0 \quad \Leftrightarrow \quad (x-a) \text{ is a factor of } f(x)}$$

Worked Example

Given that $(x+3)$ is a factor of $f(x)$ where $f(x)=2x^3-ax+12$ find the constant a.

Express $f(x)$ as a product of linear factors. (LU 1981)

Solution

If $(x+3)$ is a factor of $f(x)$ we require $f(-3)=0$.

$$f(-3) = 2(-3)^3-a(-3)+12$$

$$= -54+3a+12$$

$$\therefore \quad f(-3) = 3a-42$$

Since $f(-3) = 0$

$$3a - 42 = 0$$
$$\therefore \quad a = 14$$

Hence $\quad f(x) = 2x^3 - 14x + 12$

Let $f(x) = 2g(x)$ where $g(x) = x^3 - 7x + 6$.

If $g(x) = (x+3)(x+\alpha)(x+\beta)$ we know from the properties of roots of cubic equations that

$$3\alpha\beta = 6$$
$$\therefore \quad \alpha\beta = 2$$

The integer solutions to this equation are $\alpha = 2$, $\beta = 1$ or $\alpha = -2$, $\beta = -1$.

$$g(2) = 2^3 - 7(2) + 6$$
$$= 0 \qquad \therefore \quad (x-2) \text{ is a factor}$$
$$g(1) = 1^3 - 7(1) + 6$$
$$= 0 \qquad \therefore \quad (x-1) \text{ is a factor}$$

Hence $\quad g(x) = (x+3)(x-2)(x-1)$

$$\therefore \quad f(x) = 2(x+3)(x-2)(x-1)$$

EXERCISE

1. When the expression $x^3 + ax^2 + bx + c$ is divided by $x^2 - 4$ the remainder is $18 - x$ and when it is divided by $x + 3$ the remainder is 21. Find the remainder when the expression is divided by $x + 1$. (AEB 1980)

2. When $f(x)$, where $f(x) = x^4 - 2x^3 + ax^2 + bx + c$, is divided by $x - 2$ the remainder is -24. When $f(x)$ is divided by $x + 4$ the remainder is 240. Given that $x + 1$ is a factor of $f(x)$, show that $x - 1$ is also a factor. (AEB 1981)

3. Show that $x = 2$ is a root of the equation $x^3 + 3x - 14 = 0$. Given that the other roots are α and β, show that $\alpha + \beta = -2$ and find the value of $\alpha\beta$. Find the equation with numerical coefficients whose roots are
   (i) $\alpha + 3$ and $\beta + 3$
   (ii) 5, $\alpha + 3$ and $\beta + 3$ (AEB 1982)

4. (i) One of the roots of the equation $x^3 + ax^2 + bx + c = 0$ is equal to the sum of the other two. Show that $a^3 - 4ab + 8c = 0$. Find the real value of a, such that the equation $x^3 + ax^2 + 8 = 0$ has a root equal to the sum of the other two and solve the equation in this case.
   (ii) The roots of the equation $x^4 + 2x^2 - 3x + 4 = 0$ are α, β, γ and δ. Find the values of $\Sigma\alpha^2$, $\Sigma 1/\alpha$ and $\Sigma\alpha^4$. (SUJB 1980)

5. If α, β and γ are the roots of $x^3 + qx - r = 0$, show that

$$\frac{\alpha}{\beta} + \frac{\beta}{\alpha} = \frac{\gamma^3}{r} - 2$$

Hence or otherwise show that the equation with roots

$$\frac{\alpha}{\beta} + \frac{\beta}{\alpha}, \ \frac{\beta}{\gamma} + \frac{\gamma}{\beta} \quad \text{and} \quad \frac{\gamma}{\alpha} + \frac{\alpha}{\gamma}$$

can be put in the form

$$r^2(y+1)^3 + q^3(y+2) = 0$$ (SUJB 1982)

Worked Solutions

1. Let $f(x) = x^3+ax^2+bx+c$

Since division of $f(x)$ by (x^2-4) gives a remainder of $(18-x)$, we have

$$f(x) = (x^2-4)Q(x)+(18-x)$$

where $Q(x)$ is a linear expression.

$f(2) = 16$ [since $R = 18-x$ and also $R = f(a)$]

$\therefore\ 8+4a+2b+c = 16$

$\therefore\ 4a+2b+c = 8$ (1)

$f(-2) = 20$

$\therefore\ -8+4a-2b+c = 20$

$\therefore\ 4a-2b+c = 28$ (2)

Solving these simultaneously

(1)−(2) $4b = -20$

$\therefore\ b = -5$

Also $f(-3) = 21$

$\therefore\ -27+9a+15+c = 21$ (using $b = -5$)

$\therefore\ 9a+c = 33$ (3)

Substituting for b in (2) gives

$4a+10+c = 28$

$4a+c = 18$ (4)

(3)−(4) $5a = 15$

$\therefore\ a = 3$

Substituting for a in (4)

$12+c = 18$

$\therefore\ c = 6$

Hence $f(x) = x^3+3x^2-5x+6$

$\therefore\ f(-1) = (-1)^3+3(-1)^2-5(-1)+6 = 13$

$\therefore$ remainder on division by $x+1$ is 13

2. $f(2) = 2^4-2\times 2^3+a\times 2^2+2b+c = -24$ (remainder theorem)

$\therefore\ 4a+2b+c = -24$ (1)

$f(-4) = (-4)^4-2(-4)^3+a(-4)^2-4b+c = 240$ (remainder theorem)

$\therefore\ 16a-4b+c = -144$ (2)

$f(-1) = (-1)^4-2(-1)^3+a(-1)^2+b(-1)+c = 0$ (factor theorem)

$\therefore\ a-b+c = -3$ (3)

The equations (1), (2) and (3) have to be solved simultaneously.

(1)−(3) $3a+3b = -21$ (4)

(2)−(3) $15a-3b = -141$ (5)

(4)+(5) $18a = -162$

$\therefore\ a = -9$

Substituting in (4) gives

$-27+3b = -21$

$3b = 6$

$\therefore\ b = 2$

EXERCISE

Substituting for a and b in (3) gives

$$-9-2+c = -3$$
$$\therefore \quad c = 8$$

Hence $\quad f(x) = x^4-2x^3-9x^2+2x+8$

$$\therefore \quad f(1) = 1^4-2-9+2+8 = 0$$
$$\therefore \quad (x-1) \text{ is a factor}$$

3. Let $\quad f(x) = x^3+3x-14 \qquad (1)$

$$\therefore \quad f(2) = 2^3+3\times 2-14 = 0$$

Hence $x=2$ is a root of $x^3+3x-14=0$.

Since the coefficient of the x^2 term is zero, the sum of the roots is 0.

$$\therefore \quad \alpha+\beta+2 = 0$$
$$\therefore \quad \alpha+\beta = -2$$

From (1) product of roots is 14

$$\therefore \quad 2\alpha\beta = 14$$
$$\therefore \quad \alpha\beta = 7$$

(i) The equation with roots $\alpha+3$ and $\beta+3$ will be the quadratic equation:

$$x^2-(\alpha+\beta+6)x+(\alpha+3)(\beta+3) = 0$$
$$x^2-4x+[\alpha\beta+3(\alpha+\beta)+9] = 0 \qquad (\alpha+\beta=-2,\ \alpha\beta=7)$$
$$\therefore \quad x^2-4x+10 = 0$$

(ii) The equation with roots 5, $\alpha+3$ and $\beta+3$ will be a cubic given by

$$(x-5)(x^2-4x+10) = 0$$
$$\therefore \quad x^3-9x^2+30x-50 = 0$$

4. (i) Let α, β, γ denote the roots of the equation $x^3+ax^2+bx+c=0$.

$$\alpha+\beta+\gamma = -a \qquad \text{(sum of roots)}$$

but $\quad \alpha = \beta+\gamma \qquad$ (one root = sum of other roots)

$$\therefore \quad 2(\beta+\gamma) = -a$$
$$\beta+\gamma = \frac{-a}{2} \qquad (1)$$

Also

$$\alpha\beta+\alpha\gamma+\beta\gamma = b \qquad \text{(product of roots in pairs)} \qquad (2)$$

and $\quad -\alpha\beta\gamma = c \qquad$ (product of roots) $\qquad (3)$

$$\therefore \quad -\beta\gamma(\beta+\gamma) = c \qquad (\text{since } \alpha=\beta+\gamma)$$
$$\beta\gamma\frac{a}{2} = c \qquad [\text{substituting for } (\beta+\gamma)]$$
$$\therefore \quad \beta\gamma = \frac{2c}{a} \qquad (4)$$

Substituting (4) in (2) gives

$$\alpha(\beta+\gamma)+\frac{2c}{a} = b$$
$$(\beta+\gamma)^2+\frac{2c}{a} = b \qquad (5)$$

$$\frac{a^2}{4}+\frac{2c}{a} = b \qquad (6)$$

(6) × 4a $\qquad a^3+8c = 4ab$

$$a^3-4ab+8c = 0$$

If $x^3+ax^2+8=0$, $b=0$, $c=8$

hence $\qquad a^3+64 = 0$

$$\therefore \quad a = -4$$

$$\therefore \quad x^3-4x^2+8 = 0 \text{ is the required equation}$$

Substituting for a in (1) gives

$$\beta+\gamma = 2$$

$$\beta\gamma = -4 \qquad \text{[from (4)]}$$

$$\gamma(2-\gamma) = -4$$

$$\gamma^2-2\gamma-4 = 0$$

$$\therefore \quad \gamma = 1\pm\sqrt{5}$$

and $\qquad \beta = 1\mp\sqrt{5}$

The required roots are $\alpha=2$, $\beta=1+\sqrt{5}$, $\gamma=1-\sqrt{5}$.

(ii) $\qquad \alpha+\beta+\gamma+\delta = 0 \qquad$ (sum of roots) $\qquad$ (7)

$\alpha\beta+\alpha\gamma+\alpha\delta+\beta\gamma+\beta\delta+\gamma\delta = 2 \qquad$ (product of roots in pairs) (8)

$\alpha\beta\gamma\delta = 4 \qquad$ (product of all roots) $\qquad$ (9)

Now $\qquad (\alpha+\beta+\gamma+\delta)^2 = (\alpha+\beta)^2+2(\alpha+\beta)(\gamma+\delta)+(\gamma+\delta)^2$

$$= \alpha^2+\beta^2+\gamma^2+\delta^2 + 2(\alpha\beta+\alpha\gamma+\alpha\delta+\beta\gamma+\beta\delta+\gamma\delta) \qquad (10)$$

$$\alpha^2+\beta^2+\gamma^2+\delta^2 = -2(\alpha\beta+\alpha\gamma+\alpha\delta+\beta\gamma+\beta\delta+\gamma\delta)$$

[using (7)]

$$\therefore \quad \sum\alpha^2 = -4$$

Since α, β, γ and δ are roots of the equation we have

$$\alpha^4+2\alpha^2-3\alpha+4 = 0 \qquad (11)$$

$$\beta^4+2\beta^2-3\beta+4 = 0 \qquad (12)$$

$$\gamma^4+2\gamma^2-3\gamma+4 = 0 \qquad (13)$$

$$\delta^4+2\delta^2-3\delta+4 = 0 \qquad (14)$$

Addition of the equations (11) to (14) gives

$$(\alpha^4+\beta^4+\gamma^4+\delta^4)+2(\alpha^2+\beta^2+\gamma^2+\delta^2)-3(\alpha+\beta+\gamma+\delta)+16 = 0$$

$$\therefore \quad \sum\alpha^4 = -16-2\sum\alpha^2 \qquad \left[\text{since } \sum\alpha=0 \text{ from (7)}\right]$$

$$= -16-2(-4)$$

$$= -8$$

$$\sum\frac{1}{\alpha} = \frac{1}{\alpha}+\frac{1}{\beta}+\frac{1}{\gamma}+\frac{1}{\delta}$$

$$= \frac{\beta\gamma\delta+\alpha\gamma\delta+\alpha\beta\delta+\alpha\beta\gamma}{\alpha\beta\gamma\delta} \qquad (15)$$

but $\qquad \alpha\beta\gamma+\alpha\beta\delta+\beta\gamma\delta+\delta\alpha\gamma = 3 \qquad$ [using (15.12)]

and $\qquad \alpha\beta\gamma\delta = 4 \qquad$ [from (9)]

EXERCISE

$$\therefore \quad \sum \frac{1}{\alpha} = \frac{3}{4}$$

5.
$$\frac{\alpha}{\beta}+\frac{\beta}{\alpha} = \frac{\alpha^2+\beta^2}{\alpha\beta}$$
$$= \frac{(\alpha+\beta)^2-2\alpha\beta}{\alpha\beta}$$
$$\therefore \quad \frac{\alpha}{\beta}+\frac{\beta}{\alpha} = \frac{(\alpha+\beta)^2}{\alpha\beta}-2 \qquad (1)$$

Using the standard results for the sum and the product of the roots of a cubic equation we have

$$\alpha+\beta+\gamma = 0 \qquad \text{(coefficient of } x^2 \text{ is zero)}$$
$$\therefore \quad \alpha+\beta = -\gamma \qquad (2)$$
$$\alpha\beta\gamma = r$$
$$\therefore \quad \alpha\beta = \frac{r}{\gamma} \qquad (3)$$

Substituting (2) and (3) in (1) gives

$$\frac{\alpha}{\beta}+\frac{\beta}{\alpha} = \frac{\gamma^2}{(r/\gamma)}-2$$

giving
$$\frac{\alpha}{\beta}+\frac{\beta}{\alpha} = \frac{\gamma^3}{r}-2 \qquad (4)$$

From the original cubic equation we have

$$\gamma^3+q\gamma-r = 0$$

i.e.
$$\gamma^3-r = -q\gamma$$
$$\frac{\alpha}{\beta}+\frac{\beta}{\alpha} = \frac{\gamma^3-2r}{r} = \frac{-q\gamma-r}{r}$$
$$\therefore \quad \frac{\alpha}{\beta}+\frac{\beta}{\alpha} = \frac{-q\gamma}{r}-1 \qquad (5)$$

Let
$$l = \frac{\alpha}{\beta}+\frac{\beta}{\alpha}+1$$

Using (5) we have
$$l = \frac{-q\gamma}{r} \qquad (6)$$

Also, defining

$$m = \frac{\beta}{\gamma}+\frac{\gamma}{\beta}+1 \quad \text{and} \quad n = \frac{\gamma}{\alpha}+\frac{\alpha}{\gamma}+1$$

it follows that
$$m = \frac{-q\alpha}{r} \qquad (7)$$

and
$$n = \frac{-q\beta}{r} \qquad (8)$$

The cubic equation with roots given by (6), (7) and (8) has

$$l+m+n = -\frac{q}{r}(\alpha+\beta+\gamma)$$
$$\therefore \quad l+m+n = 0 \qquad [\text{since } (\alpha+\beta+\gamma = 0 \text{ from } (2)] \qquad (9)$$

Also

$$lm + mn + nl = \frac{q^2}{r^2}(\alpha\gamma + \alpha\beta + \beta\gamma)$$

but $\alpha\gamma + \alpha\beta + \beta\gamma = q$ (product of roots in pairs)

$$\therefore \quad lm + mn + nl = \frac{q^3}{r^2} \qquad (10)$$

and $lmn = \dfrac{-q^3}{r^3}\alpha\beta\gamma$ [from (6), (7) and (8)]

$$\therefore \quad lmn = \frac{-q^3}{r^2} \quad \text{(since } \alpha\beta\gamma = r\text{)} \qquad (11)$$

From (9), (10) and (11) the required cubic is

$$u^3 + \frac{q^3 u}{r^2} + \frac{q^3}{r^2} = 0$$

$$r^2u^3 + q^3u + q^3 = 0$$

If we let $u = y + 1$, we have

$$r^2(y+1)^3 + q^3(y+1) + q^3 = 0$$

$$r^2(y+1)^3 + q^3(y+2) = 0 \quad \text{(as required)}$$

EXERCISE

16 COMPLEX NUMBERS

COMPLEX NUMBERS

A fundamental theorem in algebra is that every polynomial equation of degree n has n roots. In particular, the solutions to the quadratic equation

$$ax^2 + bx + c = 0$$

are given by

$$x = \frac{-b \pm \sqrt{b^2 - 4ac}}{2a}$$

For ease of reference we let $D = b^2 - 4ac$. In the case where $D \geqslant 0$, the solutions are real. If $D < 0$ it is necessary to find the square root of a negative number and in order that every quadratic equation has two roots we define $\mathrm{i}^2 = -1$. The introduction of i in this manner allows us to find the square root of any negative number.

Example 1

$$\begin{aligned} (-9)^{1/2} &= 9^{1/2} \times (-1)^{1/2} \\ &= \pm 3\mathrm{i} \end{aligned}$$

There are two roots because every positive number has a positive and a negative square root.

Example 2

$$\begin{aligned} (-16)^{1/2} &= 16^{1/2} \times (-1)^{1/2} \\ &= \pm 4\mathrm{i} \end{aligned}$$

Because these numbers possess no real part they are called imaginary.

DEFINITION OF A COMPLEX NUMBER

A complex number is the combination of a real number and an imaginary number by either addition or subtraction. All complex numbers can be written in the form

$$a + \mathrm{i}b$$

where both a and b are real numbers.

ADDITION AND SUBTRACTION OF COMPLEX NUMBERS

The rules for the addition or subtraction of complex numbers are shown below

$$(a_1 + \mathrm{i}b_1) + (a_2 + \mathrm{i}b_2) = (a_1 + a_2) + \mathrm{i}(b_1 + b_2)$$

The addition or subtraction of complex numbers is effected by adding or subtracting the real part of the numbers and doing the same to the imaginary part.

MULTIPLICATION OF COMPLEX NUMBERS

The product of two complex numbers is obtained by the same procedure as for multiplying out brackets in algebra. The result is then simplified by collecting together real and imaginary parts.

Example

$$\begin{aligned}(a_1+ib_1)(a_2+ib_2) &= a_1a_2+ia_2b_2+ia_2b_1+i^2b_1b_2 \\ &= a_1a_2+ia_2b_2+ia_2b_1-b_1b_2 \qquad \text{(since } i^2=-1\text{)} \\ &= (a_1a_2-b_1b_2)+i(a_1b_2+a_2b_1)\end{aligned}$$

COMPLEX CONJUGATES

Let
$$z = x+iy$$
We define the complex conjugate of z, denoted by $\bar{z}$, to be given by
$$\bar{z} = x-iy$$

DIVISION OF COMPLEX NUMBERS

Let
$$z_1 = x_1+iy_1 \quad \text{and} \quad z_2 = x_2+iy_2$$
Then
$$\begin{aligned}\frac{z_1}{z_2} &= \frac{x_1+iy_1}{x_2+iy_2} \\ &= \frac{(x_1+iy_1)(x_2-iy_2)}{(x_2+iy_2)(x_2-iy_2)} \qquad \text{(multiplying both numerator and denominator by } \bar{z}_2\text{)} \\ &= \frac{x_1x_2-ix_1y_2+ix_2y_1+y_1y_2}{x_2^2+y_2^2}\end{aligned}$$
$$\therefore \quad \frac{z_1}{z_2} = \frac{(x_1x_2+y_1y_2)}{x_2^2+y_2^2}+\frac{i(x_2y_1-x_1y_2)}{x_2^2+y_2^2}$$

REAL AND IMAGINARY PARTS OF A COMPLEX NUMBER

Sometimes it is necessary to refer to the real or imaginary part of a complex number in isolation. If $z = x+iy$, the real part of z is $\text{Re}(z)$ and is given by
$$\text{Re}(z) = x$$
Similarly, the imaginary part of z is given by
$$\text{Im}(z) = y$$

THE ARGAND DIAGRAM

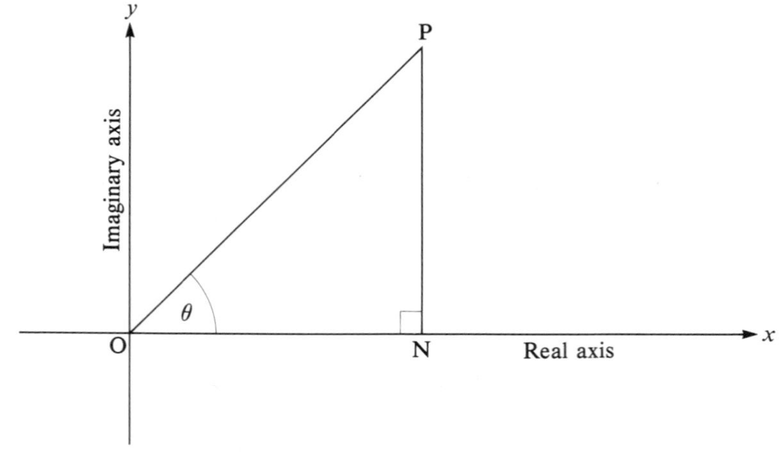

Fig. 16.1

The Argand diagram is a useful device for representing complex numbers. The y-axis is used to represent the imaginary part of the complex number, and the x-axis is used for the real part. Fig. 16.1 shows the point P, corresponding to the complex number $x + iy$, plotted on the Argand diagram. If we connect O to P, the resulting line OP is the position vector of the point P on the Argand diagram.

THE MODULUS AND ARGUMENT OF A COMPLEX NUMBER

The representation of a complex number on the Argand diagram enables us to apply geometrical concepts to complex numbers. We define the modulus of z, denoted by $|z|$, to be the length of the position vector $\overrightarrow{OP}$. Applying Pythagoras' theorem to the right-angled triangle ONP, we have

$$OP^2 = ON^2 + NP^2$$

Since $OP = |z|$, $ON = x$ and $NP = y$ substitution gives the result

$$z^2 = x^2 + y^2$$

$$\therefore \quad |z| = \sqrt{x^2 + y^2}$$

The argument of the complex number z is the angle which the position vector $\overrightarrow{OP}$ makes with the positive direction of the x-axis. Referring to the diagram above, simple trigonometry gives the result

$$\tan\theta = \frac{y}{x}$$

$$\therefore \quad \theta = \tan^{-1}\frac{y}{x}$$

Sometimes we write $\arg z = \theta$.

Worked Example

(i) Solve the equation $x^2 - 4x + 13 = 0$, giving both complex roots.

(ii) Sketch on the Argand diagram, the point (radius vector) corresponding to $w = 3 - 4i$. Indicate clearly the modulus and argument of w.

(iii) Multiply out $(\cos\theta + i\sin\theta)(\cos\phi + i\sin\phi)$, simplifying the answer.

(iv) If $z = 5 - 12i$, express (a) $1/z$ and (b) $z/(5 - 7i)$ in the form $a + ib$, where a and b are both real. (SUJB 1979)

Solution

(i) $x^2 - 4x + 13 = 0$ i.e. $a = 1$, $b = -4$, $c = 13$. Using the standard formula for the solution of quadratic equations we have

$$x = \frac{4 \pm \sqrt{(-4)^2 - 52}}{2}$$

giving

$$x = 2 \pm \tfrac{1}{2}\sqrt{-36}$$
$$= 2 \pm 3i$$

$$\therefore \quad x = 2 + 3i \quad \text{or} \quad x = 2 - 3i$$

(ii) The argument of w is the angle that the radius vector $\overrightarrow{OP}$ makes with the positive x-axis when the angle is measured in the anticlockwise direction. By Pythagoras' theorem we have

$$|w| = \sqrt{3^2 + 4^2} = 5 \quad \text{and} \quad \theta = \arctan -4/3 \approx 307^\circ$$

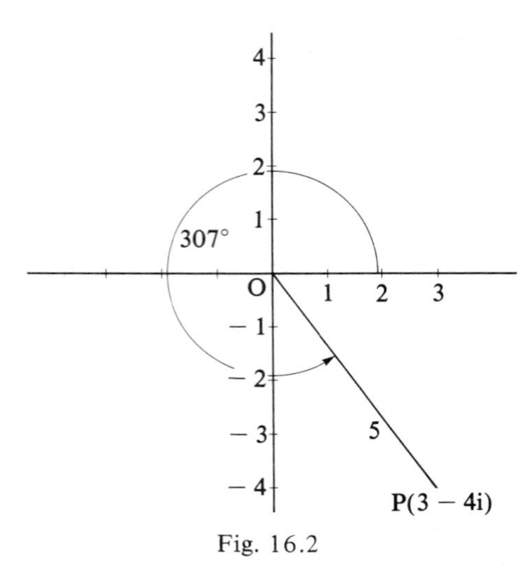

Fig. 16.2

(iii)

$$(\cos\theta + i\sin\theta)(\cos\phi + i\sin\phi) = \cos\theta\,\cos\phi + i\sin\phi\,\cos\theta + i\sin\theta\,\cos\phi - \sin\theta\,\sin\phi$$

$$= (\cos\theta\,\cos\phi - \sin\theta\,\sin\phi) + i(\sin\phi\,\cos\theta + \sin\theta\,\cos\phi)$$

$$= \cos(\theta + \phi) + i\sin(\phi + \theta)$$ (using the addition formulae)

(iv) (a)

$$\frac{1}{z} = \frac{1}{5 - 12i}$$

$$= \frac{(5 + 12i)}{(5 - 12i)(5 + 12i)}$$ (multiplying numerator and denominator by $\bar{z}$)

$$= \frac{5 + 12i}{25 + 144}$$

$$= \frac{5 + 12i}{169}$$

$$= \frac{5}{169} + \frac{12i}{169}$$

(b)

$$\frac{z}{5 - 7i} = \frac{(5 - 12i)(5 + 7i)}{(5 - 7i)(5 + 7i)}$$

$$= \frac{25 + 35i - 60i + 84}{25 + 49}$$

$$= \frac{109 - 25i}{74}$$

$$= \frac{1}{74}(109 - 25i)$$

THE MODULUS AND ARGUMENT OF A COMPLEX NUMBER

THE CARTESIAN AND POLAR FORM OF A COMPLEX NUMBER

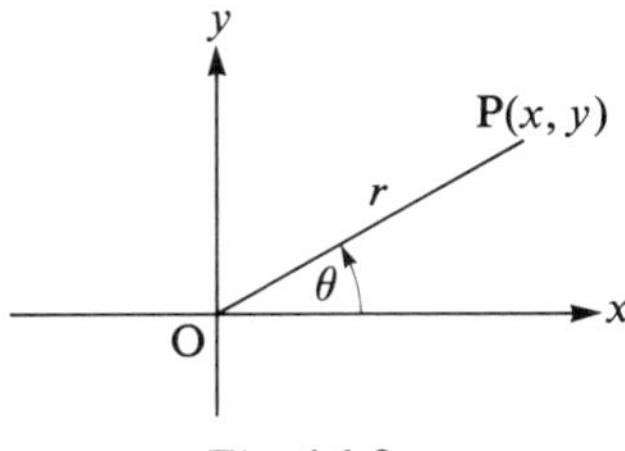

Fig. 16.3

In coordinate geometry there are two basic methods for labelling points in the plane. The widely used rectangular cartesian coordinates are measured relative to mutually perpendicular axes. For this reason a number given in the form $z = x + \mathrm{i}y$ is said to be in the Cartesian form.

In contrast to this method, the polar coordinates (r, θ) of the point P specify the length of the radius vector $\overrightarrow{\mathrm{OP}}$ and the angle that it makes with the positive x-axis (Fig. 16.3). The Argand diagram enables us to identify these quantities as the modulus and argument of z, respectively.

Trigonometry allows us to relate Cartesian coordinates to polar coordinates and vice versa. Using the basic identities of the trigonometric ratios for right-angled triangles, we have

$$x = r\cos\theta \quad \text{and} \quad y = r\sin\theta$$

The complex number $z = x + \mathrm{i}y$ can now be rewritten in the polar form as

$$z = r\cos\theta + r\sin\theta \times \mathrm{i}$$

which can be conveniently factorised to

$$z = r(\cos\theta + \mathrm{i}\sin\theta) \tag{16.1}$$

where $r = |z|$ and $\theta = \arg z$.

THE EXPONENTIAL FORM FOR COMPLEX NUMBERS

If we take the exponential series for e^x and let $x = \mathrm{i}\theta$, we have

$$\begin{aligned} \mathrm{e}^{\mathrm{i}\theta} &= 1 + \mathrm{i}\theta + \frac{(\mathrm{i}\theta)^2}{2!} + \frac{(\mathrm{i}\theta)^3}{3!} + \frac{(\mathrm{i}\theta)^4}{4!} + \dots \\ &= 1 + \mathrm{i}\theta - \frac{\theta^2}{2!} - \frac{\mathrm{i}\theta^3}{3!} + \frac{\theta^4}{4!} + \dots \end{aligned}$$

Collecting together real and imaginary parts gives

$$\mathrm{e}^{\mathrm{i}\theta} = \left(1 - \frac{\theta^2}{2!} + \frac{\theta^4}{4!} + \dots\right) + \mathrm{i}\left(\theta - \frac{\theta^3}{3!} + \frac{\theta^5}{5!} - \frac{\theta^7}{7!} + \dots\right)$$

Using the Maclaurin expansions for $\cos\theta$ and $\sin\theta$, this result is equivalent to

$$\mathrm{e}^{\mathrm{i}\theta} = \cos\theta + \mathrm{i}\sin\theta \tag{16.2}$$

which is a standard result referred to as Euler's identity.

The Euler identity enables us to rewrite (16.1) in the exponential form as

$$z = r\mathrm{e}^{\mathrm{i}\theta} \tag{16.3}$$

DE MOIVRE'S THEOREM

If $z = r\mathrm{e}^{\mathrm{i}\theta}$

$$\begin{aligned} z^n &= (r\mathrm{e}^{\mathrm{i}\theta})^n \\ &= r^n\mathrm{e}^{\mathrm{i}n\theta} \\ &= r^n(\cos n\theta + \mathrm{i}\sin n\theta) \end{aligned} \tag{16.4}$$

However, in polar form, we have

$$z = r(\cos\theta + \mathrm{i}\sin\theta)$$

Hence $$z^n = r^n(\cos\theta + \mathrm{i}\sin\theta)^n \qquad (16.5)$$

The RHS of (16.4) must be identical to the RHS of (16.5).

Equating gives $$(\cos\theta + \mathrm{i}\sin\theta)^n = \cos n\theta + \mathrm{i}\sin n\theta \qquad (16.6)$$

which is De Moivre's theorem. This is valid for positive and negative integers as well as rational and irrational indices.

Example

De Moivre's theorem can be used to establish trigonometric identities. If we put $n = 3$ in (16.6), we have

$$(\cos\theta + \mathrm{i}\sin\theta)^3 = \cos 3\theta + \mathrm{i}\sin 3\theta$$

Expanding the LHS by the binomial theorem, we have

$$\cos^3\theta + 3\cos^2\theta\,(\mathrm{i}\sin\theta) + 3\cos\theta(\mathrm{i}\sin\theta)^2 + (\mathrm{i}\sin\theta)^3 = \cos 3\theta + \mathrm{i}\sin 3\theta$$

Collecting together real and imaginary parts gives

$$(\cos^3\theta - 3\cos\theta\sin^2\theta) + \mathrm{i}(3\cos^2\theta\sin\theta - \sin^3\theta) = \cos 3\theta + \mathrm{i}\sin 3\theta$$

Equating real and imaginary parts

$$\cos 3\theta = \cos^3\theta - 3\cos\theta\sin^2\theta \qquad (1)$$

and $$\sin 3\theta = 3\cos^2\theta\sin\theta - \sin^3\theta \qquad (2)$$

The RHS of (1) can be expressed in terms of $\cos\theta$ by replacing $\sin^2\theta$ by $(1 - \cos^2\theta)$. This gives

$$\cos 3\theta = \cos^3\theta - 3\cos\theta(1 - \cos^2\theta)$$

$$\therefore \quad \cos 3\theta = 4\cos^3\theta - 3\cos\theta \qquad (3)$$

Similarly, by replacing $\cos^2\theta$ by $(1 - \sin^2\theta)$, we can obtain a formula for $\sin 3\theta$ from (2). We have

$$\sin 3\theta = 3(1 - \sin^2\theta)\sin\theta - \sin^3\theta$$

$$\therefore \quad \sin 3\theta = 3\sin\theta - 4\sin^3\theta \qquad (4)$$

Another standard application of De Moivre's theorem is to the calculation of roots of a number. This technique is illustrated in the following example.

Worked Example

Express in the form $a + \mathrm{i}b$

(i) $\dfrac{3+4\mathrm{i}}{5-2\mathrm{i}}$

(ii) $\left(\cos\dfrac{\pi}{6} + \mathrm{i}\sin\dfrac{\pi}{6}\right)^5$

(iii) $\mathrm{e}^{\mathrm{i}\pi/3}$

Solve the equation $z^3 + 27 = 0$ and represent the roots on an Argand diagram. The equation $z^3 + pz^2 + 40z + q = 0$ has a root $(3 + \mathrm{i})$, where p and q are real. Find the values of p and q. (AEB 1981)

Solution

(i) $$\frac{3+4\mathrm{i}}{5-2\mathrm{i}} = \frac{(3+4\mathrm{i})(5+2\mathrm{i})}{(5-2\mathrm{i})(5+2\mathrm{i})}$$

$$= \frac{15 + 26\mathrm{i} - 8}{25 + 4}$$

$$= \frac{(7+26i)}{29}$$

$$= \frac{7}{29} + \frac{26i}{29}$$

(ii) $$\left(\cos\frac{\pi}{6} + i\sin\frac{\pi}{6}\right)^5 = \cos\frac{5\pi}{6} + i\sin\frac{5\pi}{6} \qquad \text{(De Moivre's theorem)}$$

$$= -\frac{\sqrt{3}}{2} + \frac{1}{2}i$$

(iii) $$e^{i\pi/3} = \cos\frac{\pi}{3} + i\sin\frac{\pi}{3}$$

$$= \frac{1}{2} + \frac{\sqrt{3}}{2}i$$

If $z^3 + 27 = 0$

$$z^3 = -27$$

$$z^3 = 27(\cos\pi + i\sin\pi) \qquad (\text{since } \cos\pi = -1,\ \sin\pi = 0) \qquad (1)$$

However, since both the sine and cosine ratios have a period of 2π, this can be rewritten as

$$z^3 = 27[\cos(2n-1)\pi + i\sin(2n-1)\pi] \qquad (2)$$

for $n = 1, 2, 3, 4, \ldots$

$$\therefore \quad z = 27^{1/3}[\cos(2n-1)\pi + i\sin(2n-1)\pi]^{1/3}$$

$$z = 3\left[\cos\frac{(2n-1)}{3}\pi + i\sin\frac{(2n-1)}{3}\pi\right]$$

for $n = 1, 2, 3, 4, \ldots$

First root: if $n = 1$

$$z = 3\left(\cos\frac{\pi}{3} + i\sin\frac{\pi}{3}\right)$$

$$\therefore \quad z = 3\left(\frac{1}{2} + \frac{\sqrt{3}}{2}i\right) \qquad (3)$$

Second root: if $n = 2$

$$z = 3(\cos\pi + i\sin\pi)$$

$$\therefore \quad z = -3 \qquad (\cos\pi = -1,\ \sin\pi = 0) \qquad (4)$$

Third root: if $n = 3$

$$z = 3\left(\cos\frac{5\pi}{3} + i\sin\frac{5\pi}{3}\right)$$

$$\therefore \quad z = 3\left(\frac{1}{2} - \frac{\sqrt{3}}{2}i\right) \qquad (5)$$

Integer values of n such that $n > 3$ will only repeat the three solutions (3), (4) and (5). These three solutions are shown on the Argand diagram in Fig. 16.4.

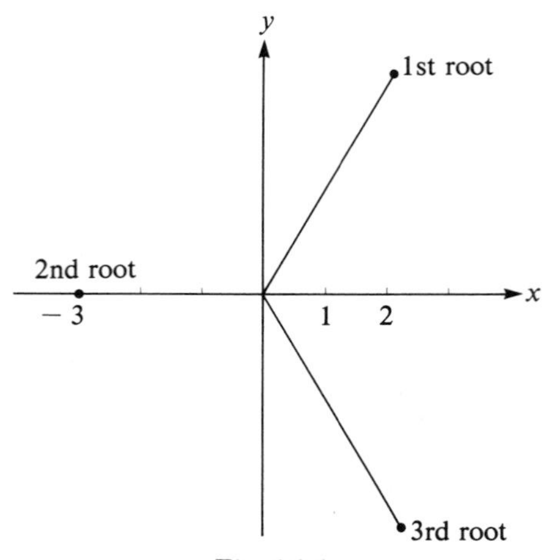

Fig. 16.4

Let α, β and γ denote the roots of the cubic equation

$$z^3 + pz^2 + 40z + q = 0$$

Complex roots occur in conjugate pairs. Hence $\beta = \bar{\alpha}$, where $\alpha = 3 + \mathrm{i}$. This gives $\beta = 3 - \mathrm{i}$. We now use the following relationships between the roots and the coefficients of this cubic equation

$$\alpha + \beta + \gamma = -p \qquad (6)$$

$$\alpha\beta + \alpha\gamma + \beta\gamma = 40 \qquad (7)$$

$$-\alpha\beta\gamma = q \qquad (8)$$

Substituting the values of α and β in equations (6) and (7) gives

In (6) $$(3 + \mathrm{i}) + (3 - \mathrm{i}) + \gamma = -p$$

$$6 + \gamma = -p \qquad (9)$$

$$(3 + \mathrm{i})(3 - \mathrm{i}) + \gamma(3 + \mathrm{i}) + \gamma(3 - \mathrm{i}) = 40$$

$$10 + 6\gamma = 40$$

$$\therefore \quad \gamma = 5 \qquad (10)$$

Substituting (10) in (9) gives $p = -11$.

From (8) we have

$$-5(3 + \mathrm{i})(3 - \mathrm{i}) = q$$

$$-5 \times 10 = q$$

$$\therefore \quad q = -50$$

The required values are $p = -11$, $q = -50$.

EXERCISE

1. (i) If z_1 and z_2 are complex numbers, solve the simultaneous equations $4z_1 + 3z_2 = 23$, $z_1 + \mathrm{i}z_2 = 6 + 8\mathrm{i}$, giving both answers in the form $x + \mathrm{i}y$.

(ii) If $(a + \mathrm{i}b)^2 = -5 + 12\mathrm{i}$, find a and b given that they are both real. Give the two square roots of $-5 + 12\mathrm{i}$.

(iii) In each of the following cases define the locus of the point which represents z in the Argand diagram.

Illustrate each statement by a sketch.

(a) $|z - 2| = 3$, (b) $|z - 2| = |z - 3|$. (SUJB 1981)

DE MOIVRE'S THEOREM/EXERCISE

2. (i) Solve the equation $z^3 = -8i$, giving answers in the form $a + ib$, and show the results on an Argand diagram.

(ii) If $w = \dfrac{z+2i}{z-4}$ where $z = x + iy$ (x and y real), find the real and imaginary parts of w.

P is the point which represents z in an Argand diagram. If w is purely imaginary, prove that the locus of P is a circle. If w is real, find the locus of P. (SUJB 1981)

3. If $z = \cos\theta + i\sin\theta$, find $|z-1|$ in its simplest form and show that $\arg(z-1) = \frac{1}{2}(\pi + \theta)$. Hence find the arguments of the cube roots of $i-1$ in terms of π. Find also the modulus of these cube roots to 3 significant figures.

If $z = x + iy$ is represented in an Argand diagram by the point P, sketch the locus of P when $|z| = 2|z - i + 1|$. (AEB 1980)

4. (i) Verify that $\alpha_1 = -1 - 3i$ is a root of the equation

$$z^2 + iz + 5(1-i) = 0$$

By considering the coefficient of z in the equation, or otherwise, find the second root α_2.

Find the modulus and argument of β where

$$\frac{1}{\beta} = \frac{1}{\alpha_1} + \frac{1}{\alpha_2}$$

(ii) (a) Show that the locus of points in the Argand plane satisfying the equation

$$z\bar{z} + (1+i)z + (1-i)\bar{z} = 1$$

is a circle.

(b) Find the complex numbers corresponding to the points where the locus

$$z^2 + \bar{z}^2 - 14z\bar{z} + 48 = 0$$

crosses the imaginary axis.

(c) Show that the locus

$$2z^2 + 2\bar{z}^2 - z\bar{z} + 15 = 0$$

does not cross the real axis. (WJEC 1982)

Worked Solutions

1. (i) We need to solve simultaneously the equations

$$4z_1 + 3z_2 = 23 \qquad (1)$$

$$z_1 + iz_2 = 6 + 8i \qquad (2)$$

$$(2)\times 4 \qquad 4z_1 + 4iz_2 = 24 + 32i \qquad (3)$$

$$(3)-(1) \qquad (4i-3)z_2 = 1 + 32i$$

$$z_2 = \frac{1+32i}{4i-3}$$

$$\therefore \quad z_2 = \frac{(1+32i)(-3-4i)}{(4i-3)(-3-4i)}$$

$$= \frac{-3-4i-96i+128}{9+16}$$

$$= \frac{125-100i}{25}$$

giving $$z_2 = 5-4i \qquad (4)$$

Substituting (4) in (1) gives

$$4z_1+3(5-4i) = 23$$
$$4z_1+15-12i = 23$$
$$\therefore \quad 4z_1 = 8+12i$$
$$\therefore \quad z_1 = 2+3i \qquad (5)$$

(ii)
$$(a+ib)^2 = -5+12i$$
$$\therefore \quad (a^2-b^2)+2abi = -5+12i$$

Equating real and imaginary parts gives

$$a^2-b^2 = -5 \qquad (6)$$
$$2ab = 12 \qquad (7)$$
$$b = \frac{6}{a} \qquad (8)$$

Substituting (8) in (6) gives

$$a^2-\left(\frac{6}{a}\right)^2 = -5$$
$$\therefore \quad a^4+5a^2-36 = 0$$
$$(a^2-4)(a^2+9) = 0$$

Since a is real the only possible solutions are given by

$$a^2 = 4$$
$$\therefore \quad a = 2 \quad \text{or} \quad a = -2$$

If $a=2$ $\quad b = 3 \quad$ [from (8)]

If $a=-2$ $\quad b = -3 \quad$ [from (8)]

If $(a+ib)^2 = -5+12i$

$$a+ib = (-5+12i)^{1/2}$$

hence $$(-5+12i)^{1/2} = 2+3i$$

or $$(-5+12i)^{1/2} = -2-3i$$

(iii) (a) If $|z-2| = 3$

$$|(x+iy)-2| = 3$$
$$|(x+iy)-2|^2 = 9$$
$$|(x-2)+iy|^2 = 9$$
$$(x-2)^2+y^2 = 9$$

which represents a circle centre at $(2, 0)$ of radius 3 (Fig. 16.5).

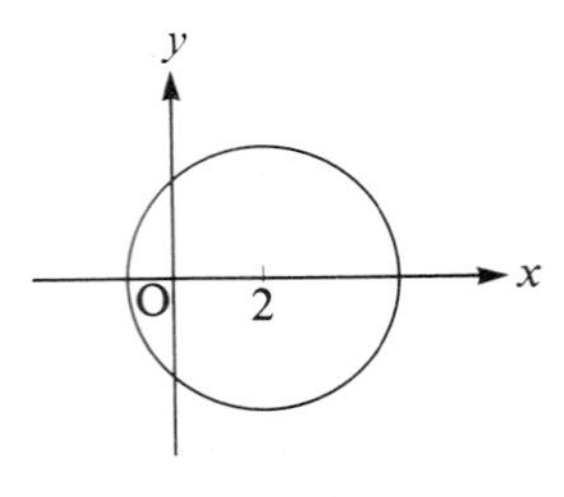

Fig. 16.5

EXERCISE

(b)

$$
\begin{aligned}
|z-2| &= |z-3| \\
\therefore \quad |z-2|^2 &= |z-3|^2 \\
|(x+iy)-2|^2 &= |(x+iy)-3|^2 \\
|(x-2)+iy|^2 &= |(x-3)+iy|^2 \\
(x-2)^2+y^2 &= (x-3)^2+y^2
\end{aligned}
$$

giving

$$
\begin{aligned}
(x-2)^2 &= (x-3)^2 \\
\therefore \quad x^2-4x+4 &= x^2-6x+9 \\
2x &= 5 \\
x &= \frac{5}{2}
\end{aligned}
$$

which is a straight line parallel to the y-axis (Fig. 16.6).

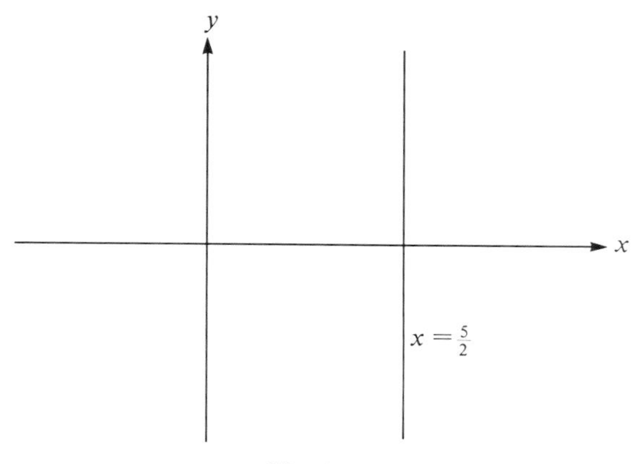

Fig. 16.6

2. (i) If $z^3 = -8i$

then
$$z^3 = 8\left(\cos\frac{3\pi}{2} + i\sin\frac{3\pi}{2}\right)$$

In general, since $\cos\theta$ and $\sin\theta$ have a period of 2π, this can be written as

$$z^3 = 8\left(\cos\frac{(4n-1)}{2}\pi + i\sin\frac{(4n-1)}{2}\pi\right)$$

$n = 1, 2, 3, 4, \ldots$

$$
\begin{aligned}
\therefore \quad z &= 2\left(\cos\frac{(4n-1)}{2}\pi + i\sin\frac{(4n-1)}{2}\pi\right)^{1/3} \\
&= 2\left(\cos\frac{(4n-1)}{6}\pi + i\sin\frac{(4n-1)}{6}\pi\right) \qquad \text{(De Moivre's theorem)}
\end{aligned}
$$

First solution $n = 1$:

$$
\begin{aligned}
z_1 &= 2\left(\cos\frac{\pi}{2} + i\sin\frac{\pi}{2}\right) \\
&= 2i
\end{aligned}
$$

Second solution $n = 2$:

$$z_2 = 2\left(\cos\frac{7\pi}{6} + i\sin\frac{7\pi}{6}\right)$$

$$= 2\left(-\frac{\sqrt{3}}{2} - \frac{1}{2}i\right)$$

Third solution $n = 3$:

$$z_3 = 2\left(\cos\frac{11\pi}{6} + i\sin\frac{11\pi}{6}\right)$$

$$= 2\left(\frac{\sqrt{3}}{2} - \frac{1}{2}i\right)$$

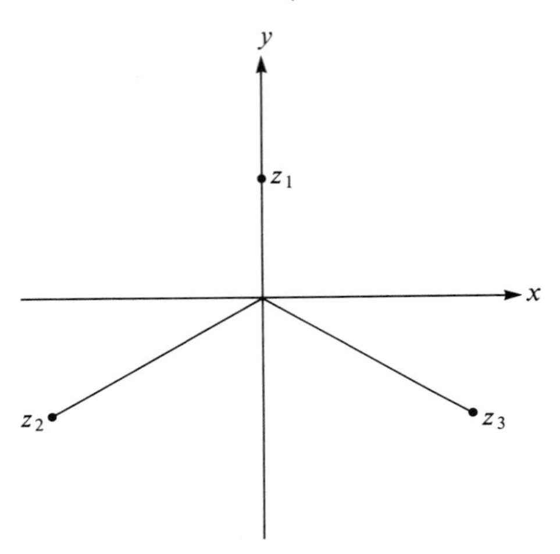

Fig. 16.7

(ii)

$$w = \frac{x + iy + 2i}{x + iy - 4}$$

$$= \frac{x + i(y+2)}{(x-4) + iy}$$

$$\therefore \quad w = \frac{[x + i(y+2)]\,[(x-4) - iy]}{[(x-4) + iy]\,[(x-4) - iy]}$$

$$= \frac{x(x-4) - ixy + i(x-4)(y+2) + y(y+2)}{(x-4)^2 + y^2}$$

$$= \frac{(x^2 - 4x + y^2 + 2y) + i(xy + 2x - 4y - 8 - xy)}{(x-4)^2 + y^2}$$

$$= \frac{(x^2 - 4x + y^2 + 2y)}{x^2 - 8x + y^2 + 16} + \frac{i(2x - 4y - 8)}{x^2 - 8x + y^2 + 16}$$

If w is imaginary then $\text{Re}(w) = 0$

$$\therefore \quad x^2 - 4x + y^2 + 2y = 0$$

This is the equation of a circle as required.

If w is real then $\text{Im}(w) = 0$

EXERCISE

$$\therefore \quad 2x - 4y - 8 = 0$$

$$\therefore \quad y = -2 + \frac{x}{2}$$

which is the equation of a straight line.

3.

$$\begin{aligned} |z-1| &= |\cos\theta + \mathrm{i}\sin\theta - 1| \\ &= |(\cos\theta - 1) + \mathrm{i}\sin\theta| \\ &= \sqrt{(\cos\theta - 1)^2 + \sin^2\theta} \\ &= \sqrt{\cos^2\theta - 2\cos\theta + 1 + \sin^2\theta} \\ &= \sqrt{2(1-\cos\theta)} \end{aligned}$$

but $\cos\theta = 1 - 2\sin^2\dfrac{\theta}{2}$ (half-angle formula)

$$\therefore \quad |z-1| = \sqrt{4\sin^2\frac{\theta}{2}} = 2\sin\frac{\theta}{2}$$

$$\tan\arg(z-1) = \frac{\sin\theta}{(\cos\theta - 1)} = \frac{\sin\theta}{-2\sin^2\theta/2} = \frac{2\sin\theta/2\,\cos\theta/2}{-2\sin^2\theta/2} = -\cot\theta/2$$

If $\phi = \arg(z-1)$ this can be written as

$$\tan\phi = -\cot\frac{\theta}{2}$$

$$\therefore \quad \phi = \frac{1}{2}(\pi + \theta) \qquad \text{since } \tan\left(\frac{\pi}{2} + x\right) = -\cot x$$

In order to find the modulus and the arguments of the cube roots of $\mathrm{i} - 1$ from $z - 1$, we put

$$z = \mathrm{i}$$

$$\therefore \quad z_1 = \mathrm{e}^{\pi\mathrm{i}/2} \qquad \therefore \quad \theta_1 = \pi/2 \qquad (1)$$

$$z_2 = \mathrm{e}^{5\pi\mathrm{i}/2} \qquad \therefore \quad \theta_2 = 5\pi/2 \qquad (2)$$

and

$$z_3 = \mathrm{e}^{9\pi\mathrm{i}/2} \qquad \therefore \quad \theta_3 = 9\pi/2 \qquad (3)$$

hence

$$\arg(z_1 - 1) = \frac{1}{2}\left(\pi + \frac{\pi}{2}\right) = \frac{3\pi}{4} \qquad \therefore \quad \arg(z_1 - 1)^{1/3} = \frac{\pi}{4}$$

$$\arg(z_2 - 1) = \frac{1}{2}\left(\pi + \frac{5\pi}{2}\right) = \frac{7\pi}{4} \qquad \therefore \quad \arg(z_2 - 1)^{1/3} = \frac{7\pi}{12}$$

$$\arg(z_3 - 1) = \frac{1}{2}\left(\pi + \frac{9\pi}{2}\right) = \frac{11\pi}{4} \qquad \therefore \quad \arg(z_3 - 1)^{1/3} = \frac{11\pi}{12}$$

To find the modulus we use the result

$$|z-1| = 2\sin\frac{\theta}{2}$$

$$|z_1 - 1| = 2\sin\frac{\pi}{4} = (2)^{1/2}$$

$$\therefore \quad |(z_1 - 1)^{1/3}| = 2^{1/6} = 1.12$$

If $|z| = 2|z-\mathrm{i}+1|$

$$|x+\mathrm{i}y|^2 = 4|(x+\mathrm{i}y)-\mathrm{i}+1|^2$$
$$|x+\mathrm{i}y|^2 = 4|(x+1)+\mathrm{i}(y-1)|^2$$
$$\therefore\ x^2+y^2 = 4[(x+1)^2+(y-1)^2]$$
$$= 4[(x^2+2x+1+y^2-2y+1)]$$
$$\therefore\ 3x^2+3y^2+8x+4-8y+4 = 0$$
$$x^2+y^2+\frac{8x}{3}-\frac{8y}{3}+\frac{8}{3} = 0$$

which is the equation of a circle centre

$$\left(\frac{-4}{3}, \frac{4}{3}\right), \quad \text{and radius} \quad \sqrt{\left[\left(\frac{4}{3}\right)^2+\left(\frac{-4}{3}\right)^2-\frac{8}{3}\right]} = \frac{2}{3}\sqrt{2}$$

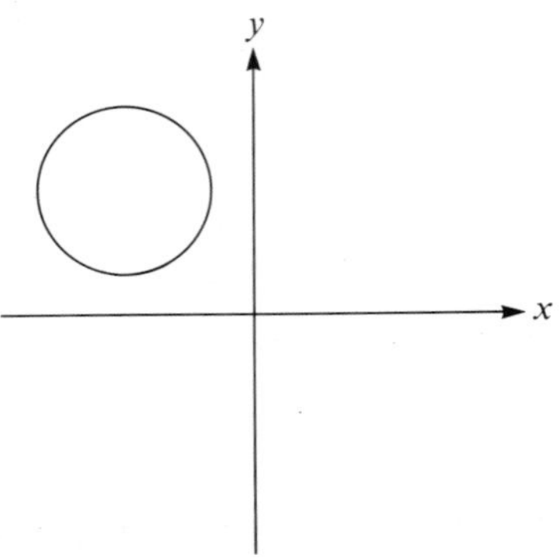

Fig. 16.8 The locus of P when $|z| = 2|z-\mathrm{i}+1|$.

4. (i) If $\alpha_1 = -1-3\mathrm{i}$

$$\alpha_1^2 = (-1-3\mathrm{i})^2$$
$$= 1+6\mathrm{i}+(3\mathrm{i})^2$$
$$\therefore\ \alpha_1^2 = 6\mathrm{i}-8$$

and

$$\mathrm{i}\alpha_1 = \mathrm{i}(-1-3\mathrm{i})$$
$$\therefore\ \mathrm{i}\alpha_1 = -\mathrm{i}+3$$

Substituting these values in the equation

$$\alpha_1^2+\mathrm{i}\alpha_1+5(1-\mathrm{i}) = 6\mathrm{i}-8-\mathrm{i}+3+5-5\mathrm{i}$$
$$= 0 \qquad \text{(as required)}$$
$$\alpha_1+\alpha_2 = -\mathrm{i} \qquad \text{(sum of roots} = -b/a)$$
$$\therefore\ \alpha_2 = -\mathrm{i}-(-1-3\mathrm{i})$$
$$\alpha_2 = 1+2\mathrm{i}$$
$$\frac{1}{\alpha_1}+\frac{1}{\alpha_2} = \frac{\alpha_1+\alpha_2}{\alpha_1\alpha_2}$$
$$= \frac{\text{sum of roots of the quadratic}}{\text{product of the roots of the quadratic}}$$
$$= \frac{-\mathrm{i}}{5(1-\mathrm{i})}$$

EXERCISE

$$\therefore \quad \beta = -5\frac{(1-i)}{i}$$

$$= 5-\frac{5}{i}$$

giving $\quad \beta = 5+5i$

$$\therefore \quad |\beta| = 5\sqrt{2} \quad \text{and} \quad \arg\beta = \frac{\pi}{4}$$

(ii) (a) If $z\bar{z}+(1+i)z+(1-i)\bar{z} = 1$

$$(x+iy)(x-iy)+(1+i)(x+iy)+(1-i)(x-iy) = 1$$

$$x^2+y^2+x+iy+ix-y+x-iy-ix-y = 1$$

$$x^2+y^2+2x-2y-1 = 0$$

which, as required, is the equation of a circle.

(b) If $z^2+\bar{z}^2-14z\bar{z}+48 = 0$

$$(x+iy)^2+(x-iy)^2-14(x+iy)(x-iy)+48 = 0$$

$$x^2+2ixy-y^2+x^2-2ixy-y^2-14(x^2+y^2)+48 = 0$$

$$12x^2+16y^2-48 = 0$$

The locus crosses the imaginary axis when $x = 0$.

Hence $\quad 16y^2 = 48$

$$y^2 = 3$$

$$\therefore \quad y = \sqrt{3} \quad \text{or} \quad y = -\sqrt{3}$$

hence $\sqrt{3}\,i$ and $-\sqrt{3}\,i$ are the complex numbers corresponding to where the locus cuts the imaginary axis.

(c) If $2z^2+2\bar{z}^2-z\bar{z}+15 = 0$

$$2(x+iy)^2+2(x-iy)^2-(x+iy)(x-iy)+15 = 0$$

$$2(x^2+2ixy-y^2)+2(x^2-2ixy-y^2)-(x^2+y^2)+15 = 0$$

Simplifying to $\quad 3x^2-5y^2+15 = 0$

In order to find the points of intersection on the real axis we put $y = 0$

$$\therefore \quad 3x^2 = -15$$

i.e. no real values of x satisfy the points of intersection. Hence the locus does not cross the real axis.

INDEX